James E. Bro...

McGraw-Hill Series in the Geological Sciences

ROBERT R. SHROCK, *Consulting Editor*

MICROSCOPIC PETROGRAPHY

McGraw-Hill Series in the Geological Sciences

ROBERT R. SHROCK, *Consulting Editor*

Microscopic Petrography

E. WM. HEINRICH

Department of Mineralogy
University of Michigan
Ann Arbor, Michigan

McGRAW-HILL BOOK COMPANY, INC.

New York **Toronto** **London**

1956

MICROSCOPIC PETROGRAPHY

Library of Congress Catalog Card Number 55–11171

THE MAPLE PRESS COMPANY, YORK, PA.

For
EDITH

PREFACE

Because of the diversity of rocks, the several ways in which they are formed, and the enormous size variation of the units which they compose and which compose them (batholiths to submicroscopic crystallites), the science of petrology utilizes several contrasting modes of investigation in seeking answers to problems of petrogenesis. Among the most important of these approaches are:

1. Geological (field) techniques
2. Chemical techniques
3. Experimental techniques
4. Petrographical techniques

The petrographical approach concerns itself principally with texture and mineral composition, the latter involving not merely mineral identification but, for chemically complex species, an approximation of their composition through measurement of their optical properties. Considerable petrographic information can be obtained by the megascopic examination of outcrops and hand specimens, usually with the aid of a hand lens. However, most of the available data are obtainable by means of the petrographic polarizing microscope, and for some refinements (e.g., clay mineral identities, perthite studies) other techniques capable of higher resolution, such as x-rays and the electron microscope, have become both desirable and necessary.

Petrography today stands as a petrological tool and no longer as an end itself. Nor can it be employed as the sole means of effective rock investigation. Yet it remains as the method that can contribute, under proper application, the greatest amount of information to the deductive approach in the science of rocks.

This book is intended as a text to serve on the initial to intermediate level of the systematic microscopic study of rocks. Its use presupposes that the student is familiar with the techniques of mineralogical optical microscopy and with the general optical characteristics of the more common rock-forming and accessory minerals.

Few modern textbooks have been devoted principally to petrography, most of the more recent books being preoccupied with petrogenesis. This preponderance of emphasis has forced students to refer to older books for petrographic information. Yet many new petrographic data and many fine recent petrographic studies have supplemented or revised older petrographic descriptions, particularly with respect to the variation in mineral composition in rocks and its significance. It is hoped that this book will bring some of this scattered information within the ken of the student.

No new rock names or group names have been introduced, and relatively few varietal names are listed. Even such listing does not necessarily imply approval of their continued use. The use of a very few names, such as *phonolite*, has been somewhat extended over historical usages in order to simplify groupings. In citing examples of rock types the writer has attempted to list well-known United States or North American examples wherever possible.

Mr. Fred Anderegg has prepared most of the photomicrographs. Credit is given separately for all photomicrographs originated by other individuals. The writer is greatly indebted to his colleagues in the Department of Mineralogy for continuous advice and assistance, particularly to Prof. Walter F. Hunt. Edith Dunn Heinrich assumed much of the difficult task of checking the manuscript and proofreading. Mrs. F. L. Everett performed much of the laborious stenographic work. Despite careful preparation, editing, and proofreading, errors of commission and omission will no doubt appear. The writer will consider it a favor if readers will bring these to his attention.

E. WM. HEINRICH

CONTENTS

Contents

1

METHODS OF MICROSCOPIC STUDY

THIN SECTIONS

General

Thin slices of rocks, mineral aggregates, and synthetic substances provide undisturbed sectional samples of the material that are not only effective for rapid identification of most of the common species present but are also particularly adapted for a study of their spatial relations and grain size, i.e., texture and fabric. Thin sections also have the advantage of showing a particular mineral among its normal associates, commonly in a manner that is sufficiently characteristic to facilitate identification. No other laboratory method has been as extensively employed for the detailed study of rocks. For teaching purposes, thin sections of crystals oriented to show specific optical characteristics have been widely used in the past. The use of thin sections of groups of randomly oriented crushed grains is also an aid in demonstrations. In petrography thin sections are indispensable for a complete rock investigation, yet it is well to realize that a study by means of thin sections alone is not always desirable nor does it always yield all the required information. Thin sections by themselves are inadequate under the following circumstances:

1. If the rock is very coarse grained and mineralogically variable, as is the case for some conglomerates, breccias, agglomerates, and pegmatites.

2. If the mineral constituents are sufficiently unusual so that their refractive indices must be measured to aid in their identification.

3. Generally if it is required to determine the position of a species in an isomorphous series or group. This can normally be done more quickly and more accurately by means of optical data determined in immersion.

4. If the rock contains a very small percentage of genetically significant accessory constituents, only a very few grains of which might be cut by a thin section. This applies particularly to the insoluble residue minerals of carbonate and saline sedimentary rocks and to the accessory detrital and authigenic minerals, both heavy and light fractions, in sandstones and related rocks.

Preparation

Although in the past the petrologist commonly prepared his thin sections himself, today relatively few do so, the task being carried out by trained preparators or by commercial technicians. It is well, however, for the beginning student in petrography to complete several thin sections by himself, in order that he may appreciate some of the difficulties involved and learn to handle the finished product with proper care.

The operation of preparing the section may be divided into the following stages:

1. Cutting a slice
2. Mounting the slice to object glass
3. Cutting the section
4. Final grinding
5. Mounting the cover slip

These steps follow closely the procedures developed and described by Meyer (*Econ. Geol.*, **41**: 166, 1946) whose studies first brought about a major improvement in the rapid production of high-quality sections.

Normally all specimens can be trimmed to uniform size on a diamond saw using a kerosene–water lubricant. On a rock slab about ¼ to ⅜ in. thick is traced the outline of the object glass, and saw cuts are made inside the lines. Most sections are made to fit on glass slides that measure 50×25 mm, but for special purposes, such as the study of mineral relations in banded rocks, much larger, "giant" sections may be prepared with considerably more labor and care. The surface that is to be mounted against the object glass must be carefully flattened. This can be accomplished through the use of —500-mesh silicon carbide, as a 10 per cent suspension in kerosene, on a revolving cast-iron lap. The long edge of the rock slice should be held at an angle to the lap motion, and the slice should be moved from near the lap center to the margins and back in a continuous back-and-forth motion. After the surface is perfectly flat the section is washed to remove abrasive and lubricant. Additional insurance of a tight bond between glass and slice is obtained by frosting the side of the glass on which the mount is to be made.

The thermoplastic cement, Lakeside No. 70, is a very satisfactory mounting and binding agent. Its properties are:

1. Essentially colorless in thin films
2. $n = 1.536$, unchanged with age
3. Insoluble in petroleum lubricants
4. Easy to apply and grind
5. Has superior adhering powers and resistance to shock
6. More viscous than Canada balsam, thus preventing spreading of the thin section during covering
7. Melts readily at 140°C to a uniform film, but is likely to form bubbles above 150°C

Since it is available in inexpensive stick form,[1] it is only necessary to brush the stick across the object glass and the rock slice, which have been heated to 140°C on a hot plate. Overheating, causing excessive bubbles, must be avoided. If the cement is too cool, its viscosity may be such that a nonuniform layer is formed between the rock and the glass; thus the two surfaces are not parallel, and in the final grinding, part of the rock slice will be ground off. Remove the coated rock slice from the hot plate, place the coated object glass on the polished surface, and with a slight pressure, force all air bubbles from the contact. The mounted slice is then cooled to room temperature.

The long tedious grinding formerly required is obviated through a specially adapted diamond saw, by means of which the sections are cut directly and rapidly to thicknesses in which quartz shows uniformly low-order colors. The following description is by Meyer (*Econ. Geol.*, 41: 168–169, 1946).

The saw is adapted from the bearing and shaft assembly of an old (Eimer and Amend) faceting machine and a discarded machine-lathe compound. The only essential features of the bearings are that they are true and free from end play. The compound feed must be fairly heavy and tight and mounted on a turntable (Fig. 1*J*) so that its track can be brought into perfect alignment with the saw blade.

On top of the compound is mounted a section-holding device. This consists essentially of a steel block (Fig. 1*B*), capable of swing adjustment (Fig. 1*D*) to align it laterally, and a lift (Fig. 1*E*) to align it

[1] From the Lakeside Chemical Corporation, Chicago, Ill.

vertically, exactly parallel with the saw blade. This block serves as the
buttress against which the object glass of the mounted rock slice is
placed. To hold the slice in place a universal clamp (Fig. 1A) is
brought against it on the side opposite the object glass and bolted in
place. Flanges at the leading edge of the buttress block and the trail-

Fig. 1. Diamond-saw assembly for cutting thin sections. *A*, Universal clamp block;
B, buttress block; *C*, base block; *D*, swing above feed track; *E*, vertical "lift"
adjustment; *F*, clamp bar for universal clamp; *G*, mounted rock slice; *H*, lubricant
dispenser; *J*, turntable; *K*, end bolt, for thickness adjustment. (*Courtesy of Charles
Meyer and Economic Geology.*)

ing edge of the universal clamp prevent the rock slice (Fig. 1G) from
slipping backward or forward during cutting. A later improvement
holds the slide onto the block through suction applied to the rear of
the slide by means of two holes through the block. The bottom edge
of the object glass rests on that slight projection of the base block
(Fig. 1C) which forms one wall of the notch where the saw blade

travels. The bottom of the blade, while making the cut, should pass at least ¼ in. below the lower edge of the object glass. The base block is capable of movement on a track oriented perpendicularly to the axis of the compound. This adjustment is made by tightening the two end bolts (Fig. 1*K*) against one another. It controls the thickness of the resulting section. A 6-in. sintered-diamond blade is used on the machine. Kerosene, the lubricant, is supplied to the cutting edge by jets on either side of the blade (Fig. 1*H*). With experience, sections may be cut directly to a uniform thickness of 0.08 mm. The section is then hand-finished to 0.03 mm, using a coarse polishing abrasive in water or kerosene on a flat lap or on a glass plate.

After the thin section has been prepared, it is best to use Canada balsam in mounting the cover slip. The balsam should be heated to about 110°C, at which temperature it flows readily, but at which the Lakeside is merely soft. A wooden spatula cut to the width of the glass slide is used to spread a film of balsam over the surface of the section. One stroke of the spatula is best in order to avoid air bubbles. Both the section and the cover slip should be preheated gently. A small ridge of balsam is placed down the center of the cover slip with the side of the spatula. The cover slip is then touched to the glass slide at the top end and allowed to descend under its own weight upon the full surface of the slide. A small weight in the shape of a rectangular block is then placed upon the cover slip in order to press out the excess balsam, which may be removed with xylol.

In old thin sections the balsam may have partly crystallized to polarizing, randomly oriented needles or minute spherulites. Gentle heating should restore its isotropic character.

Friable specimens can first be impregnated with lucite (methyl methacrylate) monomer, using a vacuum. The lucite may be cut and ground with the constituents of the rock and does not soften noticeably at 130 to 140°C.

The inhibitor in the methacrylate is first removed with either a 2 or 3 per cent aqueous solution of potassium hydroxide. This solution is added in small amounts until the hydroxide solution remains colorless and is not tinged brown by the inhibitor. Two washings accompanied by thorough shaking are generally sufficient; three may be necessary. The solution is then washed three times with thorough shaking with water. Water that remains is removed by adding dehydrated calcium chloride several times in amounts of about 1 g each time, agitating the mixture and collecting the water that drains off. This is repeated until the liquid lucite is entirely clear.

The specimen to be impregnated is placed smooth surface down in a disposable glass jar. A piece of benzoyl peroxide about the size of a large rice grain is placed on top of the specimen. The prepared lucite is then run through filter paper (No. 41) onto the specimen in the jar, and the benzoyl peroxide is dissolved.

The jar is stoppered tightly with a suitable rubber stopper penetrated by a thick-walled glass tube connected to an aspirator vacuum pump. The pump, which should have a suitable trap to prevent the return flow of water, is started slowly, and pressure is diminished gradually. Generally 2 min will suffice for smaller specimens, although materials such as clays may require as much as 20 min. Observe the jar closely, and when most of the large bubbles of air have been withdrawn, small bubbles will begin to form. This may indicate that the lucite is boiling under reduced pressure. The formation of these bubbles will be accompanied by a rapid decline in temperature of the jar. In covering the specimen an excess of about 20 per cent of lucite should be used. For jars 2 in. or so in diameter this amounts to a height of about 1½ in. above the specimen. After the material has been completely evacuated, the pump should be released, and air pressure will force the lucite into the evacuated openings.

The lucite is cured at 90°C in the covered jar for a period of 10 to 12 hr; overnight is not too long. The jar is then broken to remove the specimen, which may be sawed and trimmed as any other.

Various other impregnating media have been used for bonding friable sediments, volcanic debris, and other incoherent natural and synthetic materials for thin-section preparation. Canada balsam has been employed, as have kollolith, which has nearly the same index as balsam, and bakelite varnish, with $n = 1.60$ to 1.64. The application of these media is hindered by their relatively high viscosity, and they must be used in some solvent, whose evaporation is attended by the formation of bubbles within the specimen unless special precautions are observed. A liquid of lower viscosity is aroclor 4465 with $n = 1.66+$, by means of which friable materials may be impregnated quickly and effectively through capillary action, without any solvent.

Thin sections of saline rocks containing water-soluble minerals present some special difficulties. The rock must be cut dry or with paraffin. If deliquescent minerals are present, the rock slice must be kept moist during final grinding. Paraffin will slowly dissolve Canada balsam. If halite is the only soluble mineral, the section may be cut and ground in a saturated NaCl brine. Rock slices that contain gypsum should not be heated strongly, but even if this precaution is observed, calcium sulfate hemihydrate may form during grinding but may be reconverted to gypsum by wetting the surface.

It may be advantageous not to cover sections of salines, in order to observe reactions in moist air. Deliquescent salts will collect moisture. Etching with water and various brines will also assist identification and bring out microstructural details. Some minerals may be detected because of their marked efflorescence. Sections of deliquescent minerals should be stored in a $CaCl_2$ dessicator.

Staining

In some cases, particularly if rocks contain two or more mineral species that are optically similar superficially or if the speed and accuracy of Rosiwal determinations are to be increased, selective staining of minerals in uncovered thin sections may be highly advantageous. Although stains have been described for many mineral species, in practice only a few are necessary and in common use:

1. To distinguish nepheline from potash feldspar and plagioclase
2. To distinguish potash feldspar from untwinned or very finely twinned plagioclase
3. To distinguish between calcite and dolomite
4. To distinguish between brucite and serpentine

PROCEDURE FOR NEPHELINE

1. Spread with glass rod a thin film of sirupy phosphoric acid over section; allow to remain 3 min.
2. Wash by dipping gently in water.
3. Immerse slide in 0.25 per cent solution of methylene blue 1 min.
4. Wash off excess dye by dipping gently in water.

By this technique nepheline, sodalite, and analcite are stained deep blue, melilite a light blue; potash feldspar, plagioclase, and leucite are unaffected. Zonal structure in nepheline may be revealed, the unstained zones being richer in SiO_2.

PROCEDURE FOR NEPHELINE AND PLAGIOCLASE

1. Spread, with pipette, concentrated HCl on slide surface; allow to remain 4 min.
2. Wash by dipping gently in water.
3. Spread, with pipette, solution of malachite green (1 g in 200 ml of distilled H_2O) over wet slide; allow to stand for 50 to 60 sec. Nepheline is stained strong green.

4. Dry in air 24 hr.

5. Cover backs of slides with cellophane or paint with thin solution of rubber cement in xylol.

6. Place in lead fuming box or plastic tray containing HF; expose to HF fumes at 30 to 40°C for 45 sec or generally less. The green nepheline stain is temporarily lost but restored in the next step.

7. Immerse slide with very gentle agitation in concentrated solution of sodium cobaltinitride (3 to 4 g, in 6 ml of H_2O) for 2 to 3 min. Feldspars of some volcanic rocks require as long as 10 to 15 min. Potash feldspar is stained yellow, including that of perthites; plagioclase is unstained; nepheline green is restored.

8. Wash in gentle stream of water.

If nepheline is absent, steps 5 to 8 may be used to stain potash feldspar. This technique will also separate leucite from analcite, and alunite from kaolinite.

Procedure for Brucite-Serpentine and Calcite-Dolomite

1. Immerse slide in dilute HCl in which a few crystals of potassium ferrocyanide have been dissolved. Immersion time varies; watch progress of stain. Brucite is stained blue; serpentine, pale green.

2. Wash gently.

3. Immerse in Lemberg solution for about 1 min. Calcite is stained lilac; dolomite is unaffected. Lemberg solution: 6 g of logwood extract, 4 g of $AlCl_3$, 60 ml of water. Boil for 20 min, adding water lost by evaporation; filter.

4. Wash gently.

For dolomite and calcite without brucite and serpentine, use steps 3 and 4.

Micrometric Mineralogical Analysis

One of the simplest and most satisfactory techniques by which it is possible to determine the quantitative mineralogical composition (the mode) of a rock is the linear method of micrometric analysis, also generally known as the Rosiwal or Delesse-Rosiwal method. In this method a thin section is placed on the stage of a recording micrometer attached to the stage of the microscope. The micrometer is fitted usually with five or six screws, to each of which a mineral or a mineral group is assigned. The carriage holding the thin section is moved across the field of vision by turning the screws, each screw being turned for the traverse across the particular mineral or minerals to which it is assigned. The screws have graduated micrometer heads so that, after a traverse across the section has been completed, the total distance traversed across grains of each mineral species (or groups) may be read directly and recorded. The micrometer screws are returned to zero positions, the section is moved a fixed distance, and the traverse is repeated. The entire analysis consists of a series of parallel, equidistant traverses, in the course of which the lengths of lines crossing mineral grains of different species are totaled for each of the species (or groups).

A widely used recording micrometer is the Hunt-Wentworth instrument (Fig. 2), in which the five micrometer screws, all on the same side, are turned by hand. Another by Leitz has six spindles, three on each side, and also is hand-operated (Fig. 3). The Dollar stage also has six spindles and is constructed to permit the stage to be rotated

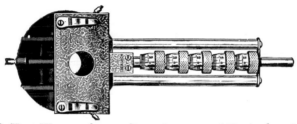

Fig. 2. Hunt-Wentworth recording micrometer. (*Eberbach and Son.*)

through a full 360°, an advantage it possesses uniquely. The Hurlbut electric counter (Fig. 4), which has the recording unit separate from the microscope stage, consists of two parts, an electrically operated recording unit and a mechanical microscope stage, joined by a flexible cable. Six minerals can be measured at one time, in traverses made alternately right and left across the thin section, and the sums of all traverses appear on the recording unit counters. A total counter automatically adds the subtotals of the individual counters. This instrument greatly reduces the time required for an analysis.

In the Glagolev modification of micrometric analysis, as developed by Chayes, the regular spacing between traverses is retained, but the individual traverses are broken into merely a series of equally spaced points. The mineral under the cross hairs is identified, the appropriate key is punched, and this tabulatory key controls a mechanism that moves the stage with its thin section a fixed distance along the traverse line. The line is run, the section is shifted a regular interval, and the new line is traversed in points. The instrument consists of two parts:

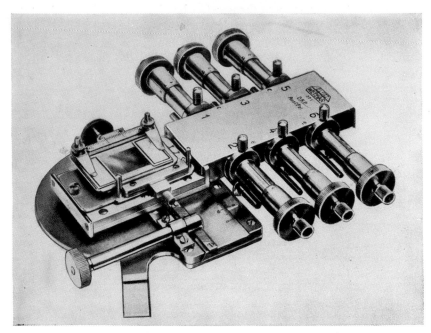

FIG. 3. Leitz integrating stage. (*E. Leitz, Inc.*)

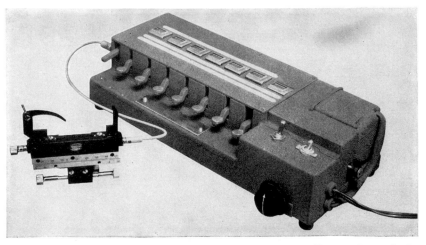

FIG. 4. Hurlbut electric counter. (*Courtesy of C. S. Hurlbut and Cambridge Thermionic Corp.*)

an adapted mechanical stage (Fig. 5) and an electrically operated tabulator unit of the counting-block type, either five- or six-cell. Details of the construction are given by Chayes (*Am. Mineralogist*, **34:** 1–11, 600–601, 1949; **40:** 126–127, 1955). A modified mechanical stage operated with an integrating unit based on electromagnetic counters has been devised by Ford (*J. Sci. Instr.*, **31:** 164–165, 1954).

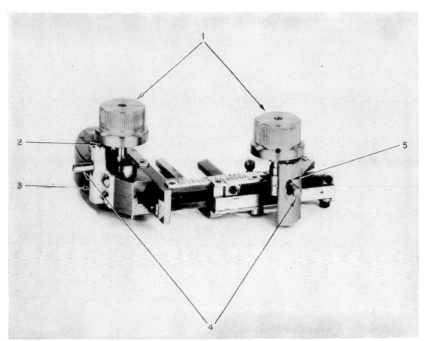

Fig. 5. Mechanical stage with stop mechanisms, for use as Chayes point counter. 1, Oversized knobs with 24 holes drilled from below; 2, stop pin; 3, pinholder; 4, lockscrew; 5, elongated hole for locking lockscrew. By turning knob 1, the stop pin 2 jumps from one hole to the next in steps of 0.5 mm. (*Courtesy of Felix Chayes and Baltimore Instrument Co.*)

The fundamental premise of the technique is that linear (and thus arcal) measurements are directly proportional to the volumes of the grains measured, regardless of the shape of the individual grains. The quality or precision of the result is determined by the total length of line traversed or the total frequency of points recorded. For an accuracy of about 1 per cent it is necessary to make approximately fifteen traverses about 1 mm apart across an average section. Errors in measurement increase with decreasing grain size because of (1) the exaggeration of the cumulative error from the surface-boundary estimation of the opaque minerals and (2) the increased difficulty in recognizing the mineral species. The difficulties of proper sampling increase, on the other hand, with increasing grain size, owing to (1) the limited number of grains per section, (2) the greater probability of nonuniform mixing, and (3) the increased possibility of the systematic tearing out of certain good-cleavage minerals during construction of the section. In any event, sections with numerous holes should be discarded. In practice the error resulting from the failure of the measuring process to represent adequately the section to which it is applied usually can be made smaller than the error resulting from failure of the section to provide a proper sample of the rock. Best results are to be expected on rocks in which the minerals are uniformly distributed and the grains are about 1 mm across.

In strongly lineated or foliated rocks the variance stemming from orientation will be markedly reduced by choosing sections normal to the lineation and by pooling results without regard to the orientation of the sections. In mineralogically banded rocks it is preferable, for bands that are wide in relation to thin-section width, to sample each band individually. For bands that are thin with respect to thin-section width, sections normal to the layering will provide an efficient estimate of the frequencies and volumes of the bands.

As expressed by Chayes (*J. Geol.*, **62**: 100–101, 1954), "The inaccuracy of a micrometric analysis is never the result of a failure in the basic theory relating area to volume. It is always traceable to unsatisfactory technique or to sampling which is either inadequate or inefficient. . . . It is always a potentially accurate procedure."

THE IMMERSION METHOD

Although the immersion method has been applied primarily to the recognition of species in a monomineralic aggregate and to the accurate measurement of their optical constants, it also has wide practicability in the microscopic study of rocks and other polymineralic aggregates. For the determination of the essential rock constituents, usually no concentration or separation is necessary; aggregates or rocks consisting of three, four, or even more main minerals may be crushed and the powdered mixture studied effectively. Indeed this technique offers some advantages over thin sections alone, although crushed-fragment studies do not replace thin-section examinations. Crushed-fragment studies are helpful, therefore, not only for mineral identification and thus for rock identification, but also for the determination of the approximate composition of some species, chiefly by measuring their refractive indices, a task that cannot be performed in thin section. On the other hand, for studying rock textures, thin sections remain indispensable.

EXAMINATION WITH THE BINOCULAR MICROSCOPE

Considerable information on both clastic and chemical sedimentary rocks may be obtained through the study of samples by means of the binocular microscope, and this technique is widely applied to the examination and description of well samples, of either the cable-tool or rotary type, after the fragments have been washed clean of drilling mud. It is also useful, however, in the laboratory study of outcrop samples.

Information that may be obtained by this method includes:

1. Color. Of considerable value in the standardization of color nomenclature is the Rock Color Chart, a *U.S. Geological Survey Special Publication* in 1948, obtainable from the National Research Council, Division of Geology and Geography, Washington 25, D.C.

2. General textural features, i.e., clastic, granular, etc.

3. Grain size and sorting. Good qualitative descriptions may readily be made by comparing the samples against a standard set of grain samples mounted as a unit on a slide.

4. Shape, roundness, and surface features of grains.

5. Identity of the minerals of the grains and of the minerals of the cement. Acid testing for effervescence.

6. Identity of fossils.

7. Rock designation.

Most of these features are described in greater detail in Chap. 4. Although the technique has been applied to fragments of sedimentary rocks, it may also be used for samples of the other types.

OTHER METHODS

For the study of mineral aggregates from ore deposits, in which both opaque and nonopaque species are abundantly represented, polished thin sections may prove desirable. Since such sections are difficult to prepare, comparable results may be obtained by preparing both thin and polished sections of the ores or rocks, using one face of the slabbed specimen for the thin section and the opposing counterpart for the polished section. Polished sections of both igneous and metamorphic rocks may reveal a wealth of detailed and complex textural features in the opaque grains—information of considerable significance in deciphering their paragenetic history but not obtainable through thin sections.

Other microscopic methods that apply principally to sedimentary rocks and are thus described in Chap. 4 include the examination of accessory detrital grains and insoluble residues.

2

IGNEOUS ROCKS—GENERAL

EARTH STRUCTURE AND PRIMARY MAGMAS

Seismological data, other geophysical evidence, and astronomical calculations indicate that the earth is a concentrically layered body consisting of three main divisions—crust, mantle, and core. Regarding the composition and structure of the crust, the upper parts of which are available for direct sampling and study, there is a general concordance of ideas. Within it two principal shells underlie continental areas—an upper of generally granitic composition (the sial), with a mean thickness of 11 km, and a lower of basaltic composition (the sima), whose mean thickness is 24 km. Beneath the oceanic basins the granitic shell is absent or very thin. Covering the continental areas as a whole is a veneer of metamorphic and sedimentary rocks which, although locally many kilometers thick, have only a very minor total mass when compared to that of the entire crust.

For the mantle and core there is less general agreement as to their composition, but many geologists believe, again largely on the basis of seismological evidence, that the mantle, at least in its outer part, i.e., directly beneath the major discontinuity that separates it from the heterogeneous crust, consists of material approximating in composition various peridotitic rocks, especially those consisting essentially of olivine or of olivine and pyroxene combined. Most theorists believe that the core, which begins at a depth of about 2,900 km, consists of iron and nickel. Much of the disagreement on earth composition centers on the composition of the mantle and on whether the mantle and crust are liquid or crystalline or both.

It is either within the crustal layers or the uppermost part of the mantle that we must look for the original sources of many igneous rocks. Igneous rocks are formed by the solidification (generally crys-

15

tallization) of magmas that have cooled. A magma is a mutual solution, dominantly silicate in composition, consisting chiefly of Si, O, Al, alkali elements, alkaline-earth elements, and Fe, together with minor amounts of other elements including the volatile components—CO_2, H_2O, F, Cl, S, P, etc. A magma is initially hot and under great pressure, and it possesses mobility.

Granites, granodiorites, and quartz monzonites constitute about 95 per cent of all intrusive igneous rocks, whereas basalts and pyroxene-bearing andesites form nearly 98 per cent of all extrusive igneous rocks. From this and other lines of evidence many geologists believe that there are and have been two main types of primary magmas—a granitic type derived by fusion of material from the sialic layer, and a basaltic formed by fusion of material from the shell of sima. The possibility of the existence of a third type of primary magma, much less common, has been suggested to explain the origin of peridotites and anorthosites—tapping and fusion of the uppermost part of the mantle. Igneous rocks, other than granite, basalt, and possibly some peridotites are considered to result largely from the crystallization of secondary magmas—those derived by various modifications of primary magma, especially the basaltic type.

There also exist a considerable body of thought and some evidence that suggest that some plutonic bodies of rock, usually classed as igneous, were at no time in a completely liquid (magma) state, but were formed through metasomatism, i.e., largely by reactions in the solid state as the result of ionic migration along mineral grain boundaries and through the crystalline framework of minerals while the rock as a whole remained solid or at least nearly so. This process, along with several modifications of it, is generally referred to as granitization, and the numerous adherents of this theory hold to somewhat different ideas regarding the details of the mechanism and the scope on which it operates.

DEVELOPMENT OF SECONDARY MAGMAS

Differentiation

Primary magmas may crystallize without undergoing fractionation, or they may divide into secondary magmas that differ in composition both from each other and from their parent. This general phenomenon of evolution is referred to as magmatic differentiation. Early ideas on magmatic differentiation placed considerable emphasis upon the importance of such processes as (1) gaseous transfer of volatile constituents, (2) separation into two different portions through liquid immiscibility, and (3) the migration of material by means of diffusion along a temperature gradient (Soret effect). Generally geologists no longer regard these mechanisms as effective in producing large-scale inhomogeneities in initially uniform magmas.

Of utmost importance is differentiation resulting from crystal fractionation (fractional crystallization or crystal differentiation). In a cooling magma the early precipitated crystals, which are initially in equilibrium with magma remaining, may be prevented in various ways from further reaction with the liquid as it continues to cool and thus from changing their composition in order to remain in equilibrium with it. For the mineralogical changes that result from reactions at equilibrium see Fig. 8. Incomplete reaction or the prevention of reaction results in the formation of a crystalline portion and a liquid portion which differ in composition from each other and also from the original magma. Reaction may be prevented by (1) rapid cooling or chilling, (2) sinking or floating of crystals under gravity, (3) gas flotation of crystals, and (4) filter pressing to squeeze off remaining liquid from a partly crystallized magma through tectonic movements or renewed magmatic surges.

Examples of intrusive bodies that were differentiated *in situ* largely or in part through gravitative settling of crystals are some of the peridotitic layered lopoliths (Stillwater Complex, Montana); some diabasic sills (Palisade sill, New Jersey); some alkaline gabbro sills (Lugar, Scotland); and some shonkinitic laccoliths (Shonkin Sag, Montana). Clear-cut examples of differentiation through floating of crystals appear to be less common; one of the best described is the headed dike studied by Buie in the Highwood Mountains of Montana, in which leucite crystals accumulated near the arcuate roof in a shonkinitic magma.

The fractional crystallization of basaltic magma under different geological environments (e.g., in active orogenic belts; in volcanic provinces; under plutonic conditions) is believed to yield various series of secondary magmas that were intruded or extruded at intervals to crystallize as sequences, such as:

1. Basalt, trachyte, phonolite
2. Basalt, andesite, rhyolite
3. Gabbro, tonalite, granodiorite, (minor) granite

No doubt in some cases the processes of crystal fractionation have been combined with other mechanisms leading to secondary magmas (e.g., assimilation) to modify this straight-line or "normal" magmatic descent. In addition, many investigators also believe that the sima differs somewhat in composition from place to place or with depth and that there are two main varieties of primary basaltic magmas: an olivine basaltic type and a slightly less basic type—the flood or plateau basaltic magma (tholeiitic type).

The crystal differentiation of primary granitic-granodioritic–type magmas is considered to yield secondary magmas that crystallize as rocks in such associations as:

1. Rhyolite, quartz latite, dacite
2. Rhyolite, latite, andesite
3. Granodiorite, tonalite, diorite
4. Granite, quartz syenite, syenite
5. Granite, aplite, pegmatite

Syntexis

Syntexis refers to the assimilation of foreign material by magmas by means of various mechanisms—melting, solution, and reaction. One of the most widely accepted theories for the origin of some feldspathoidal syenites postulates large-scale reaction between granitic magmas and calcareous sedimentary or metamorphic rocks involving either desilication of the granitic magma through the formation of Ca or Ca-Mg silicates or through the enrichment of the magma in CO_2, or both. Another group of rocks that apparently have crystallized from basaltic-type magmas modified by the assimilation of sialic material are the mafic potassic rocks—leucite basalts and their kindred. The formation of some diorites has been ascribed to reaction between granitic magma and mafic wall rocks such as amphibolites or gabbros or even limestones or marbles. The development of spilitic basalts has been explained, under one of several theories, by assuming an incorporation of associated graywacke sedimentary material and/or sea water.

Mingling of Magmas

The mixing of partly crystalline magmas of different composition prior to eruption (e.g., basaltic with rhyolitic) has been suggested to explain the origin of certain volcanic rocks, especially andesites (San Juan Mountains, Colorado), which contain plagioclase phenocrysts of markedly diverse composition or with abnormal zoning.

GRANITIZATION

By granitization is meant the processes that convert various solid rocks to rocks of granitic composition and structure without the intervention of a magmatic stage. The term denotes different processes to different adherents, but it is not generally applicable to selective fusion or even remelting of parts of the sialic layer or of granites previously intruded and crystallized (anatexis). The chief variations are:

1. Granitization by fluids genetically associated with intruded bodies of cooling magma; restricted to the contact aureole

2. Granitization by "mobilized and reactivated" solutions derived from connate water and/or from remelted rocks

3. Granitization without fluids—by large-scale and long-distance solid diffusion of ions moving along grain boundaries, through spaces in crystal structures and from position to position in crystal structures (atomic or ionic "shunting"), the movements following gradients in chemical potential resulting from gradients in physical conditions

Proponents of this last viewpoint, known as transformationists, believe large granitic batholiths have been developed by the migration toward a locus of concentration of light "active" ions of such elements as Na, K, Al, and Si and the opposing diffusion of heavier "less active" ions of elements such as Ca, Mg, and Fe (basic fronts).

A process analogous to granitization has been suggested to explain the formation of some of the Alnö Island, Sweden, nepheline syenites and also the nepheline syenites of the Bancroft, Ontario, region. This process, called nephelinization, involves the reaction of granitic or syenitic "juices" upon limestone (Bancroft) or an intense reaction between a "carbonatitic magmatic liquid" and migmatite (Alnö). Similarly, to explain the genesis of the leucitic lavas of East Africa Holmes has postulated the action of a highly complex and energized series of "emanations" upon various rocks including peridotite, biotite pyroxenite, granite, and sediments.

CLASSIFICATION

No single classification of igneous rocks satisfies all petrographers. Indeed, the number of different classifications closely approaches the number of outstanding petrographers that have appeared since the start of the science. Igneous rocks have been classified on the basis of their geological occurrence, on geographic occurrence, on geologic age, on megascopic structure, on chemical compositions through comparison of oxide ratios or calculated artificial mineral composition (the norm), on color index, and on microscopic mineral composition, both qualitative and quantitative. No one basis is entirely suitable.

The classification here adopted is quantitative and mineralogical, modified and simplified from that of Johannsen. Obviously such a basis is disadvantageous for very fine grained and glassy rocks. The main criteria here employed in establishing families and their boundaries are usability by the student and general petrographic usage. From the standpoint of ease of teaching, it seems desirable to begin with the granite family, which shows less mineralogical variation and fewer complex alteration products than do mafic or ultramafic rocks, although from the genetic viewpoint, excellent arguments may be advanced for studying first basalts or even peridotites. Because the classification is mineralogical, the lamprophyre dike rocks are not considered separately but are placed with the groups they most closely resemble. However, pyroclastic rocks are considered as a unit in a

TABLE 1. CLASSIFICATION OF IGNEOUS ROCKS

Granite-rhyolite family	Felsic; essential quartz; alkali feldspar exceeds sodic plagioclase
Granodiorite–quartz latite family	Felsic; essential quartz; sodic plagioclase equals or exceeds alkali feldspar
Syenite-trachyte family	Felsic; neither essential quartz nor feldspathoids; alkali feldspar exceeds sodic plagioclase, which may be absent
Monzonite-latite family	Felsic to intermediate; neither essential quartz nor feldspathoids; sodic plagioclase equals or exceeds alkali feldspar
Foidal syenite–phonolite family	Felsic; essential feldspathoids; alkali feldspar generally exceeds sodic plagioclase
Tonalite-dacite family	Felsic to intermediate; essential quartz and sodic plagioclase; no essential alkali feldspar
Diorite-andesite family	Intermediate; no essential quartz or alkali feldspar; essential sodic plagioclase
Gabbro-basalt family	Intermediate to mafic (except for anorthosites); essential calcic plagioclase; no essential quartz or alkali feldspar
Foidal gabbro–foidal basalt family	Intermediate to mafic; essential feldspathoids; calcic plagioclase essential to absent
Peridotite family	Ultramafic; no essential calcic plagioclase

Pyroclastic rocks

separate subdivision. Since many pyroclastics are contaminated by sedimentary material or have been reworked, some advantage may be gained by studying them after the student is familiar with sedimentary rocks.

No new igneous names have been introduced; no old obscure names have been resuscitated; the number of varietal types described is small, and their appearance is not necessarily indicative of approval for their continued usage.

In Table 1, felsic indicates that the amount of light-colored constituents exceeds that of dark; intermediate, the two groups are nearly equal; mafic, dark-colored minerals exceed light-colored ones; essential, 10 per cent or more; sodic plagioclase, Ab_{100-50}; calcic plagioclase, Ab_{50-0}.

TEXTURES AND MICROSTRUCTURES

Individual Minerals

The form of individual minerals is largely a reflection of the degree of crystallization and the perfection of their normal outline. The

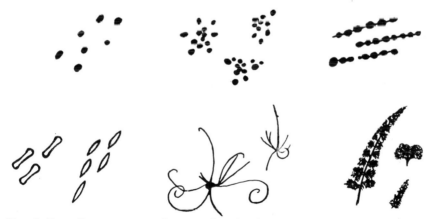

Fig. 6. Crystallites. *Top row, left to right,* globulites, cumulites, margarites; *lower row, left to right,* belonites, trichites, scopulites.

smallest are crystallites, which are minute, nonpolarizing units of various aspects (Fig. 6), which cannot be identified as to species. Microlites are small polarizing crystals whose identity usually can be established. Skeletal crystals are incomplete frameworks.

Based on form perfection are three categories (Fig. 7):

1. Euhedral (idiomorphic, automorphic): maximum development of characteristic crystal forms

2. Subhedral (hypidiomorphic, hypautomorphic): partial development of characteristic crystal forms

3. Anhedral (xenomorphic, allotriomorphic): nondevelopment of characteristic crystal forms

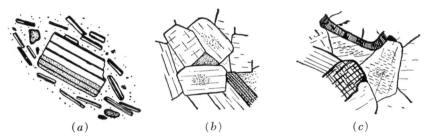

(a)   (b)   (c)

Fig. 7. Shape of grains. (a) Euhedral plagioclase phenocryst in andesite, (b) subhedral plagioclase in diorite, (c) anhedral plagioclase in gabbro.

Terms used to describe the habit of minerals are:

1. One direction greatly developed: fibrous, needlelike, acicular, prismatic, columnar, lathlike

2. Two directions greatly developed: platy, tabular, micaceous

3. Three dimensions equally developed: blocky, equant, equidimensional

Many minerals show variations that are internal to single grains. These are usually systematically arranged, as in general zones that reflect the symmetry of the mineral, or in face zones, that reflect the development of a particular crystal form (hourglass structure). Zoning appears through color variations, variations in birefringence, extinction angle and 2V, systematically placed inclusions, or selective alteration. In some species internal variations in color and optical properties may be distributed in a pattern that is crystallographically irregular (tourmaline, staurolite).

Mineral Combinations and Groups

Minerals of the same or different species form numerous regular to semiregular intergrowths that may be characteristic:

1. Parallel and subparallel aggregates (sillimanite). If arranged in a linear pattern of contiguous grains: synneusis texture (magnetite).

2. Radial, spherulitic, or sheaflike clusters: divergent elongate crystals extending from a common center. Example: tourmaline (Fig. 9c), dumortierite, alkali feldspar spherulites (Fig. 12c).

3. Poikilitic: a single crystal host including numerous grains or crystals of another or other species unsystematically distributed. Examples: hornblende, melilite.

4. Perthite-type intergrowths. A single crystal host including oriented to suboriented plates, films, or blebs of another mineral. Perthite specifically involves host alkali feldspar and guest sodic plagioclase, and antiperthite is the converse. Similar intergrowths occur in the pyroxenes. Commonly the result of exsolution or deuteric replacement.

5. Micrographic. A single crystal host with evenly distributed but irregular blebs and vermicular units of another mineral, which are commonly of uniform optical orientation, although separate. Such quartz in alkali feldspar forms micropegmatite, micrographic intergrowth, or granophyre (Fig. 10b). Such quartz in plagioclase forms myrmekite. Numerous other mineral combinations form similar intergrowths.

6. Overgrowths and reaction rims. Borders of one or more minerals around another acting as a nucleus. The border may consist of a single grain or of numerous units, not uncommonly arranged normal to the contact with the nucleus. Corona structure usually refers to pyroxenes and amphiboles about olivine (Fig. 19a); kelyphitic, to various minerals overgrown on garnet.

7. Relict textures. Irregular, normally subordinate remnants of an original mineral in a host formed by replacement.

Texture

The texture of an igneous rock partakes of the following factors: (1) degree of crystallinity: hyaline, hypocrystalline, cryptocrystalline, holocrystalline; (2) grain size; (3) shape, relative sizes, and arrangement of the mineral grains with respect to each and any glass that may be present.

Glassy rocks have a hyaline texture; those with some crystals in a glassy base are hypocrystalline (Fig. 11a). Some glasses are perlitic, containing clustered concentric shell-like fractures produced by contraction upon cooling (Fig. 12b). Others show flow banding (eutaxitic texture) (Fig. 11b). Rocks with grains of submicroscopic size, but which show faint polarization effects, are cryptocrystalline (Fig. 11b); this may result from the postsolidification crystallization of glass (devitrification). Holocrystalline rocks are without glass. The finest-grained are microcrystalline (Fig. 11c), in which the grains are distinguishable only microscopically. A commonly accepted grain-size classification is:

	Average diameter
Fine-grained............	<1 mm
Medium-grained............	1–10 mm
Coarse-grained............	1–3 cm
Very coarse................	>3 cm

The granitic texture is holocrystalline, in which the constituents are equigranular-anhedral. Aplitic, in a textural sense, is similar, but fine-grained, equigranular-anhedral (Fig. 10a); saccharoidal is its equivalent; mosaic is similar (Fig. 23a). Pegmatitic implies extra coarse-grained and in some instances, uneven-grained or heterogranular.

The porphyritic texture is one in which relatively large (usually euhedral or corroded euhedral) crystals (phenocrysts) of one or more species are set in a finer-grained or glassy matrix or groundmass (Fig. 11a). If the phenocrysts are grouped or clustered, the texture is glomeroporphyritic. In some rocks the sizes of the phenocrysts vary gradually or in a continuous series from large phenocrysts through phenocrysts and microphenocrysts—the seriate-porphyritic texture (Fig. 18c). And some species that display this size gradation also vary chemically in analogous fashion, e.g., plagioclase, olivine, and pyroxenes. A xenocryst is an included foreign grain or crystal (Fig. 18c).

Porphyritic rocks may have various matrix textures. A porphyritic rock with a glassy matrix is a vitrophyre (Fig. 11a). In the trachytic texture matrix microlites of lathlike feldspar are subparallel, winding around phenocrysts in flow lines (Fig. 14c).

The relations between crystallinity of the matrix and abundance of phenocrysts may be expressed as follows (using as an example the granite-rhyolite family):

Matrix aphanitic (i.e., grains not discernible without magnification)
1. Relatively few phenocrysts, predominant glassy matrix. Extrusive: rhyolite vitrophyre.
2. Phenocrysts subordinate to the predominately crystalline or holocrystalline matrix. Extrusive or hypabyssal (near-surface intrusive): porphyritic rhyolite (generally for extrusives), rhyolite porphyry (more usually for hypabyssal types).

3. Phenocrysts predominate over holocrystalline matrix, which usually is coarser than that of rhyolite porphyries. Hypabyssal: granite porphyry.

Matrix phaneritic (i.e., grains visible without magnification)

4. Phenocrysts in a granitic (fine- to coarse-grained) matrix. Plutonic: porphyritic granite.

In some holocrystalline rocks the texture is pilotaxitic, consisting of small lathlike or needlelike microlites of feldspar in subparallel position, with interstitial granular mafic minerals. If the needlelike feldspar microlites occur in glass, the texture is hyalopilitic. With an increased number of microlites the glass becomes subordinate, appearing in interstitial wedge-shaped pieces, resulting in an intersertal texture. If the rock is holocrystalline and the needlelike feldspar microlites are unoriented, the texture is felted.

Some rhyolitic rocks consist chiefly of orthoclase grains with micrographically, vermicularly to radially intergrown quartz inclusions and are called granophyres (Fig. 10*b*). Many diabases have a texture of randomly arranged feldspar laths with large anhedral-interstitial or molding pyroxene—the ophitic texture (Fig. 20*b*). In the panidiomorphic texture the bulk of the constituents tends toward euhedralism, as is the case in some lamprophyric dike rocks.

Some holocrystalline igneous rocks display a parallel orientation of minerals—the mafics or feldspar, in some cases even with a crude segregation in stringers. If this directional texture is the result of primary movements during magmatic crystallization, it is called gneissoid. If granulation, fracturing, and strain effects result from these primary movements, the texture is called autoclastic. If the textures result from postcrystallization metamorphic forces, the directional texture is gneissic and the crushed texture is cataclastic.

The distinction between textural and structural features is not sharp. Generally if the feature is on a relatively large scale—that of an outcrop or large specimen—it is referred to as a structure. Some such features, however, may also be studied microscopically. Orbicular textures have minerals segregated in concentric shells to form distinct spheroidal masses. Within the shells the texture may be radial or granular. Vesicular rocks contain numerous gas cavities—rounded, ellipsoidal, or lenticular. In amygdaloidal rocks, such ellipsoidal to rounded cavities are filled by secondary minerals. Lithophysae are spheroidal cavities in some hyaline rocks, bordered by shell-like concentric layers. They are associated with and related to spherulites.

Miarolitic cavities are small, irregular open spaces, usually in coarse-grained rocks, on whose walls commonly appear euhedral, inwardly projecting crystals.

Various prefixes and adjectives have been applied to the dark- and light-colored mineral groups and also to color variations in rocks resulting from variations in proportions of these groups. The light-colored minerals (quartz, feldspars, feldspathoids or foids) are grouped as felsic; rocks rich in them are felsic rocks. Rocks of any one family that are abnormally rich in the minerals of this group may be described by adding the prefix *leuco-*, as leucogranite, leucogabbro, etc. The dark-colored group of minerals (biotite, amphiboles, pyroxenes, olivine) are the mafics, and rocks in which they predominate are mafic rocks. If mafic minerals are the sole essential constituents, the rocks are ultramafic. Similarly, if a rock of a specific family contains an abnormal amount of mafic minerals it may be referred to by the prefix *mela-*, as a melagranite, meladiorite, melasyenite, etc.

Sequence of Crystallization

The general order of crystallization from igneous magmas may be illustrated by Bowen's reaction series (Fig. 8). As a result of cooling, crystals that are precipitated at a given temperature are in equilbrium with the remaining liquid at that temperature. With continued cooling, earlier crystallized minerals no longer are in equilibrium with the magma, but will, if cooling takes place slowly, react with the liquid to change their composition or to form as new minerals. Thus the left-hand branch of the reaction series (Fig. 8) is discontinuous (involving formation of new species at the expense of different, older minerals), whereas the right-hand arm is continuous (forming plagioclase of progressively different composition). In many cases the time available for complete reaction was insufficient, and early minerals appear corroded, as relicts, cores, or zones.

It should not be assumed that one mineral completes its growth before others begin theirs, but rather that irregular time overlapping occurs. The exact sequence also depends in part on the composition of the magma, and in some cases simultaneous or partly simultaneous crystallization of mineral pairs takes place. In general the sequence is:

1. Early accessory minerals: magnetite, ilmenite, apatite, zircon, sphene

2. Anhydrous ferromagnesian silicates (olivine, pyroxenes) and calcic plagioclase

3. Hydrous ferromagnesian silicates (amphiboles, biotite) and intermediate to sodic plagioclase

4. Alkali feldspars and quartz
5. Late accessories: muscovite, fluorite, tourmaline
6. Exsolution minerals

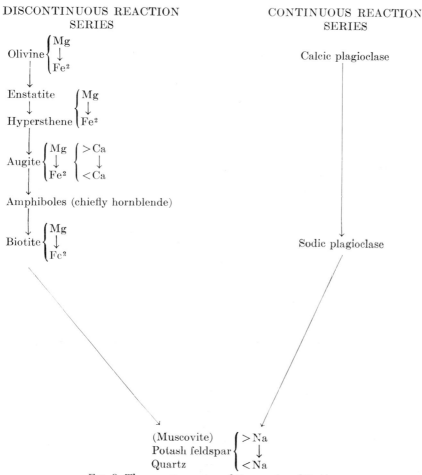

DISCONTINUOUS REACTION
SERIES

CONTINUOUS REACTION
SERIES

Olivine $\begin{cases} Mg \\ \downarrow \\ Fe^2 \end{cases}$

Calcic plagioclase

Enstatite
$\downarrow$
Hypersthene $\begin{cases} Mg \\ \downarrow \\ Fe^2 \end{cases}$

Augite $\begin{cases} Mg \\ \downarrow \\ Fe^2 \end{cases} \begin{cases} >Ca \\ \downarrow \\ <Ca \end{cases}$

Amphiboles (chiefly hornblende)

Biotite $\begin{cases} Mg \\ \downarrow \\ Fe^2 \end{cases}$

Sodic plagioclase

(Muscovite)
Potash feldspar $\begin{cases} >Na \\ \downarrow \\ <Na \end{cases}$
Quartz

FIG. 8. The reaction series of Bowen (modified).

In some nepheline syenites the sequence of crystallization is, in a general way, the reverse of that of calc-alkaline rocks, being:

1. Nepheline
2. Alkali feldspars
3. Zr and Ti silicates
4. Alkali (Na-Fe) pyroxenes
5. Alkali (Na-Fe) amphiboles

The large amounts of Na and Fe in the pyroxenes and amphiboles increase their solubility, and consequently they cannot separate until after feldspathoids and alkali feldspar and appear as interstitial anhedral units. This texture is called agpaitic.

Deuteric changes are those that take place during the last stages of magmatitic consolidation by reaction between remaining interstitial liquid and crystallized minerals: myrmekite, replacement perthite, muscovitization of biotite, and cancrinite replacing nepheline.

Hydrothermal alteration products are postmagmatic; the solutions may have been derived from the magma from which the rock crystallized or from unrelated magmatic sources. Common hydrothermal changes in igneous rocks result in the formation of albite, sericite, kaolinite and other clay minerals, carbonates, epidote, tourmaline, quartz, chlorite, zeolites, and serpentine. Many changes involve the formation of characteristic mineral aggregates—greisen, propylite, and saussurite. Some secondary minerals (limonite, kaolinite) also are formed by ground-water alteration and weathering.

Various textural criteria are available to aid in determining sequences of mineral formation, but many are ambiguous or open to more than one interpretation:

1. If one crystal encloses another (particularly of euhedral form), the enclosed crystal is earlier. This applies if the enclosed mineral crystallized from the magma and did not form by reaction in the solid state or through metasomatic replacement (which may be difficult to determine).

2. Early crystals are generally more nearly euhedral than later ones. Completely anhedral, interstitial grains, whose shapes are molded by the surrounding crystals, are normally last to form.

3. If a mineral forms crystals of different sizes, the presumption is that the larger crystals began to grow first. Phenocrysts are earlier than matrix minerals, but the distinction between phenocrysts and metacrysts in coarse-grained rocks may be difficult to make. In hypocrystalline rocks crystals formed prior to the solidification of glass.

4. In reaction rims and overgrowths the outer minerals are younger than the interior. Corroded relicts are older than the replacing materials.

5. Anhedral-granular, mosaic, and some micrographic textures indicate essentially simultaneous deposition.

6. Exsolved minerals are younger than their hosts.

3

DESCRIPTIONS OF IGNEOUS ROCKS

GRANITE-RHYOLITE FAMILY

Granite

Definition. Granite is plutonic and hypabyssal, holocrystalline, phaneritic, containing:

Quartz	10–40%
Potash feldspar	30–60
Sodic plagioclase (excluding perthite)	0–35
Mafics (biotite, hornblende)	35–10

If plagioclase exceeds potash feldspar, the rock becomes a granodiorite. With decrease in quartz the rocks pass into syenites.

Mineralogy. Two general groups of granites are commonly separated: (1) the more widespread, or calc-alkali, granites and (2) the alkali granites, typically rich in sodium. Each has a characteristic mineralogy:

Calc-alkali granite	*Alkali granite*
Perthitic orthoclase or microcline	Strongly perthitic orthoclase or microcline, anorthoclase
Oligoclase or rarely andesine	Albite or sodic oligoclase
Biotite ± muscovite	Iron-rich biotite
Hornblende	Hastingsite, arfvedsonite, riebeckite
Diopside or augite	Aegirine-augite, aegirine, rarely hedenbergite

The potash feldspar is orthoclase or microcline, more commonly the former. Both are usually crypto- or microperthitic. Anorthoclase occurs in some sodic granites. A gradation exists from cryptoperthite, through

29

microperthite and perthite to orthoclase (or microcline) plus albite in discrete grains. Coarsely perthitic microcline is associated with highly undulant or granulated quartz in some granites; the exsolution was facilitated by the stresses that deformed the quartz.

Orthoclase, anorthoclase, and also much less commonly microcline may show zoning. Carlsbad twinning is common in orthoclase and may also occur in microcline along with the ubiquitous gridiron twinning. Rarely the two feldspars occur together; if so, the microcline is the younger. Microcline is the normal feldspar in muscovite-biotite granites. Inclusions of hematite, zircon, apatite, plagioclase, quartz, and mafic minerals may be common. In some rocks, droplike inclusions of

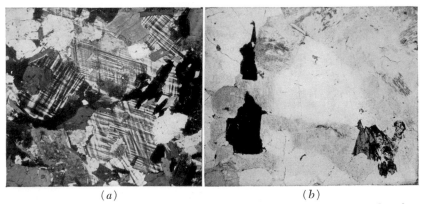

(*a*)   (*b*)

Fig. 9*a, b.* (*a*) Granite, Woodbury, Vermont. Microcline, quartz, oligoclase, biotite. Nicols crossed, ×9.5. (*b*) Alkali granite, Quincy, Massachusetts. Quartz, kaolinized orthoclase, riebeckite, zircon. Nicols not crossed, ×9.5.

quartz are especially abundant, and in a few cases the feldspar becomes poikilitic, enclosing quartz and/or oligoclase. Micropegmatite is widespread and abundant; some orthoclase grains grade into rims of micropegmatite. Anorthoclase, either twinned or untwinned, also may show zoning. In some cases a broad core with nonuniform extinction is set in a narrow, uniform frame. Rims of albite also occur, and inclusions of aegirine needles are common.

In porphyritic granites the phenocrysts are commonly microcline or orthoclase. All matrix minerals may be included, but biotite inclusions are particularly common. In granite porphyries sanidine also forms phenocrysts.

Potash feldspars are altered to kaolinite, other clay minerals, sericite (or coarse muscovite), and less usually to zeolites or chlorite. The feldspars commonly have a turbid aspect. Alteration may be zonal, along cleavages, or irregular.

In normal granites the plagioclase (exclusive of that in perthites) is sodic to intermediate oligoclase. In granites richer in mafics or containing pyroxene, andesine may be present. In alkali types the plagioclase is albite or oligoclase. Zoning of the normal type is common; very fine albite or albite plus Carlsbad twinning is characteristic. Rounded quartz inclusions may be zonally arranged. Myrmekite forms interstitial patches or marginal rims. Antiperthite also occurs. Plagioclase, which forms uncommon phenocrysts in some granite porphyries, shows zoning and may be rimmed by alkali feldspar. Plagioclase alters to sericite or coarse muscovite and clay minerals. Zonal replacement or even selective replacement of one set of twin lamellae is not uncommon. Usually plagioclase is altered before potash feldspar.

Quartz is normally interstitial, except in some granite porphyries in which it forms bipyramidal phenocrysts that may be corroded, deeply embayed, or even rounded. Much quartz also occurs in graphic intergrowths with the feldspars—with potash feldspar as micropegmatite and granophyre, and with plagioclase as myrmekite. In plutonic quartz inclusions of hairlike rutile may be present. Minute, irregularly distributed liquid–gas inclusions are common ("bubble trains"). Apatite and tourmaline are also included. Strain effects are widespread—undulatory extinction, anomalous biaxial character, mortar structure, or even crushing of the entire grain.

Biotite, the most common mafic mineral, is in some granites the only mafic; in others it occurs with muscovite, in still others with amphibole. The biotite of alkali granites is iron-rich, either Fe^2, Fe^3, or both, showing very strong absorption, and has usually been called lepidomelane. In calc-alkali granites the biotite is lighter brown, rarely green. Bird's-eye extinction is characteristic. Inclusions are zircon with its usual pleochroic halos, magnetite, ilmenite, apatite, allanite, xenotime, and quartz. Intergrowths with and overgrowths by muscovite are conspicuous in some granites. In granite porphyries biotite, as uncommon phenocrysts, shows partial or complete resorption to magnetite or magnetite and pyroxene. Biotite alters to chlorite (commonly pennine) with by-product magnetite, sphene, or rutile. Prior to this conversion, the biotite may be bleached green.

Muscovite occurs with biotite, very rarely alone. Much of it clearly replaces biotite, along margins, cleavages, or even in micrographic intergrowths; magnetite may be a by-product of this replacement. Some

coarse muscovite also forms by replacement of plagioclase. Pleochroic halos appear around zircon, and bird's-eye-extinction mottling
characterizes coarse flakes.

In calc-alkali granites the amphibole is green or brownish green
hornblende. Zoning may occur, and twinning on (100) is common.
Inclusions are magnetite, ilmenite, apatite, sphene, and zircon (with
halos). In some granite porphyries hornblende or oxyhornblende
forms phenocrysts, resorbed marginally or generally.

In alkali granites the amphibole is a sodic type—hastingsite, arfvedsonite, or riebeckite. Zoning is not uncommon, especially in arfvedsonite, in which brown cores are mantled by blue rims, or in which the
ends of irregular grains grade into riebeckite. Inclusions of aegirine
and aenigmatite may be present, and some arfvedsonite is mantled
by aegirine.

Uncommon diopside and augite are the pyroxenes in calc-alkali
granites; ferroan hypersthene is rare. Usually the pyroxene survives
as an irregular core in hornblende. Twinning on (100) is not uncommon, and various accessories, including haloed zircon, form inclusions.
In alkali types, aegirine-augite, aegirine (including acmite), or rarely
hedenbergite occur. Aegirine is replaced by riebeckite or arfvedsonite.

Accessories include magnetite, ilmenite, hematite, pyrite, apatite,
xenotime, monazite, zircon (may be zoned), allanite, sphene, tourmaline, fluorite, fayalite, and garnet (especially in muscovite types).
The allanite may be overgrown by epidote. Less widespread are andalusite, cordierite, and sillimanite. Alkali varieties may also contain
aenigmatite, astrophyllite, pyrochlore, and thorite. Astrophyllite occurs in elongate, light brown sheaves, usually in radial groups.

The alteration minerals are chlorite, calcite, epidote-clinozoisite,
zoisite, quartz, kaolinite and other clay minerals, sericite, zeolites,
leucoxene, sphene, rutile, magnetite, hematite, and limonite. Some
granite walls of hydrothermal cassiterite deposits show extensive replacement to greisen—an aggregate of quartz, lithium mica, topaz,
tourmaline, fluorite, and cassiterite. Others are transformed to topaz-
quartz aggregates, or are tourmalized (luxullianites) (Fig. 9c).

The main mineralogical types are biotite granite ("normal"), muscovite-biotite granite (binary or two-mica granite), hornblende-biotite
granite, hornblende granite, pyroxene granite, tourmaline granite,
riebeckite granite, arfvedsonite granite and aegirine granite. Some rare
granites are rich in quartz, containing nearly 60 per cent. The term
alaskite is an unnecessary name for a leucogranite. Granitite is an
obsolete name for the normal, i.e., biotitic, granite. Silexite and

arizonite were names given to quartzose-vein materials of presumed magmatic origin.

Textures and Microstructures. Granites are anhedral-granular, even-grained, fine- to coarse-grained, with the mafic constituents and plagioclase usually somewhat subhedral to euhedral and quartz and potash feldspar anhedral (Fig. 9a). Zircon, apatite, sphene, and magnetite are euhedral, but fluorite is characteristically interstitial. In alkali granites (Fig. 9b), the mafics may be entirely anhedral and even interstitial (agpaitic texture). Riebeckite, particularly, forms spongy, irregular crystals, including grains of feldspar and quartz.

Mafic minerals may be clustered in aggregates, as is biotite, or in strings, as is pyroxene (synneusis texture). In addition to the graphic quartz-feldspar intergrowths similar to dactylic intergrowths occur between biotite-muscovite, biotite-quartz, and biotite-orthoclase. In gneissoid types the mafics are sub-parallelly oriented, as are any phenocrysts.

Granites are not uncommonly porphyritic, the phenocrysts being orthoclase or microcline. In granite porphyries, however, phenocrysts of the mafic minerals as well as the feldspars and quartz occur. Quartz

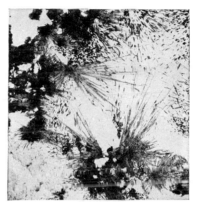

Fig. 9c. Tourmalinized granite, Cornwall, England. Fibrous tourmaline, quartz, topaz, *lower left*. Nicols not crossed, ×9.

may show considerable embayment or granophyric rims, and plagioclase phenocrysts may be armored by potash feldspar. Microgranites are merely very fine grained types.

Cataclastic effects are common—undulatory and biaxial quartz, mortar structure, bent feldspar cleavages and twin lamellae, mosaic structure in quartz and feldspar, and bent mica plates.

The aplitic texture is fine- and even-grained, saccharoidal, with sutured to interlocking grain boundaries. Aplites in the narrow sense are leucogranites with these textures (Fig. 10a), but all rock families contain representatives with aplitic textures. Likewise, pegmatite, in the narrow sense refers to leucogranitic dike and sill rocks of very coarse grain, but all families have pegmatitic types. Granitic and granodioritic pegmatites are by far the most common. In the rapakivi texture large porphyritic ovoids of orthoclase are surrounded by a

mantle of oligoclase and are set in a matrix of smaller rounded oligoclase grains, quartz, biotite, and hornblende. Orbicular structures
are well represented among granites. Miarolitic structures also occur.

Occurrence. Granites occur in all types of plutonic and hypabyssal
bodies, especially in batholiths, stocks, and plutons of various shapes
and sizes. Three general categories of granitic bodies are recognized:

1. Enormous plutons of pre-Cambrian shields
2. Batholiths in the cores of mountain ranges
3. Minor intrusives

Two contrasting structural types of granitic batholiths can be distinguished: (1) a type of rather variable composition, gneissic struc-

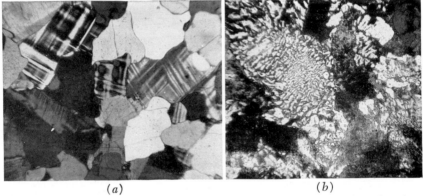

         (*a*)   (*b*)

FIG. 10. (*a*) Aplite, Waynesville, North Carolina. Microcline, quartz, oligoclase.
Nicols crossed, ×19. (*b*) Granophyre, San Luis Rey Quadrant, California. Orthoclase with intergrown quartz; magnetite. Nicols crossed, ×19.

ture with numerous oriented xenoliths, generally conformable
contacts, and migmatitic aureoles; (2) a type of more uniform composition, poor or nonfoliated structure, with crosscutting, sharp contacts, and a contact metamorphic aureole.

From the viewpoint of association, granite masses occur (1) by
themselves, (2) with subordinate quartz syenites and quartz monzonite, (3) with quartz syenites and alkali syenites, (4) as minor phases
of complex batholiths consisting mainly of tonalite and granodiorite,
and (5) rarely with syenites and nepheline syenites. Granite porphyries occur in independent stocks, laccoliths, and sheets or as
marginal phases of granite stocks.

Well-known examples of alkali granites include those of North

Conway, New Hampshire, and Quincy, Massachusetts. As examples of calc-alkali types may be cited the Pikes Peak and Silver Plume granites of Colorado, the granite of the Beartooth Range of Wyoming, and various granites of the Appalachian Mountains.

Rhyolite

Definition. Rhyolite is extrusive and hypabyssal; holocrystalline to hypocrystalline; with aphanitic matrix. Mineral composition is similar to granite. Alkali feldspar exceeds plagioclase; otherwise the rock belongs with the quartz latites. With a reduction in quartz, there is a gradation into trachytes.

Mineralogy. Two main types are present: potassic rhyolites, the more common, and sodic rhyolites. Their mineralogical differences resemble those of the two types of granite. Quartz occurs both as phenocrysts and in the matrix. Phenocrysts are bipyramids of α-quartz, pseudomorphous after β-quartz. They usually contain irregular inclusions of glass, which themselves carry bubbles of vapor. Matrix quartz may be very fine grained, or intergrown with alkali feldspar in complex patterns. Tridymite is not uncommon, either concentrated in coarser and more porous parts of the matrix or minutely disseminated through the matrix. Some of it forms aggregates of tiny plates, showing negative relief and low birefringence. It also occurs in vesicles as complexly twinned groups and is intergrown with alkali feldspar. Cristobalite is a rare, submicroscopic matrix constituent, whose identification usually requires x-ray methods.

The alkali feldspar is usually sanidine, but in hypabyssal types orthoclase microperthite and anorthoclase (in alkali types) may be present. Sanidine phenocrysts are usually clear and may be untwinned or twinned according to the Carlsbad law. Glass, rounded droplike quartz, and aegirine or aegirine-augite microlites are enclosed. The sanidine phenocrysts may show some optical (and compositional) variation from one to another in the same rock. Barian feldspars also appear, but not commonly. Spherulites of potash feldspar appear in the matrix of some types.

If plagioclase is present, it is usually in phenocrysts; matrix plagioclase is rare. The composition is normally oligoclase, but albite occurs in sodic types, and andesine also has been reported in a few rocks. In some rocks there is a considerable compositional variation in different plagioclase phenocrysts in the same rock.

Biotite, brown or less usually green, is likewise normally in phenocrysts, although scattered matrix flakes occur in some holocrystalline varieties. Phenocrysts are marginally or entirely resorbed to magnetite and pyroxene. Amphibole alone is rare; it typically occurs as phenocrysts with biotite and shows the usual resorption effects. Some rocks contain rare matrix amphibole. In potassic rhyolites the amphibole is brown or green hornblende. In sodic rhyolites and their porphyries, riebeckite, arfvedsonite, or hastingsite occurs. Riebeckite, which alters to acmite or a fine-grained magnetite-hematite-goethite-zircon mixture, may contain Zr.

Pyroxene-bearing rhyolites are not common. Diopside, augite, or rarely hypersthene are represented, either as phenocrysts or matrix granules. In sodic types diopside with aegirine-augite or aegirine rims, aegirine-augite, or aegirine forms phenocrysts. Aegirine and acmite appear in the matrix.

Accessory minerals are tridymite, cristobalite, titanian magnetite, cordierite, sphene, zircon, apatite, fayalite, garnet, fluorite (in holocrystalline types), rare graphite, and rare leucite (in alkali types and usually zeolitized). In the matrix of some rhyolites tridymite may be the chief or sole silica mineral, achieving the status of an essential constituent. Rhyolites with quartz phenocrysts also may have considerable matrix tridymite. Minerals of lithophysae include quartz, opal, sanidine, fayalite, tridymite, garnet, topaz, tourmaline, pseudobrookite, and cassiterite. The more common alteration products include quartz, chalcedony, calcite, magnetite, hematite, goethite, limonite, rutile, leucoxene, sphene, chlorite, kaolinite, sericite, epidote, and piedmontite.

Varietal names are at a minimum. The name quartz porphyry was applied to pre-Tertiary rhyolites. Liparite and nevadite are synonyms for rhyolite; panterellite for alkali rhyolite. Felsite is a general field or hand-specimen name for megascopically aphanitic, light-colored volcanic rocks, including rhyolite, quartz latite, trachyte, latite, dacite, and in some cases also andesite.

Textures and Microstructures. Many rhyolites are porphyritic, and a great variety of matrix textures are present.

Holocrystalline
  1. Microgranular (Fig. 11c)
  2. Pilotaxitic or felted
  3. Trachytic
  4. Granophyric (Fig. 10b)
  5. Spherulitic
  6. Cryptocrystalline; devitrified

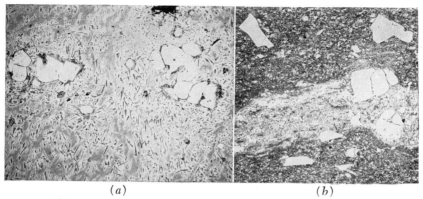

(a)   (b)

FIG. 11a, b. (a) Rhyolite vitrophyre, Arran, Scotland. Embayed quartz phenocrysts, augite microlites, glass. Nicols not crossed, ×8. (b) Rhyolite, Tendoy
Mountains, Montana. Quartz phenocrysts in a flow-banded crypto- to microcrystalline matrix. Nicols not crossed, ×8.

Hypocrystalline
1. Hyalopilitic—mainly microcrystalline with interstitial glass
2. Vitreous with cryptocrystalline patches
3. Vitreous with disseminated microlites
4. Vitreous with spherulites

Vitreous (rhyolite vitrophyres)
1. Glass alone or with disseminated crystallites (Fig. 11a)
2. Banded, streaked, swirly, and fluidal (eutaxitic)

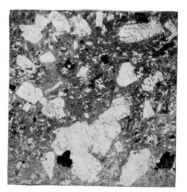

FIG. 11c. Rhyolite, San Juan Mountains, Colorado. Sanidine and biotite phenocrysts in microcrystalline matrix. Nicols not crossed, ×8.

Phenocryst minerals are quartz, sanidine, rare sodic plagioclase, biotite,
amphibole, and pyroxene. Anorthoclase and perthitic orthoclase also form
phenocrysts in some hypabyssal intrusives. Quartz and sanidine phenocrysts
may show embayment, corrosion, rounding, or fragmentation. The feldspars
also may be glomeroporphyritic or seriate porphyritic. Plagioclase and biotite
phenocrysts form rare parallel growths. The holocrystalline matrix
usually consists of alkali feldspar, quartz, pyroxene, and accessories.
Matrix potash feldspar forms anhedral grains of euhedral, stubby laths.
Granophyric texture consists of micrographic, vermicular, and lacy

intergrowths of guest quartz in host alkali feldspar (orthoclase and sanidine). Granophyre occurs as zones around feldspar crystals (both orthoclase and plagioclase), as interstitial patches between crystals, as general matrix material, and rarely as phenocrysts—large feldspar euhedra with intergrown quartz. Some dike rocks that consist to a large extent of this intergrowth are also called granophyres (Fig. 10*b*). Minor granophyre is a differentiate of many large diabase dikes and sills, but many rocks called granophyres are granodioritic in composition. Other granophyres are of metasomatic origin. Matrix albite or oligoclase in rhyolites may be anhedral or in stellate lath groups.

Spherulites are spheroids with radial-fibrous structure, in some cases combined with concentric layers. Most of the fibers are alkali feldspar. Many are straight, but forked, aborescent, and feathery types also occur. The spherulites display the characteristic pseudo interference figure. Where abundant spherulites are formed in juxtaposition, they assume polygonal outlines against one another. In some isolated spherulites, prismatic feldspar crystals project beyond the general periphery of the spherulite, so that the aggregate resembles an irregular cogwheel. Spherulites may be arranged in coalesced groups, elongated following flow directions. Axiolites, or ellipsoidal spherulites, may also be so oriented. Flow lines continue without interruption through spherulites. Although alkali feldspar is the chief constituent, cristobalite interstitial to the feldspar may also be present. In some alkali rhyolite dikes, alkali feldspar, sodic plagioclase, riebeckite, and acmite make up spherulites, some of which radiate from central phenocrysts of quartz or microperthitic feldspar. Matrix riebeckite is usually dendritic, poikilitic, or spongy.

Occurrence. Rhyolites occur as flows and other volcanic types and in hypabyssal intrusives, particularly dikes and sills. They are abundant and widespread in thick volcanic accumulations of orogenic regions, associated with andesite and basalt and minor latite and quartz latite. Well-studied rhyolites occur in the San Juan Mountains of Colorado and in Yellowstone National Park.

Obsidian and Related Rocks

Constituents. Obsidian is natural glass of rhyolitic composition. Phenocrysts are rare, but crystallites are common. Crystallites are skeletal crystal embryos (Fig. 6) whose development did not reach the stage at which the minute aggregate could polarize light; consequently they are isotropic. Round crystallites are called globulites; grouped globulites are cumulites. Rodlike forms are longulites; fernlike forms are scopulites; hairlike clusters or snarls are trichites; and beaded aggregates are margarites. The mineral forming the crystallites cannot be determined optically. With continued growth crystallites become microlites, small polarizing crystals that may be recognized as a particular mineral species. These are usually lath- or rodlike in form, and augite or feldspar are common. Spherulites also are constituents of rhyolitic glasses (Fig. 12c).

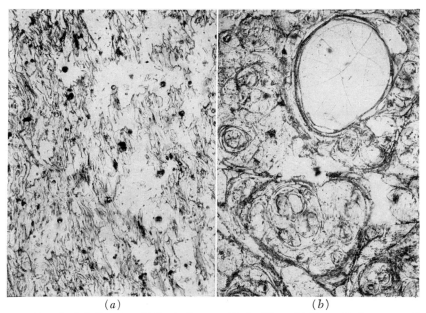

(a)   (b)

FIG. 12a, b. (a) Pumice, Millard County, Utah. Glass, highly vesicular, some directional texture. Nicols not crossed, ×11. (b) Perlite, Chaffee County, Colorado. Glass with multiple concentric fractures. Nicols not crossed, ×11.

A volcanic glass may represent the bulk composition of an igneous rock, but where phenocrysts or microlites are present, the composition of the glass generally differs from that of the rock as a whole.

The indices of refraction vary with the composition: rhyolitic glasses have an index range of 1.480 to 1.510, with a mean of about 1.495. For glasses of the composition of dacites, trachytes, and andesites the index varies from 1.490 to 1.530, with a mean near 1.512. Tachylites or basaltic glasses range in index from 1.505 to 1.620 and average around 1.575. Palagonite (altered basaltic glass) has a great variation in index, depending partly on the original composition and partly on the degree of alteration. The amount of any one element or oxide, even a major one, does not alone determine the index of the glass. Two glasses differing in their compositions by as much as 14 per cent SiO_2 may have the same index, or glasses with the same amounts of SiO_2 can show differences of as much as 0.065 in their refractive indices. However, a moderately close correlation between index and a major constituent (generally SiO_2) can be obtained by confining the study to glassy rocks belonging to the same petrographic province. Each province, however, has its own characteristic refractive index–composition curve for its glasses.

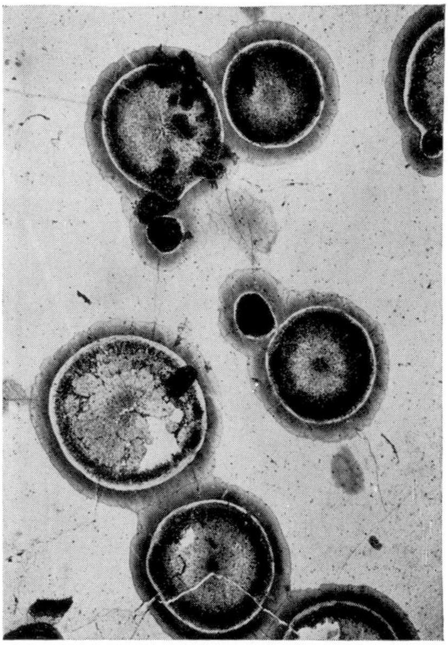

FIG. 12c. Spherulitic obsidian, Lipari, Italy. Feldspathic spherulites in glass. Nicols not crossed, ×11.

Many "glasses" are actually microcrystalline, for with age all glasses will eventually crystallize by means of a process called devitrification. Rocks older than Miocene generally contain devitrified "glass" rather than true glass. Devitrification, which is initiated along cracks, results in a submicroscopic mixture of various rock minerals and their alteration products. Usually individual mineral species are indistinguishable, but the jumbled aggregate is faintly birefringent (test with gypsum plate). In some cases mineral species can be recognized, and feldspars, clay minerals, and various forms of silica have been recorded as devitrification products.

Glasses are colorless to gray, brownish, or faintly red in thin section. The color is rarely diagnostic of the composition, even in hand specimen, for black glasses may be either rhyolitic or basaltic. Red glasses, however, are more typically rhyolitic.

Textures and Microstructures. Obsidians may be massive, but flow structures formed by the alignment of crystallites, microlites, spherulites, or differently colored bands commonly are present. Irregular swirls, streaks, and turbulent structures occur as well as lamellar flow structures.

Lithophysae and perlitic structures (Fig. 12b) also occur, and some rhyolitic glasses are highly vesicular. Lithophysae may contain a variety of well-crystallized minerals.

Varieties. Pitchstone is an obsidian with a waxy rather than glassy luster, which contains 4 to 10 per cent H_2O. In obsidian the water content is usually 1 per cent or less. Perlite is marked by numerous groups of multiple concentric cracks, arranged as onionlike partings (Fig. 12*b*). The centers of these fracture-encircled parts may break out as subrounded to subangular obsidian "pebbles" with concave surfaces. Pumice (Fig. 12*a*) is natural glass froth in which the volume of air space approaches, equals, or even exceeds the volume of glass. The cavities are usually attenuated, either straight or irregularly curved.

Occurrence. Obsidian occurs in individual flows rarely, usually as marginal parts of more crystalline flows. Pumice forms crusts on flows or volcanic ejectamenta—bombs and cinders. Some tuffs also consist principally of volcanic glass. The natural glass of Obsidian Cliff of Yellowstone Park is well known; other examples occur in south-central Colorado, in New Mexico, and in Arizona.

GRANODIORITE–QUARTZ LATITE FAMILY

Granodiorite

Definition. Granodiorite is intrusive, holocrystalline, phaneritic, containing:

Potash feldspar	20–40%
Sodic plagioclase	25–45
Quartz	35–10
Mafics (biotite, hornblende)	30–10

Granodiorite, as here defined, requires that the plagioclase equal or exceed the potash feldspar. If potash feldspar is in excess of plagioclase, the rock is placed with granite. If potash feldspar is present only in accessory amounts, the rock is a tonalite.

Mineralogy. The potash feldspar is orthoclase, or microcline, or their microperthitic and cryptoperthitic variants. The plagioclase, which averages oligoclase or less usually andesine, may be zoned. In some pyroxene-bearing types cores of laboradorite occur. Some antiperthite not uncommonly is present. The common mafic mineral is brown biotite, rarely green. Green hornblende is widely associated with it, in some types with incomplete shells of flaky biotite. Some varieties contain pyroxene, usually diopside or augite, very rarely hypersthene, which is rimmed or replaced by hornblende. Common accessories are apatite, magnetite, ilmenite, zircon, allanite, sphene, and garnet. The usual alteration products are sericite, kaolinite, calcite, chlorite, sphene, limonite, hematite, leucoxene, and quartz. Plagioclase may be saussuritized.

Mineralogical varieties are biotite granodiorite ("normal") (Fig. 12*d*), hornblende-biotite granodiorite, hornblende granodiorite, augite granodiorite, and hypersthene granodiorite. Lindgren restricted granodiorite to rocks in which plagioclase is at least double the potash feldspar. Rocks with less plagioclase he placed with quartz monzonites. Thus his divisions, on the orthoclase-plagioclase ratio, were 13⅓, 33⅓, and 66⅔ for tonalite, granodiorite, and quartz monzonite, respectively. These divisions are difficult to establish, whereas it is usually simpler to decide which feldspar predominates. Thus rocks called quartz monzonites are here partly in the granodiorite family, partly in the granite family. Adamellite is a substitute for quartz monzonite or even for quartz monzonite and granodiorite (Lindgren's sense) combined.

Fig. 12*d*. Granodiorite, Bitterroot Mountains, Idaho. Quartz, zoned oligoclase, biotite, orthoclase. Nicols crossed, ×9.5.

Textures and Microstructures. Granodiorite is usually equigranular, medium-grained. Aplitic and pegmatitic types also occur. Porphyritic granodiorites are not common; granodiorite porphyries are perhaps a little more common. Phenocrysts are potash feldspar, plagioclase, and mafic minerals; some potash feldspar phenocrysts are poikilitic. Some porphyries show fluidal patterns.

The normal texture is subhedral-granular, with gradations toward anhedral-granular in types richer in potash feldspar. Plagioclase and mafics show tendencies toward subhedralism; quartz and potash feldspar are anhedral. Quartz may show wavy extinction. Myrmekite, common in some types, is usually interstitial. A few rare types display orbicular structures; others may be gneissoid and even autoclastic.

Occurrence. Granodiorite occurs as a very common and widespread rock, in batholiths (both compound and simple), stocks, large sills and dikes, and irregular plutons. Granodiorite porphyries occur in dikes and sills and as marginal phases of larger granodiorite bodies.

Associated rocks are tonalites, gabbros, and subordinate granite, as in the great batholith of southern California, in which granodiorites are estimated to constitute 34 per cent. Other major granodiorite occurrences in the United States are in the Boulder batholith of Montana, in the Idaho batholith, in the Sierra Nevada Mountains of California, and in the Front Range of Colorado. Numerous and varied hydrothermal ore deposits are genetically associated with granodiorites.

Quartz Latite

Definition. Quartz latite is extrusive and hypabyssal, with aphanitic matrix; holocrystalline to vitreous, usually porphyritic; containing:

> Potash feldspar.......... 20–30%
> Sodic plagioclase........ 30–50
> Quartz................... 35–10
> Mafics................... 20–10

If quartz becomes accessory, the rocks grade into latites. With orthoclase reduced to an accessory, the gradation is into dacites. With more potash feldspar than plagioclase, the rocks are rhyolites. Types with abundant glass are difficult to classify.

Mineralogy. Sanidine is the usual potash feldspar. It may appear as phenocrysts alone, in the matrix alone, or in both. Plagioclase of the high-temperature type is the most common phenocryst mineral, usually normally or oscillatorily zoned and complexly twinned. The composition averages calcic andesine to oligoclase; cores of labradorite are uncommon. Biotite forms phenocrysts which are usually marginally or entirely resorbed. Green to olive hornblende, also as phenocrysts, shows various degrees of irregular alteration to oxyhornblende and marginal resorption to iron oxides. Some are entirely replaced by aggregates of augite, magnetite, and feldspar. In a few cases hornblende phenocrysts have been centrally replaced by biotite aggregates and marginally by magnetite-augite. Augite appears both as phenocrysts and matrix grains; hypersthene is uncommon. Rarely augite shows narrow hornblende coronas, which themselves are partly resorbed. Glass is an abundant constituent of some types. Some quartz latites contain quartz phenocrysts, and sphene also may appear in phenocrysts. Magnetite, ilmenite, apatite, sphene, zircon, tridymite, cristobalite, and rare garnet are the accessory minerals. The chief essential silica mineral of the groundmass not uncommonly is tridymite. Chlorite, epidote, zoisite, sericite, kaolinite, quartz, calcite, and hematite are the usual alteration products.

The names dellenite and rhyodacite are equivalents of quartz latite.

Textures and Microstructures. The texture is usually porphyritic with a holocrystalline, hypocrystalline, cryptocrystalline, and vitreous (quartz latite vitrophyre) groundmass. Glasses of this composition also occur. Phenocrysts can be any of the essential minerals; matrix minerals include chiefly the feldspars, quartz, and pyroxene. Feldspar phenocrysts may be broken and healed by matrix material. Quartz phenocrysts may show resorption embayments and large rounded inclusions of the matrix, which also appear in feldspar phenocrysts. Some types are seriate porphyritic with a very fine grained to cryptocrystalline matrix of potash feldspar and quartz. Biotite may form irregular nests of interlocking flakes, all enclosed in a large irregular biotite plate along with quartz and accessories. Matrix fabrics are trachytic, felted, microgranular, and locally micropegmatitic. In glassy and cryptocrystalline types, flow structures may be conspicuous. Tuffaceous and volcanic breccia types are also known

Occurrence. Quartz latites occur as flows and other volcanic rocks and also as sills and dikes (quartz latite porphyries), associated with rhyolites, dacites, and trachytes. Examples are found in Utah, Montana, California, and Colorado.

SYENITE-TRACHYTE FAMILY

Syenite

Definition. Syenite is intrusive, holocrystalline, phaneritic, containing:

Potash feldspar	30–80%
Sodic plagioclase	5–25
Mafics (biotite, amphibole, pyroxene)	40–10

Plagioclase may be absent or accessory. If plagioclase exceeds alkali feldspars, the rock is a monzonite.

Mineralogy. Syenites occur in two main types: (1) calc-akali, "normal," syenites and (2) alkali syenites. Their mineralogies contrast:

Calc-alkali syenite	*Alkali syenite*
Orthoclase, microperthitic orthoclase, rarely microcline	Micro- or cryptoperthitic orthoclase, anorthoclase
Oligoclase, less commonly andesine	Albite, sodic oligoclase
Biotite	Iron-rich biotite
Green hornblende	Arfvedsonite, hastingsite (including barkevikite)
Diopside or diopsidic augite	Titanian augite, aegirine-augite, aegirine
Accessory quartz	Accessory feldspathoids

In normal syenites (Fig. 13*a*) orthoclase or orthoclase microperthite is the dominant feldspar, in rare instances forming 90 per cent of the rocks. Microcline is much less common. Carlsbad twinning is pronounced, and hematite platelets may be included. In syenite porphyries and related hypabyssal intrusives, sanidine may form not only the phenocrysts but also the dominant matrix feldspar. Sodic plagioclase is rarely absent, and in some varieties it approaches potash feldspar in abundance. It is usually oligoclase, uncommonly andesine.

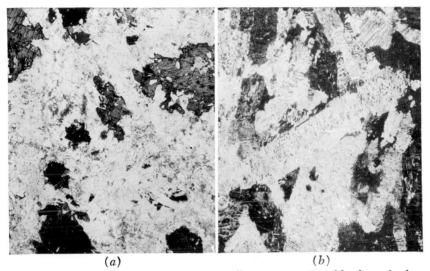

(*a*)   (*b*)

Fig. 13. (*a*) Hornblende syenite, Cuttingsville, Vermont. Hornblende, orthoclase, magnetite. Nicols not crossed, ×10. (*b*) Alkali syenite, Salem Neck, Massachusetts. Perthitic orthoclase, alkali amphibole. Nicols not crossed. ×10.

The common mafic mineral is brown biotite, but green hornblende is also widespread and may show color zoning and inclusions of various accessories. Diopside and diopsidic augite are less common. The pyroxene may be twinned and zoned with aegirine-augite rims or may be marginally uralitized.

If quartz is between 5 and 10 per cent, the rock is commonly referred to as a quartz syenite. Other accessories are zircon, apatite, sphene, magnetite, and ilmenite. A rare variety is a corundum syenite.

In alkali syenites (Fig. 13*b*) the alkali feldspars are more diversified: microperthitic, or cryptoperthitic orthoclase, or sodian orthoclase; anorthoclase; microperthitic microcline (less common); and microperthitic barian orthoclase and sanidine (in syenite porphyries). In many cases in porphyritic types anorthoclase phenocrysts may differ in composition, not only in different individuals but reportedly even in different twins of the same crystal. Zoning is widespread. Different potash feldspars have been reported together as phenocrysts in the same rock, as for example, anorthoclase plus microcline, or orthoclase plus microcline. Various combinations of porphyritic and matrix alkali feldspar occur, for example:

Phenocrysts	*Matrix*
Orthoclase microperthite.........	Orthoclase
Anorthoclase...................	Orthoclase
Anorthoclase...................	Barian orthoclase
Anorthoclase...................	Anorthoclase
Sanidine......................	Sanidine
Hyalophane...................	Sanidine

In addition to regular micro- and cryptoperthitic intergrowths, albite also is intergrown complexly as coarse blebs, patches, laths, and crystals, in some cases in such abundance that the crystals must be classed as orthoclase-albite composites. Microperthitic structure may be zonally arranged, or in rims alone, and overgrowths of albite are also common. Carlsbad twinning is common, both in phenocrysts and matrix potash feldspar. In addition to plagioclase, various other minerals such as aegirine, arfvedsonite, or sodalite may be included, and minute schiller inclusions also occur in some types.

Albite or sodic oligoclase also forms grains and crystals outside of perthitic intergrowths. In porphyritic types it is usually confined to the matrix, but albite phenocrysts also occur, some with rims of microperthite. Rarely plagioclase as calcic as andesine is present. Antiperthite and myrmekite also are recorded.

The mafic minerals also show marked compositional variations and varied combinations. Biotite is iron-rich and may become nearly opaque in position of maximum absorption. In some types the biotite is resorbed or rimmed by amphibole. The amphiboles usually are sodic—arfvedsonite and hastingsite (including barkevikite); riebeckite is less common. However, common green hornblende also occurs, either with or without sodic relatives. Zoning is not uncommon, with blue green or blue margins around green or brown interiors. Sodic amphiboles form overgrowths and replacements on sodic pyroxenes, and the converse also occurs, but less usually. Diopside and diopsidic augite as well as titanian augite are common, usually zoned with aegirine-augite or aegirine margins. Crystals of the two sodic pyroxenes also may be present together. Hypersthene is uncommon. If augite or aegirine-augite forms phenocrysts, the matrix pyroxene is aegirine. Augite may contain dark schiller inclusions along one or two sets of planes. Olivine syenites or olivine-bearing pyroxene syenites are not common. The iron-rich olivine may be crowded by ilmenite microlites parallel with (100), and borders of augite have been observed. Traces and accessory amounts of various feldspathoids, such as nepheline and sodalite, may be present, and alkali syenites grade into foidal syenites. However, other types of alkali syenites contain accessory quartz.

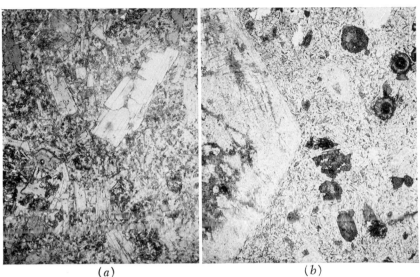

(*a*)   (*b*)

Fig. 14*a*, *b*. (*a*) Minette, New Mexico. Biotite phenocrysts in matrix of biotite, orthoclase. Nicols not crossed, ×10. (*b*) Aegirine syenite ("tinguaite"), Judith Mountains, Montana. Phenocrysts of anorthoclase, melanite (zoned), aegirine-augite (zoned) in matrix of aegirine, anorthoclase, albite. Nicols not crossed, ×10. (*Courtesy of S. R. Wallace, U.S. Geological Survey.*)

Accessories are zircon (may be very abundant), sphene, apatite, magnetite, and ilmenite. In alkali syenites, in addition, melanite (Fig. 14*b*), fluorite, calcite, aenigmatite, and eudialite may be present.

Alteration minerals are sericite, hydromica, and kaolinite (after feldspars); chlorite plus sphene (after biotite); chlorite, limonite, and calcite (after pyroxenes and amphiboles); leucoxene after ilmenite; serpentine and magnetite (after olivine); and zeolites after feldspathoids.

Among the normal syenites the main mineralogical varieties are biotite syenite, hornblende syenite, augite syenite, and quartz syenite.

Under the alkali syenites a great superfluity of varietal names has been coined, and in many cases petrographers do not even agree on their mineralogical definition. Here only a few of the more widely used (or misused!) varietal names are cited: Larvikite: cryptoperthitic sodian orthoclase or anorthoclase, oligoclase, 10 to 12 per cent mafics including diopsidic augite, aegirine-augite, and traces of hypersthene, olivine, biotite, and barkevikite; may have either accessory quartz or nepheline. Some rocks classed as larvikites are monzonites. Nordmarkite: 90 per cent orthoclase perthite or anorthoclase, no plagioclase, mafics biotite, green hornblende, or sodic amphibole, augite or aegirine, ± quartz. Bostonites are similar in mineralogy, porphyritic with a trachytic matrix. Pulaskite: chiefly orthoclase cryptoperthite, diopside and aegirine, arfvedsonite, and minor to accessory nepheline. Fenite: perthitic orthoclase or microcline, albite, 25 to 5 per cent aegirine, minor sodic hornblende.

Lamprophyric rocks of the syenite group are minette and vogesite, both dark porphyritic rocks. In minettes (Fig. 14a), biotite forms the principal phenocrysts in a matrix of sodium-rich orthoclase, biotite, and accessory hornblende and clinopyroxene. The biotite may be zoned, with light interiors and thin darker rims. In vogesites, hornblende predominates as phenocrysts in an orthoclase-hornblende matrix with accessory plagioclase, biotite, and clinopyroxene. These rocks are commonly altered markedly to calcite, chlorite, epidote, and quartz.

Textures and Microstructures. Most syenites are subhedral-granular in texture. Porphyritic syenites also occur uncommonly, but syenite porphyries are common in smaller intrusive masses. The grain size varies from fine to coarse. Gneissoid and fluidal textures result from the subparallelism of feldspar plates and laths. The bostonitic texture is fine-grained with subparallel arrangement of irregularly outlined feldspar tablets. In syenite porphyries the matrix may be trachytic. Aplitic and pegmatitic types are much less common than in the granites.

The potash feldspars tend to be subhedral rather than anhedral and form thin to thick tablets. Some micropegmatite may be present. The plagioclase is similar in development. Mafic constituents vary greatly in development—euhedral to anhedral. Biotite not rarely forms euhedral plates, hornblende slender prisms to needles. In some syenites the mafics, particularly the pyroxenes and amphiboles, are agglomerated around a single crystal of olivine or of magnetite or a group of these combined with apatite. The pyroxene generally is closest to this core, followed outward by the amphibole. Biotite similarly may be clustered around magnetite euhedra.

In general in the transition from normal to alkali syenites the mafics tend to become less euhedral, and in alkali syenites the mafics are generally anhedral.

Accessories such as apatite, zircon, sphene, melanite, and magnetite generally are euhedral, whereas quartz, fluorite, and feldspathoids are interstitial.

Occurrence. Syenites are relatively uncommon rocks. They occur as irregular plutons, stocks, dikes, and sills. Some syenites and quartz syenites occur as minor masses or border facies of large granite intrusives. Syenites, usually alkali types, have also formed as minor differentiates in layered laccoliths (Shonkin Sag, Montana). Syenites are also associated with pre-Cambrian norites (Adirondacks).

Trachyte

Definition. Trachyte is holocrystalline to hypocrystalline, rarely vitreous, with matrix aphanitic; extrusive and hypabyssal; containing:

Potash feldspar	45–80%
Sodic plagioclase	25 5
Mafics (biotite, amphibole, pyroxene)	30–10

With an increase in plagioclase, trachytes grade into latites, with more than accessory quartz into quartz latites, and with essential feldspathoids into phonolites.

Mineralogy. As in syenites, two main types are distinguished: normal and alkali (soda) trachytes. The potash feldspar is usually sanidine, less commonly anorthoclase or soda orthoclase. Perthitic structure and zonal structure are not uncommon; Carlsbad twinning may be present. Plagioclase is usually oligoclase in normal trachytes, albite in alkali trachytes, both of the high-temperature type. In some uncommon types phenocrysts of andesine and even labradorite occur sparingly. Parallel intergrowths of sanidine and sodic plagioclase have been noted, and some plagioclase phenocrysts are armored by sanidine. Sanidine phenocrysts may contain inclusions of mafic minerals, either aggregated in the center of the crystal or rarely in the margin. Peripheral zones of matrix inclusions, also glass, may be conspicuous. Where both porphyritic and matrix sanidine occur, the latter has a smaller 2V, indicating a lower sodium content. Analogously, phenocrysts of plagioclase are more calcic than any matrix plagioclase. Plagioclase phenocrysts show zoning commonly.

Biotite, the most common mafic, is brown to deep brown and nearly opaque in alkali types. It occurs almost exclusively as phenocrysts, showing partial or complete resorption to magnetite, pyroxene, and other granular minerals. In normal trachytes hornblende occurs chiefly in phenocrysts, which are usually accompanied by those of biotite and and also show resorption effects. Inclusions of various accessories are common in both minerals. In alkali trachytes the amphibole is arfvedsonite, barkevikite, or riebeckite. These amphiboles may also occur in the matrix, accompanied by accessory aenigmatite.

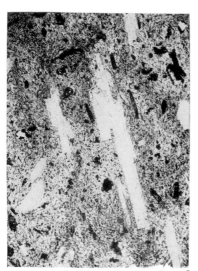

Fig. 14c. Alkali trachyte, Deadwood, South Dakota. Sanidine phenocrysts, aegirine microphenocrysts in a trachytic matrix of sanidine and aegirine. Nicols not crossed, ×10.

The pyroxene is usually diopside, in alkali types diopside, aegirine-augite, and aegirine (including acmite). Zoning of the normal type, with outer parts richer in Na and Fe^2, is widespread. Groundmass pyroxene in alkali trachytes is usually aegirine (Fig. 14c). Hypersthene also forms as uncommon phenocrysts in normal trachytes. Olivine, which occurs rarely, is normally iron-rich, but forsterite-bearing trachytes have been described.

Among the usual accessories are zircon, apatite (may show violet pleochroism), sphene, ilmenite, and magnetite. Some varieties contain quartz, in accessory amounts; others have tridymite. The alkali types may carry accessory feldspathoids—nepheline and analcite (phonolitic trachytes) and rare fluorite.

Secondary minerals are chlorite, calcite, magnetite, epidote, and opal in vesicles. Mineralogical varieties include biotite (normal) trachyte, biotite-hornblende biotite, augite trachyte, arfvedsonite (or barkevikite) trachyte, and riebeckite trachyte. Keratophyre (a deservedly obsolete term) is an albitized trachyte, usually with zeolites and epidote; some are magnetite-rich. The classic sanidinites of the Laacher Lake area, Germany, are actually pyrometamorphic-metasomatic xenoliths in trachyte flows and tuffs and are not strictly igneous rocks.

Rhomb porphyries, long regarded as alkali syenite porphyries, have been shown to be monzonite porphyries in which the rhomb-shaped feldspar phenocrysts consist of Ab_{55-60}, with exceedingly thin albite twin lamellae.

Orthoclase porphyries are hypabyssal trachyte porphyries with large, well-developed phenocrysts of orthoclase. Orthophyre is an obsolete term for older (pre-Tertiary) trachytes.

Textures and Microstructures. Most trachytes are porphyritic with a holocrystalline matrix. The phenocrysts are usually potash feldspar, biotite, or amphibole, less commonly plagioclase and pyroxene. The common matrix minerals are potash feldspar, plagioclase, alkali amphibole, and pyroxene, either augite or aegirine. A common matrix fabric is trachytic, with sanidine staves and laths in fluidal patterns around phenocrysts. If the matrix feldspars are stouter and randomly arranged, the texture is orthophyric. Vitrophyric textures are very rare, as are spherulitic and vesicular structures, although minute cavities may be filled with tridymite and opal. Tuffaceous types are not common.

Occurrence. Trachytes occur as volcanic rocks and minor hypabyssal intrusives; as subordinate components in the oceanic basalt association grading into phonolites; also as part of the continental olivine basalt association with phonolites and alkali rhyolites. Albitized types (keratophyres) occur with spilites. Some well-studied examples of North American trachytes occur near Leadville and Rosita, Colorado, and in the western part of Texas.

MONZONITE-LATITE FAMILY

Monzonite

Definition. Monzonite is intrusive, plutonic and hypabyssal, holocrystalline, phaneritic, containing:

Mafics (biotite, hornblende, augite)......... 15–60% (av. about 30)
Sodic plagioclase (andesine or oligoclase)..... 50–30
Potash feldspar (usually orthoclase)......... 45–20

Here monzonite is used in the extended sense, including not merely rocks with about equal amounts of sodic plagioclase and potash feldspar but also those in which sodic plagioclase exceeds potash feldspar (syenodiorites). With an increase in potash feldspar, so that it exceeds sodic plagioclase, monzonites grade into syenites. With a decrease in potash feldspar to accessory amounts they grade into diorites. With quartz becoming an essential mineral they pass into granodiorites.

Mineralogy. The plagioclase is andesine or oligoclase, but may be zoned (Fig. 14*d*); in some alkali types, very strongly (e.g., An_{60-15}) with labradorite cores and oligoclase rims. The alkali feldspar is usually orthoclase, rarely microcline, and may show zoning. In alkali types barian orthoclase and anorthoclase (or barian sanidine) occur, and the plagioclase may be albite.

Biotite, biotite plus hornblende, hornblende, hornblende plus augite are common mafic minerals and combinations. Augite alone also occurs, as does hypersthene, uncommonly. Olivine-bearing or olivine monzonites are not common. The olivine is of median composition. The biotite is light brown, hornblende green, and augite pale green. Augite may show color or microlite-inclusion zoning; biotite and orthoclase may also be included. In alkali monzonites titanian augite, aegirine-augite, and aegirine occur, not uncommonly in zoned crystals. In this type the amphibole is hastingsite (including barkevikite) or arfvedsonite and also may be zoned. Oxyhornblende appears in some monzonite porphyries.

FIG. 14*d*. Monzonite porphyry, Big Belt Mountains, Montana. Zoned andesine phenocrysts in microcrystalline matrix of sanidine, oligoclase, pyroxene, magnetite. Nicols crossed, ×10.

The numerous accessories include apatite, sphene, zircon, magnetite, ilmenite, allanite, garnet, pyrite, quartz or the feldspathoids nepheline, analcite, and sodalite. Alteration minerals are epidote, calcite, chlorite, kaolinite, sericite, nontronite, and serpentine.

Mineralogical varieties are biotite or biotite-hornblende monzonite, hornblende monzonite, augite monzonite, hypersthene monzonite, and olivine monzonite. Some rocks called essexites are monzonites.

Textures and Microstructures. The texture is equigranular-subhedral, fine- to medium-grained. Porphyritic monzonites are very rare, but monzonite porphyries are not uncommon (Fig. 14*d*). In the porphyries both feldspars may appear as phenocrysts, but usually potash feldspar is confined to the matrix. The mafics also form phenocrysts.

In equigranular types plagioclase is euhedral to subhedral, and potash feldspar is typically anhedral-interstitial or in large anhedra, poikilitically enclosing the other minerals. Antiperthite or potash feldspar shells may occur on plagioclase crystals, and these, in turn, may be rimmed by albite. Myrmekite may be present. Biotite and hornblende may be intergrown, and in some types biotite flakes surround magnetite-augite clusters. Hornblende replaces augite in some examples.

Aplitic, fluidal, and gneissoid textures also occur.

Occurrence. Monzonites occur as stocks, laccoliths, dikes, sills, and small plutons, also as marginal phases of granodiorite and diorite masses; not abundant. Associated rocks are syenites and foidal syenites. Well-studied representatives occur in the Big Belt and Bearpaw Mountains, Montana.

Latite

Definition. Latite is extrusive and hypabyssal intrusive; usually porphyritic with holocrystalline to vitreous aphanitic matrix. The composition is similar to that of monzonite.

Mineralogy. The plagioclase phenocrysts are of the high-temperature variety and usually zoned, with cores rarely as calcic as bytownite. Normally they are andesine, but labradorite or oligoclase phenocrysts are also known. Glass inclusions, which may be confined to cores, may be very abundant. Biotite plates are also included. Albite and albite-Ala twinning are common. Matrix plagioclase is andesine or oligoclase. Sanidine or anorthoclase forms uncommon phenocrysts, which may be corroded, but these feldspars are usually restricted to the groundmass. In some types potash feldspar shells have formed around plagioclase phenocrysts.

Biotite alone or with an amphibole or a pyroxene occurs mainly as phenocrysts, although in holocrystalline groundmasses it may also be present. The mica phenocrysts include euhedral plagioclase and apatite and may be bleached marginally or show the typical dark resorption rim. The amphibole is usually oxyhornblende or ordinary hornblende, also with the resorption border of iron oxides and pyroxene. Hornblende also may occur in a holocrystalline matrix. Diopsidic augite also may appear in two generations, more commonly as matrix microlites. Hypersthene is found in some rocks as phenocrysts. Aegirine-augite appears in some types. Olivine is very uncommon in extrusive types (mugearite).

Accessories are titanian magnetite, apatite, quartz, and tridymite or feldspathoids. Alteration minerals include calcite, quartz, chlorite, sericite, limonite, and leucoxene. Chlorite-leucoxene-sphene aggregates form pseudomorphs after amphibole; calcite-chlorite-sphene-leucoxene after pyroxene in some rocks.

Textures and Microstructures. The texture is usually porphyritic with a holocrystalline or hypocrystalline matrix; rarely with a vitreous matrix (latite vitrophyre) or very rarely entirely vitreous, without phenocrysts. Latite glasses can be distinguished mainly through chemical analysis. Many latites contain potash feldspar confined to the cryptocrystalline matrix and thus are recognized with difficulty. Holocrystalline matrix fabrics are pilotaxitic, trachytic, and microgranitic. Common phenocrysts are plagioclase, biotite, and hornblende. Latite porphyries are not common.

Occurrence. Latites occur as flows and uncommon hypabyssal intrusive bodies, associated with trachytes, quartz latites, basalts, and in some cases, rhyolites. United States examples occur on the western slope of the Sierra Nevadas and in the San Francisco Mountains of Arizona.

FOIDAL SYENITE—PHONOLITE FAMILY

Foidal Syenites

Definition. Foidal syenites are intrusive, plutonic and hypabyssal, phaneritic, holocrystalline, containing:

Alkali feldspar	35–80%
Feldspathoids	10–45
Sodic plagioclase	<5–45
Mafics (biotite, amphibole, pyroxene)	65–10

In most members of this family alkali feldspar exceeds feldspathoids; however, there are types with feldspathoids predominating, and a few rare types are feldspar-free. If plagioclase predominates over alkali feldspar, the rocks are more properly foidal monzonites. In most representatives the volume of light-colored minerals is greater than that of the dark, but in a few uncommon varieties the mafics total 50 per cent or more of the rock.

Mineralogy. Foidal syenites show a great diversity in mineral composition—the greatest of any of the rock families. Alkali feldspar varies considerably: orthoclase and microcline are not common, but orthoclase cryptoperthite, orthoclase microperthite, microcline cryptoperthite, microcline microperthite, anorthoclase, sanidine, and barian sanidine all are represented. Crystals of orthoclase and microcline may show zoning. One example has scattered central homogeneous orthoclase patches in a general core of cryptoperthite grading into a zone of coarser microperthite, and a rim of albite. Compositional zoning also may be present, as in barian sanidine, in which barium-rich cores grade into marginal zones poorer in barium. In such rocks, if porphyritic, the matrix feldspar is nearly free of barium. Carlsbad twinning is widespread; microcline shows grating twinning in various sizes. Inclusions of other minerals are very common and may be abundant

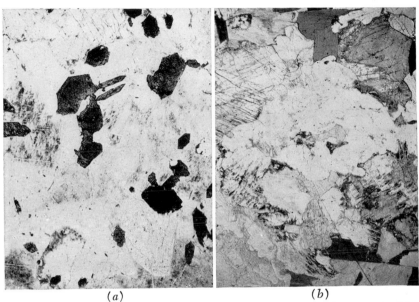

(*a*) (*b*)

FIG. 15*a, b.* (*a*) Nepheline syenite, Bearpaw Mountains, Montana. Aegirine (zoned), nepheline, orthoclase. Nicols not crossed, ×11. (*b*) Nepheline syenite, Bancroft, Ontario, Canada. Biotite, altered nepheline, orthoclase perthite, apatite, *upper right;* magnetite, calcite, *center.* Nicols not crossed, ×11.

enough to class the feldspar as poikilitic—aegirine, arfvedsonite, sodalite, nepheline, and cancrinite. Dustlike microlites also occur, and some feldspar contains oriented tiny scales of green biotite. Alkali feldspar is not uncommonly corroded and replaced by analcite. Plagioclase may be absent, but some varieties contain it in abundance. It is usually albite, less commonly oligoclase. Andesine occurs in some types rich in mafic minerals.

Nepheline is the most common feldspathoid, but in altered rocks its former presence may be very difficult to determine, for it is easily and abundantly replaced by sericite (gieseckite and liebnerite), by cancrinite, analcite, sodalite, and natrolite (including fine-grained varieties such as hydronephelite and "spreustein"). Zonal structure is not uncommon; inclusions are abundant—gas, liquid, microlites, biotite, aegirine, and sodalite.

Cancrinite, much of which is deuteric in origin, is abundant in some types. It resembles muscovite but has negative relief. Sodalite, including hackmannite in some types, is widespread. Some of it is blue or blue gray. It contains inclusions that may be zonally arranged of aegirine, arfvedsonite, and fluids. It alters to analcite and natrolite. Haüyne and nosean also occur in some rocks. Analcite is a common constituent, showing weak birefringence and cubic cleavage. Much of it is secondary and may replace feldspar, but primary potash analcite also occurs as clear phenocrysts. Leucite is not common, but does form in hypabyssal types. Much of it is altered to pseudoleucite. Main mineralogical types are commonly designated on the basis of the feldspathoids present: nepheline syenite, cancrinite syenite, analcite syenite, nepheline-cancrinite syenite, etc.

The amphibole is usually a sodic type—arfvedsonite, hastingsite (including barkevikite), less usually riebeckite. The variety kataphorite is widely reported. In some cases normal brown hornblende may be present. It is commonly zoned. Marginal and cleavage replacements by acmite together with hematite scales are not unusual. Inclusions are common and varied: apatite, magnetite, sphene, zircon, sodalite, nepheline, feldspar, and pyroxene.

The pyroxene also is sodic: aegirine-augite and aegirine (including acmite). Diopside, diopsidic augite, and titanian augite also occur. Hypersthene is exceptional, occurring only in cores of clinopyroxenes. Zonal structure is the rule, with cores of diopside, intermediate zones of aegirine-augite, and rims of aegirine, or cores of aegirine-augite and rims of aegirine (Fig. 15a). In some crystals as many as five distinct zones appear; others show oscillatory zoning instead of the normal type. The diopside core may be marginally corroded and replaced by aegirine ± fluorite. Several types of pyroxenes may occur together in separate crystals. In porphyritic types the matrix pyroxene normally is aegirine. Twinning is not conspicuous, except in titanian augite, which may also show hourglass structure. Inclusions of other minerals are common, especially centrally arranged. Cores of zoned individuals may be selectively replaced by calcite, ores, and biotite. Replacements by amphibole also occur.

Biotite (Fig. 15b), high in Fe^2, Fe^3, and Ti, usually shows golden brown to nearly black pleochroism, but some rocks contain green biotite, and in rare types two differently colored micas occur together. Darker borders framing lighter cores characterize any zonal structure. The mica replaces pyroxene; apatite, nepheline, cancrinite, and pyroxene form common inclusions.

A few rocks of the group contain essential fayalitic to intermediate olivine. The accessories are abundant and show the greatest variation of any rock family: apatite, titanian magnetite, fluorite, sphene, muscovite, melanite, perovskite, aenigmatite, zircon, eudialite, eucolite, and calcite. Rarer are corundum, astrophyllite, rinkite, lamprophyllite, mosandrite, lavenite, rosenbuschite, and sphalerite.

Alteration minerals are kaolinite, sericite, chlorite, calcite, iron oxides, epidote, analcite, natrolite, thomsonite, stilbite, pectolite, scapolite, and katapleite (after eudialite).

Because of the marked mineralogical and textural variations numerous varietal names appear in this family, most of which are of little value to petrographers. Here are listed only a few whose use has been more widespread, particularly in the older literature. Lardallites, until recently, were believed to contain anorthoclase or cryptoperthitic orthoclase feldspar. It has been shown that very finely twinned sodic plagioclase predominates. These rocks also contain nepheline ± sodalite, biotite, diopside—aegirine-augite, ± olivine, and barkevikite and thus should strictly be considered as nepheline monzonites. A miascite is a biotite-nepheline syenite with oligoclase. Shonkinite has been used for a wide variety of rocks (Fig. 16a), but as here employed it defines a mafic nepheline syenite with sanidine, augite, biotite, and olivine. In shonkinite from the type locality, Shonkin Sag laccolith, Montana, nepheline occurs only in remnants, but probably was present in considerable quantity and has been altered to natrolite and stilbite. However, shonkinite has also been used for mafic syenites containing aegiritic pyroxene, olivine, biotite, sanidine, and plagioclase (andesine to labradorite).

Among the feldspar-free members, there should be mentioned ijolite (Fig. 15c)—50 to 70 per cent nepheline, the rest mainly sodic pyroxene; urtite—70 per cent nepheline, the rest mainly sodic pyroxene; uncompahgrite—mainly melilite, a little diopside.

Textures and Microstructures. The textures of these rocks are as varied as their mineralogy. Most types tend to be equigranular, but the grain size ranges from fine to medium, to coarse, to pegmatitic. Most types tend to be equigranular, nonporphyritic. Two commonly recognized textures are the ditroitic, a subhedral-granular fabric, in which the essential minerals tend generally to be anhedral to sub-

hedral; and the foyaitic, a trachytoid fabric in which tabular feldspars and lath-shaped or prismatic mafic constituents are subparallelly
oriented, and the feldspathoids are anhedral. Between these two are
all gradations. Another fabric is the agpaitic, in which the feldspars
show a high degree of euhedralism and the mafics are anhedral,
molded between the feldspars and feldspathoids.

Cataclastic textures, with cracked, bent, and strained feldspars, are
not uncommon. Likewise, strongly fluidal textures characterize the

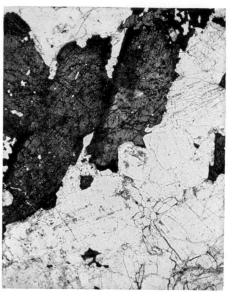

FIG. 15c. Ijolite, eastern Transvaal. Nepheline, barkevikite (zoned), apatite, *lower
right*. Nicols not crossed, ×11.

marginal parts of many intrusives. Aplitic and pegmatitic variants are
not uncommon.

Porphyritic nepheline syenites are not common, but foidal syenite
porphyries are important rocks in minor intrusives. Minerals forming
phenocrysts commonly are sanidine, barian sanidine, anorthoclase,
alkali amphibole, alkali pyroxene, and biotite. Less common as phenocrysts are olivine, nepheline, sodalite, leucite, analcite, apatite, magnetite, and lavenite.

The alkali feldspar tends to be at least subhedral, usually in tablets
with rectangular cross sections. Some grains are markedly poikilitic—
particularly toward sodalite. Nepheline is anhedral to euhedral and
may also be poikilitic with respect to sodalite as well as other min-

erals. Euhedral nepheline forms stubby to equant hexagonal prisms, with abundant inclusions that may be irregularly scattered in the core and zonally arranged in the margins. Anhedral nepheline forms large subrounded grains or angular interstitial pieces. Nepheline is rimmed and veined by sodalite and strongly corroded and replaced by analcite. Cancrinite appears as irregular flakes, rosettes, grain-boundary stringers, and pseudomorphs after nepheline. Sodalite, usually anhedral, may rarely be developed in euhedral dodecahedrons.

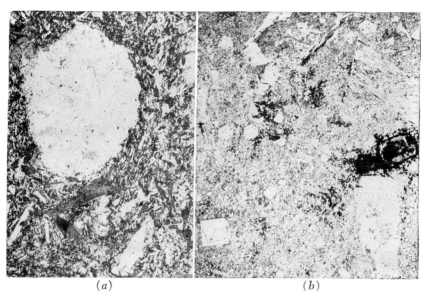

(a)　　　　　　　　　　　　　(b)

Fig. 16. (a) Pseudoleucite shonkinite, Bearpaw Mountains, Montana. Leucite phenocrysts altered to pseudoleucite; aegirine, sanidine. Nicols not crossed, ×10. (b) Nepheline phonolite, Bohemia. Phenocrysts of sanidine, nepheline, alkali amphibole (with resorption rim), in matrix of sanidine, nepheline, aegirine. Nicols not crossed, ×10.

Similarly analcite, normally anhedral and corroding feldspar and nepheline, occurs as clear icostetrahedral phenocrysts in some porphyritic types. It may be distinguished from similarly shaped leucite phenocrysts through lack of twinning and a slightly lower refractive index. Leucite may be unaltered but usually is replaced by pseudoleucite—commonly a mixture of sanidine and nepheline, with the nepheline altered in many cases to natrolite or analcite.

Amphibole is euhedral to anhedral; some large anhedra are poikilitic. Larger pyroxenes are also anhedral to euhedral, whereas smaller aegirine usually appears as needles and short, thin prisms. Intergrowths and overgrowths of both biotite and amphibole are present. Biotite forms tablets, shreds, and rosettes, the last commonly around magnetite. Aegirine-biotite aggregates rim augite grains. Biotite also forms reaction rims around olivine.

Deuteric reactions, which are widespread, result in numerous and varied overgrowths and intergrowths, some of which are micrographic. Other micrographic textures apparently are primary intergrowths.

MICROGRAPHIC INTERGROWTHS

Host	*Guest*
Alkali feldspar	Nepheline
Alkali feldspar	Cancrinite
Nepheline	Cancrinite
Nepheline	Sodalite
Aegirine	Aenigmatite
Aegirine-augite	Biotite
Arfvedsonite	Aenigmatite

Occurrence: Foidal syenites occur as stocks, laccoliths, sheets, dikes, sills, and other irregular, small to large plutons, commonly associated with alkali syenites, alkali granites, alkali and feldspathoidal gabbros, into which transitions may occur. All are rare rocks and are quantitatively insignificant compared to the total volume of granite or basalt, for example. In the United States, representatives occur at Red Hill, New Hampshire, in New Jersey, in Wisconsin, and in the Tertiary petrographic province along the front of the Rocky Mountains, particularly in Montana (Highwood Mountains) and in Texas (Big Bend area). Notable examples are also found in the Haliburton-Bancroft region of Ontario, Canada.

Phonolites

Definition. In historical usage phonolite has been restricted to rocks containing nepheline. Types without nepheline have been called trachytes with the appropriate mineralogical prefix, such as leucite trachyte, haüyne trachyte, etc. This separation is useless and confusing, and here the extended usage of phonolite is employed to cover the extrusive and aphanitic hypabyssal equivalents of all the feldspathoidal syenites. The mineral composition is:

Alkali feldspar	15–75%
Sodic plagioclase	0–30
Feldspathoids	10–40
Mafics	35–10

Sodic plagioclase is absent or subordinate to alkali feldspar. If the reverse is true, the rock belongs with the feldspathoidol latites. Rare types contain feldspathoids in excess of alkali feldspar. Normally the mafics total less than the light-colored constituents, but mafic phonolites are common in some areas.

Mineralogy. The alkali feldspar is usually sanidine, both in phenocrysts and matrix. Barian sanidine occurs in some areas; other rocks contain anorthoclase. Zoning may be conspicuous; in barian types the core typically is rich in Ba, whereas margins are poor in that element, and matrix sanidine will be largely Ba-free. Anorthoclase mantles around sanidine have been noted. Carlsbad is the usual twinning. Inclusions are abundant—magnetite, sphene, diopside, feldspathoids, either throughout the phenocrysts or in marginal parts. Matrix feldspar is generally free of inclusions and is uncommonly zoned. Alteration to zeolites is widespread. Zoned crystals may have cores selectively replaced by zeolites or sodalite. If plagioclase is present, it is normally albite or oligoclase, of the high-temperature variety in phenocrysts, although andesine characterizes some mafic phonolites. Zoning is very rare, and plagioclase phenocrysts are likewise rare.

Nepheline forms phenocrysts (Fig. 16*b*), smaller matrix euhedra, and anhedral matrix grains. If anhedral and altered, it may be very difficult to detect. In nepheline phenocrysts aegirine microlites, gas, and glass inclusions are arranged peripherally. Analcite, natrolite, other zeolites, and kaolinite are widespread as alteration minerals. Nosean, haüyne, and sodalite may be present as phenocrysts and as smaller matrix euhedra. Phenocrysts are richer in Ca, matrix euhedra poorer in Ca. Nosean also occurs interstitially. The phenocrysts are colorless, blue, blue gray, greenish, and yellowish dodecahedra, usually showing corrosion and embayment and commonly containing dust and microlite inclusions, marginally or centrally placed. The various members of the group commonly occur together. All other minerals, save the feldspars, may be included. Alterations to zeolites, calcite, and iron oxides are widespread.

Leucite, fresh, partly or entirely altered to pseudoleucite is common as trapezohedral (eight-sided) phenocrysts. A second generation of smaller, rounded crystals may occur in the matrix. The fresh phenocrysts show very weak birefringence, lamellar twinning in several directions, and inclusions of pyroxene, magnetite, apatite, and sanidine. Smaller crystals are isotropic with marginally arranged glass inclusions. Much leucite is replaced by a variably grained mixture of sanidine and nepheline (usually altered). In some rocks the coarser the matrix, the coarser the grain of the pseudoleucite, with marginal merging of the pseudoleucite units and the matrix. Pseudoleucite appears to replace either leucite or potassic analcite. Pseudoleucite appears to result chiefly from the interaction of potash-rich feldspathoid phenocrysts with the soda-rich residual liquid. However, some pseudoleucite may result from exsolution. Leucite also alters to analcite or zeolites.

Analcite occurs principally as a matrix or secondary mineral, although some rocks contain it as clear, cloudy, or zeolitized phenocrysts, which may be corroded by matrix sanidine.

Pyroxene, the most important mafic, occurs in phenocrysts and in the groundmass. In phenocrysts zoning is usual: cores of diopside, with intermediate zones of aegirine-augite and rims of aegirine; cores of aegirine-augite, rims of aegirine; rarely cores of acmite, rims of aegirine. Several green oscillatory zones may be present marginally. Some varieties are rich in Ti. Matrix pyroxene is normally aegirine. Phenocryst inclusions are matrix, apatite, magnetite, and sphene; some phenocrysts are sievelike in structure.

Amphibole, almost exclusively in phenocrysts, is usually a sodic type—commonly hastingsite and barkevikite, also arfvedsonite and riebeckite. Resorption rims of pyroxene and magnetite are very common; in some cases granular aegirine aggregates form pseudomorphs after amphibole. Biotite forms phenocrysts and also may occur in several generations of differing form and color in rocks with a granular matrix, particularly in reaction rims around pyroxene and olivine. Mica phenocrysts usually show strong resorption and may be represented only by pseudomorphs of iron oxides and pyroxenes.

Olivine occurs in some types in essential amounts, both as phenocrysts and in the matrix. The phenocrysts show resorption, with some having borders of pyroxene and magnetite, of hornblende and biotite, or of biotite alone. Iddingsite, serpentine, and magnetite replace olivine, which is magnesian to intermediate in composition.

Accessories are glass (rare), titanian magnetite, apatite, zircon, sphene, aenigmatite, pyrite, and melanite, which may be zoned. Among the alteration minerals are limonite, hematite, magnetite, chlorite, serpentine, iddingsite, sericite, calcite, kaolinite, analcite, natrolite, and chabazite. Minerals reported in vesicles include analcite, natrolite, thomsonite, and uncommon calcite and quartz crystals.

Various mineralogical prefixes can be used to designate the major varieties: leucite-nepheline phonolite, leucite phonolite ("leucite trachytes"), pseudoleucite phonolite, nosean phonolite, haüyne phonolite, sodalite phonolite, biotite phonolite, hornblende phonolite, mafic phonolite. Leucitophyre, a variably employed term, is a porphyritic leucite-nepheline-augite rock with minor sanidine. Tinguaites are green dike (or hypabyssal) phonolites, usually porphyritic, with a trachytoid to granular matrix, which normally contain alkali feldspar, nepheline, and aegirine or aegirine-augite. Other varieties of tinguaites also contain leucite, cancrinite, haüyne, analcite, biotite, melanite, arfvedsonite, or riebeckite. The term tinguaite is superfluous.

Textures and Microstructures. Most phonolites are porphyritic-holocrystalline. Although porphyritic phonolites are typical, phonolite porphyries are not uncommon. Glass is present rarely, in very minor amounts. Minerals forming phenocrysts are alkali feldspar, all feldspathoids including analcite and excepting cancrinite, zoned pyroxene, sodic amphibole, biotite, olivine, oligoclase and andesine, melanite, apatite, magnetite, and sphene. Some rocks contain analcite phenocrysts in a syneusis pattern. Many of the phenocrysts, particularly the feldspathoids, are developed in seriate porphyritic form, and there are some rocks that show three distinct generations of the same mineral.

Matrix sanidine usually forms small prismatic crystals, but much also is in anhedral patches, or in radial, plumose, lacy, or micrographic intergrowths with nepheline. Matrix nepheline is either in stubby hexagonal crystals, interstitial-anhedral, or intergrown variously and complexly with sanidine. The crystals may show rims of aegirine. Tangential aegirine needles or thin biotite plates around leucite or analcite result in a peculiar spotted appearance (ocellar texture).

Matrix textures are commonly trachytoid or granular; some approach pilotaxitic. Vesicular and amygdular structures are uncommon. The so-called tinguaitic texture covers a wide variation in fabrics, from porphyritic-trachytoid to porphyritic-granular.

Occurrence. Phonolites occur as flows and related extrusives, also in hypabyssal intrusives such as dikes, sills, and chonoliths. Phonolites are not common rocks. Minor amounts occur as associates of trachytes with oceanic olivine basalts. More commonly they occur with other volcanic and hypabyssal alkaline rocks such as orthoclase basalts, basanites, and trachytes in nonorogenic continental regions. In the United States well-studied phonolites occur in the Highwood Mountains, Montana; the Leucite Hills, Wyoming; at Cripple Creek, Colorado; as well as in the Black Hills of South Dakota and Wyoming.

TONALITE-DACITE FAMILY

Tonalite (Quartz Diorite)

Definition. Tonalite is intrusive, plutonic and hypabyssal, holocrystalline, phaneritic, containing:

Sodic plagioclase (oligoclase or andesine)........ 50–80%
Quartz...................................... 35–10
Mafics (biotite and hornblende chiefly).......... 35–10

Only accessory potash feldspar is present; with essential potash feldspar, the rocks become granodiorites. With a decrease in quartz the rocks grade into diorites.

Mineralogy. Plagioclase is usually oligoclase, less commonly andesine. Zoning may be present (Fig. 17a), although it is less common

Fig. 17a. Tonalite, San Luis Rey Quadrangle, California. Zoned andesine, quartz, hornblende. Nicols crossed, ×11.

than in diorites. In a few examples the variation is extreme, with irregular corroded core remnants of very calcic plagioclase. Examples are known of andesine cores with outer zones of potash oligoclase and overgrowth rims of anorthoclase. Fine albite lamellae are the usual twins. Inclusions of quartz, hornblende, biotite, iron oxide, and, less usually, pyroxene may be abundant. In other cases the plagioclase crystals are clouded with black, submicroscopic inclusions, generally zonally arranged. Accessory potash feldspar is normally orthoclase, less commonly microcline, rarely anorthoclase.

Biotite is the commonest mafic, either alone or with green hornblende. Hornblende alone is not common, nor are combinations of hornblende and augite. Augite alone is rare, as is the combination of augite and hypersthene. Pigeonite has been noted in the groundmass of some tonalite porphyries. Biotite is pleochroic in light brown shades; hornblende is green to brownish green and may have deep green rims and in some cases a polycrystalline fibrous core.

Accessories include magnetite, ilmenite, apatite, sphene, zircon, pyrite, garnet, and potash feldspar. Allanite is less common. Alteration minerals are chlorite, epidote, zoisite, sericite, kaolinite, sericite, limonite, and leucoxene.

A varietal name used considerably by European petrologists is trondhjemite—a quartz-rich tonalite. In this family a few rare lamprophyres are known, some of which carry labradorite phenocrysts.

Textures and Microstructures. The texture is usually medium-grained to fine-grained equigranular-subhedral. Porphyritic tonalites are rare; tonalite porphyries are uncommon. Phenocrysts can be of all the essential minerals, which occur in two generations, or the dark minerals, which may occur only in one generation. Aplitic, pegmatitic, gneissoid, and orbicular textures are uncommon to rare.

In the normal texture, biotite generally tends to be euhedral, plagioclase subhedral, quartz anhedral. Less usually plagioclase is developed in stout euhedral prisms, with quartz interstitial and mafics aggregated and molded between the feldspars. Hornblende may form overgrowth replacements on augite, and deuteric hornblende also forms veinlets transecting feldspar. In some varieties the amphibole is in large irregular crystals, poikilitically enclosing plagioclase. Quartz may appear in aggregates of grains. Any potash feldspar is usually interstitial or in rims. Minor myrmekite may be present.

Occurrence. Tonalites occur in individual plutons up to batholithic (?) dimensions (southern Alaska) more commonly as separate intrusions in complex granodiorite-tonalite batholiths. Tonalites are estimated to constitute 50 per cent of the great batholith of southern California. They also form marginal facies of dioritic bodies.

Dacite

Definition. Dacite is extrusive and hypabyssal, holocrystalline, hypocrystalline, uncommonly vitreous, with matrix aphanitic, usually porphyritic. Composition is generally like that of tonalite.

Mineralogy. The plagioclase averages andesine or oligoclase. Phenocrysts of high-temperature plagioclase usually are zoned, normally with andesine, calcic andesine, or labradorite (rarely bytownite) centers and with oligoclase and andesine margins. Phenocrysts of different size and An content may occur together. The matrix plagioclase is more sodic than that of the phenocrysts. Armoring by alkali feldspar is rare. Accessory potash feldspar, sanidine or anorthoclase, is otherwise generally confined to the matrix; rarely sanidine forms phenocrysts. Quartz occurs as phenocrysts alone, as phenocrysts and a matrix mineral, or as a matrix mineral alone. It may show marked rounding. Tridymite may be present in druses or in more coarsely crystalline parts of the groundmass. Biotite is usually present only as phenocrysts, but has been noted in small flakes in a holocrystalline matrix. Amphibole forms both phenocrysts and matrix crystals in some holocrystalline types. It is green or greenish brown hornblende or oxyhornblende (phenocrysts only). Two different types of hornblende may occur as phenocrysts in the same rock. Zoned hornblende phenocrysts consist of very pale green cores and brownish green margins. Ragged remnants of pyroxene may occur in amphibole cores.

Pyroxene dacites are apparently more common than pyroxene tonalites. The common representative is diopside or diopsidic augite, but hypersthene is widespread. Both can occur as phenocrysts and matrix constituents. Ortho- and clinopyroxenes occur singly, together, or with hornblende as phenocrysts. Hypersthene may be zoned and shows considerable variation in a single rock, with ranges as great as Fs_{32-48}.

Accessories are sanidine or anorthoclase, zircon, sphene, apatite, tridymite, fayalite, ilmenite, and magnetite. Druse minerals include tridymite, phlogopite, pargasite, and fayalite. Alteration products are sericite, kaolinite, calcite, chlorite, epidote, iron oxides, and zeolites.

Textures and Microstructures. Most dacites are porphyritic; phenocrysts are quartz, plagioclase, biotite, amphibole, pyroxene, apatite, and magnetite. A few dacites are vitreous with scattered microlites; these can be distinguished from similar rhyolites and quartz latites by chemical analysis and rarely by a determination of the refractive index of the glass. Perlitic textures are not uncommon, but spherulites are rare. Phenocrysts may be fractured and healed by glass. In the porphyritic types the matrix may be vitreous (dacite vitrophyre), hypocrystalline, or holocrystalline. With a vitreous matrix the phenocrysts tend toward a highly perfect outline but commonly are broken. In the hypocrystalline type the fabric is pilotaxitic or microgranitic. In the last, hornblende or very rarely biotite may occur in the matrix. Granophyric types are rare.

Quartz phenocrysts may show rounding and embayment. Biotite and hornblende phenocrysts have reaction rims of iron oxide, augite, and some hypersthene. Rarely hypersthene phenocrysts are rimmed by pigeonite granules or by fayalite. Matrix plagioclase is usually in small laths or is anhedral. Matrix quartz is anhedral; in some varieties radial aggregates with tridymite issue from a common center. Matrix pyroxene is granular or in slender needles. Alkali feldspar forms individual crystals, rims around plagioclase, or poikilitic inclusions in quartz.

Occurrence. Dacites occur as flows, associated with olivine basalts, andesites, and rhyolites, usually in continental orogenic regions (Cascade Range, northwestern United States).

DIORITE-ANDESITE FAMILY

Diorite

Definition. Diorite is intrusive, holocrystalline, phaneritic, containing:

Plagioclase (oligoclase or andesine). 55–70%
Mafics (commonly hornblende or biotite). 40–25

If the average plagioclase is more calcic than andesine, the rock belongs to the gabbro family. If quartz becomes essential, the rock is a tonalite. Diorites with essential feldspathoids are very rare.

Mineralogy. The plagioclase normally varies from calcic oligoclase to calcic andesine (Fig. 17*b*) and commonly shows marked normal-type zoning, so that its average composition must be estimated. Oscillatory and reverse zoning also occur. Augite diorites may even have plagioclase with labradorite cores; in some varieties albite forms the rim of zoned crystals. Included mafics, magnetite, and apatite are abundant. Potash feldspar (usually orthoclase) is present only in accessory amounts. Rare porphyritic dike rocks may contain labradorite or bytownite phenocrysts, with a predominant matrix rich in oligoclase.

The most common mafic mineral is hornblende, typically green, less commonly brownish. Color zoning may be present. Rare alkali diorites may contain a soda amphibole, near hastingsite. Biotite, brown to greenish brown, is also common, usually accompanying hornblende, with which it may be intergrown. Biotite diorites without hornblende are rare. Pyroxene is the least common type of mafic, with augite or diopsidic augite being more typical than hypersthene. Uralitic amphibole replaces pyroxene. Olivine diorites are known but are very rare.

Quartz, in accessory amounts, may be intergrown with orthoclase or very rarely microcline as micropegmatite or in some cases with plagioclase as myrmekite. Myrmekite also occurs as films along plagioclase-orthoclase grain boundaries. Other accessories are magnetite, ilmenite, apatite, sphene; less commonly, zircon, pyrite, pyrrhotite; rarely, olivine and allanite and in alkali types, nepheline.

The plagioclase alters to sericite or kaolinite, with calcic cores or zones preferentially replaced. Other secondary minerals are chlorite (from any of the mafics) accompanied by magnetite and sphene, calcite (from plagioclase, hornblende, or augite), epidote-zoisite (from plagioclase, augite, or hornblende) and hematite, limonite, and leucoxene. Accessories usually ascribed to contamination are garnet, spinel, andalusite, sillimanite, and cordierite.

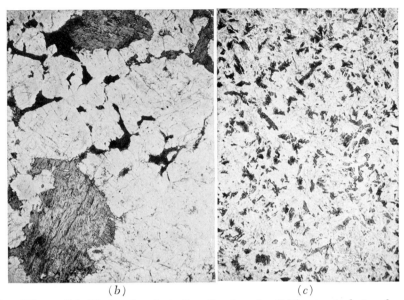

(b)   (c)

Fig. 17b, c. (b) Diorite, San Luis Rey Quadrangle, California. Andesine, hornblende, magnetite. Nicols not crossed, ×11. (c) Camptonite, Red Hill, New Hampshire. Andesine, hornblende, biotite. Nicols not crossed ×11.

Mineralogical varieties are hornblende (normal) diorite, biotite-hornblende diorite, biotite-augite diorite, augite diorite, hypersthene diorite, and olivine diorite. The dioritic lamprophyres include kersantite, spessartite, and camptonite (Fig. 17c). These are dark-colored rocks in which mafics equal or exceed the amount of feldspar. The feldspar is mainly in the matrix; plagioclase is very rare as phenocrysts. Many lamprophyres are greatly altered, and calcite may be so abundant that the rocks will effervesce with cold, dilute HCl. Other secondary minerals are chlorite, epidote, limonite, and leucoxene.

Textures and Microstructures. Diorite is usually equigranular, although porphyritic types with hornblende and/or plagioclase pheno-

	Kersantite	Spessartite	Camptonite
Plagioclase....	Matrix andesine, less commonly oligoclase	Matrix oligoclase	Matrix andesine
Biotite........	Phenocrysts and matrix	Accessory	Accessory or uncommonly as phenocrysts
Amphibole....	Subordinate green or brown hornblende usually present in matrix	Phenocrysts and matrix brown or green hornblende	Phenocrysts and matrix barkevikite
Pyroxene.....	Usually some subordinate matrix diopsidic augite or titanian augite; rarely as phenocrysts	Diopsidic augite may be accessory, rarely essential	Less common phenocrysts and matrix titanian augite
Olivine.......	Uncommon and minor as phenocrysts	Absent	Accessory to essential phenocrysts
Accessories....	Magnetite, ilmenite, apatite, pyrite, quartz, orthoclase, glass	Apatite, magnetite, sphene, orthoclase, quartz	Apatite, titanian magnetite, pyrite, sphene

crysts may be found. The texture varies from anhedral granular to subhedral granular. Plagioclase outlines may be relatively regular; quartz and orthoclase are interstitial. The mafics may be segregated in clusters. Both the mafics and plagioclase may be oriented in not uncommon gneissoid textures. In some types amphibole is markedly poikilitic. Symplectitic plagioclase-hornblende intergrowths are formed through recrystallization along grain boundaries. Orbicular structures are rare. In diorite porphyries plagioclase phenocrysts normally appear as broad laths in section. In dioritic lamprophyres the mafic minerals form the phenocrysts and also appear in the matrix; plagioclase very rarely forms phenocrysts. Some lamprophyres are nonporphyritic and are fine-, even-grained rocks with a tendency of most constituents toward euhedralism—the panidiomorphic texture. In many cases the matrix is pilotaxitic; rarely hyalopilitic. Amygdules are known.

Occurrence. Bodies of diorite occur in large intrusives such as complex batholiths, either as marginal phases (Vermilion granite, Minnesota) or as separate intrusive masses (southern California). Diorites

also form the peripheral phases of smaller dominantly granitic, granodioritic, and syenitic bodies and occur as single dikes and stocks of
limited dimensions. Another noteworthy United States occurrence is
in the Adirondacks.

Andesite

Definition. Andesite is volcanic and hypabyssal intrusive, holocrystalline or hypocrystalline, with matrix aphanitic, and having the
same general mineral composition as diorite.

Mineralogy. The normal plagioclase ranges from oligoclase to calcic
andesine. Where phenocrysts occur, the matrix plagioclase is more
sodic, and the average of all plagioclase should be more sodic than
Ab_{50} in order for the rock to qualify as an andesite. Phenocrysts of
labradorite may occur. In some districts an extreme range in plagioclase composition occurs in a single rock, with a few phenocrysts of
bytownite, some microphenocrysts of labradorite, and abundant microlites of andesine. The phenocrysts are high-temperature plagioclase,
and most of them show zoning of various types, especially normal, but
also oscillatory and calcic-core types. Cores as calcic as anorthite are
recorded. In some andesites two distinct types of plagioclase phenocrysts may be present, which differ in the details of their zoning,
twinning, and average composition. Irregular or rounded inclusions
of brown glass are common and may be abundant, usually in cores or
in zones (Fig. 18*b*). Iron ore inclusions are also prevalent, as are many
of the other rock minerals. The matrix plagioclase is not zoned. Sanidine is uncommon but has been reported as rims on plagioclase
phenocrysts. Anorthoclase occurs rarely as a matrix feldspar.

A single mafic mineral as phenocrysts is uncommon. Biotite and
hornblende commonly occur together, as do hornblende and diopside
or diopsidic augite, and diopside or diopsidic augite and hypersthene.
The most common andesite is one in which hornblende predominates
as phenocrysts. Biotite phenocrysts appear in six-sided plates or lath-
shaped cross sections, but the mineral appears rarely in the matrix.
The phenocrysts show varying degrees of corrosion and resorption. In
early stages the reaction rim is a crust of fine-grained augite, magnetite, and hematite $\pm$ feldspar. With complete resorption the former
presence of biotite is indicated only by the pseudomorph of granular
iron oxides and pyroxene. Biotite andesites commonly contain an SiO_2
matrix mineral in minor amounts. Biotite is uncommon in pyroxene
andesites.

Hornblende, brown or green, and oxyhornblende form prismatic phenocrysts. Like biotite, hornblende is exceptional as a matrix mineral. Corrosion effects similar to those of biotites typically are present. The amount of resorption increases with increasing crystallinity of the matrix, and resorption effects on phenocrysts in a glassy matrix are not pronounced.

The common pyroxene phenocrysts are diopside, diopsidic augite (Fig. 18a), and hypersthene. Sodic pyroxenes appear rarely. Augite

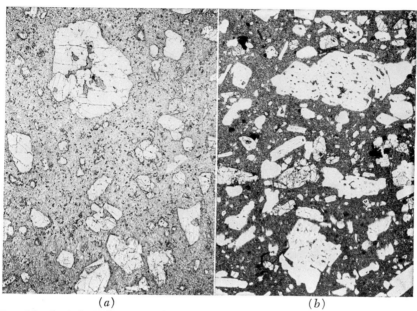

(a)   (b)

Fig. 18a, b. (a) Andesite, Tendoy Mountains, Montana. Diopsidic augite phenocrysts in matrix of andesine and augite. Nicols not crossed, ×11. (b) Andesite, San Juan Mountains, Colorado. Andesine (with inclusions of glass) and augite phenocrysts with magnetite in cryptocrystalline matrix. Nicols not crossed, ×11.

forms phenocrysts less commonly, and pigeonite appears as phenocrysts very rarely. Augite is a common matrix pyroxene, but some andesites also have pigeonite, or augite plus pigeonite, or rarely hypersthene in the groundmass. Both normal and reverse zoning occur in pyroxene phenocrysts. In augite and hypersthene the latter type is exemplified by Mg-rich borders, in pigeonite by Ca-rich borders. Inclusions of glass, magnetite, and plagioclase occur in pyroxene phenocrysts. Olivine is not uncommon in pyroxene andesites, as phenocrysts and as matrix grains. Matrix olivines contain less Mg than do phenocrysts in the same rock. Corrosion rims occur around the phenocrysts.

Quartz is rare in andesites, although it has been recorded as strongly resorbed phenocrysts (or xenocrysts?) (Fig. 18c), with granular augite coronas, and also as spongy matrix intergrowths with alkali feldspar. Cristobalite occurs in the matrix as minute spherulites attached to walls of vesicles, and tridymite also is found in gas cavities and in reaction rims on hornblende phenocrysts.

Euhedral apatite crystals appear as inclusions in mafic phenocrysts or in the groundmass; central parts may be filled with pleochroic inclusions. Magnetite granules or octahedra are important matrix constituents, and ilmenite plates are found in some andesites. Zircon and sphene are relatively uncommon. Cordierite has been reported as an unusual accessory from a number of localities.

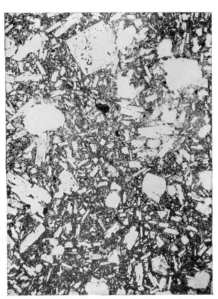

FIG. 18c. Andesite, Modoc, California. Andesine in seriate-porphyritic texture, quartz xenocryst, *upper left;* matrix andesine and augite. Nicols not crossed, ×11.

The glass of andesites is colorless, gray, pale green, yellow brown, and brown. Minute bubbles, iron oxide specks, and various crystallites are usually present. The index of refraction is in the range 1.49 to 1.54 but some andesites contain glass with $n = 1.48$, and others have some glass with $n = 1.60$. In a single specimen the index of refraction and color may show considerable variation.

Vesicle minerals are calcite, chlorite, cristobalite, quartz, opal, hornblende, piedmontite, and sodic plagioclase. Alteration products are similar to those of diorites and include sericite, calcite, epidote-zoisite, phlogopite, chlorite with sphene and magnetite, iddingsite, leucoxene, hematite, and limonite. Matrix glass may show devitrification; glass inclusions in minerals are more commonly fresh. Mineralogical varieties are designated by the name of the predominant mafic phenocryst minerals, such as biotite andesite, hornblende (normal) andesite, augite andesite, hypersthene andesite.

Textures and Microstructures. Nearly all andesites are porphyritic, and the groundmass is commonly holocrystalline. Various phenocrysts occur singly, as several intergrown in parallel position or as irregular clusters. Glassy and partly crystalline types also occur, and those varieties that contain a glassy matrix with relatively few phenocrysts (andesite vitrophyre) may be difficult to distinguish from similarly textured dacites or latites. Trachytic textures are common, with plagioclase microlites "flowing" around various phenocrysts. Pilotaxitic textures also appear, with felted microlite aggregates, and hyalopilitic textures are found in the more silicic types, with abundant glass containing various microlites. Vesicular, scoriaceous, and amygdular textures are not rare, and in some cases vesicles are filled by later infiltrations of fine-grained matrix material. In some types there is no marked size hiatus between phenocrysts and microlites, and every size intergradation appears (Fig. 18c). Mineral overgrowths include monoclinic pyroxene on hypersthene and hypersthene on olivine. Nonporphyritic, holocrystalline microgranular textures are rarely found. Other textural varieties are vesicular andesite and andesite porphyry. The term porphyrite formerly was used in referring to a pre-Tertiary andesite.

Occurrence. Andesites occur typically as flows and pyroclastic rocks associated with basalts and rhyolites in continental orogenic regions; also to a lesser extent (andesite porphyry) as sills, dikes, necks, and other minor intrusive bodies. In the United States, andesites are well represented in the San Juan Mountains of Colorado and in the Cascade Range of Washington, Oregon, and northern California.

GABBRO-BASALT FAMILY

Gabbro

Definition. Gabbro is intrusive, plutonic, holocrystalline, phaneritic, containing:

Mafics (augite, hypersthene, or olivine, less commonly
   hornblende)... 25–50%
Plagioclase (labradorite or bytownite)................... 70–45

If the plagioclase is less calcic than labradorite, the rock belongs in the diorite family. Some low-silica, dark-colored rocks containing olivine and plagioclase of the andesine range are by some investigators included as gabbros. Such rocks are better classed as mafic diorites or meladiorites.

This composition applies to all gabbroic members except anorthosite, in which the mafics become subordinate or accessory constituents, and the greatly predominant to sole essential mineral is calcic plagioclase (Fig. 20*a*). Some such rocks, field-labeled as anorthosites, actually consist primarily of andesine and should be termed andesinites.

Mineralogy. The main rock types that are included under the term gabbro in the larger sense are:

Name	Essential minerals
Gabbro (strict sense)	Augite, calcic plagioclase
Olivine gabbro	Augite, olivine, calcic plagioclase
Troctolite	Olivine, calcic plagioclase
Norite	Hypersthene, calcic plagioclase
Anorthosite	Calcic plagioclase

In addition, there are hyperites—rocks intermediate between gabbros and norites, which contain both essential clino- and orthopyroxene. Other types are olivine norites and olivine hyperites, and, if hornblende is primary, i.e., magmatic and not uralitic, there can also be distinguished hornblende gabbros and hornblende norites. A few rare types, which contain essential quartz (in excess of 5 per cent) are termed quartz gabbro and quartz norite. Some rocks erroneously called essexites ("Oslo type") are mafic gabbros, with labradorite, titanian augite, barkevikite, olivine, biotite, and variable amounts of orthoclase.

The plagioclase normally is labradorite or bytownite, but anorthite is not uncommon, for example, in the gabbroic rocks of the southern California batholith. Gabbroic rocks containing anorthite formerly were called eucrites. In a regional assemblage of gabbroic rocks the most calcic plagioclase may occur in olivine-bearing types, less calcic in clinopyroxene varieties, and least calcic in norites and hyperites. The plagioclase, which is uncommonly zoned, typically shows broad albite twin lamellae, and combined albite-Carlsbad twins are also common. Pericline twinning is not uncommon. If zoned, the zoning is usually normal or of the calcic-core type. Zoning appears to become more common with decreasing An content. The feldspar may have a grayish cast and in many cases is characterized by innumerable minute inclusions—needles, rods, plates, or spheroids, oriented parallel along various major crystallographic planes. These inclusions, which produce a schiller, may be confined to the core. They consist mainly of hematite, magnetite, and ilmenite and are formed chiefly as the result of exsolution. Other minerals, such as augite, hypersthene, and hornblende may also be included, usually in central parts. Orthoclase is absent, except as an uncommon accessory.

The pyroxene of the most common ("normal") gabbro is augite or diopsidic augite (Fig. 19b). Some of it (diallage) shows a prominent parting parallel with (100). The combination of twinning on (100) and striations parallel with (001) gives rise to "herringbone" structure. Numerous oriented inclusions of ilmenite and other iron minerals, formed by exsolution, may give rise to a schiller effect Ortho pyroxene lamellae also may be exsolved. Titanian augite may show concentric or hourglass zoning or a combination of these, as well as anomalous interference colors owing to dispersion.

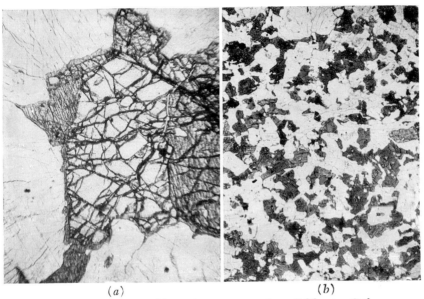

(a) (b)

FIG. 19a, b. (a) Olivine gabbro, Cuyamaca region, California. Orthopyroxene corona, followed by hornblende corona on olivine, in bytownite. Nicols not crossed, ×21. (b) Gabbro, Cuyamaca region, California. Labradorite, augite, hornblende, magnetite. Nicols not crossed, ×10.

In norites and hyperites, hypersthene becomes either the dominant or accompanying pyroxene (Fig. 19c). It may be pleochroic and also contains exsolved plates of hematite, ilmenite, etc., as minute oriented inclusions. Lamellar intergrowths with one, two, or three sets of clinopyroxene lamellae may occur. These intergrowths result from the inversion of initial pigeonite to hypersthene and the segregation of diopside or augite as exsolution lamellae. Enstatite is very uncommon in these rocks. In a related assemblage of norites iron increases in the hypersthenes as anorthite decreases in the accompanying plagioclases.

The olivine is generally of intermediate composition, but a few iron-rich gabbros (ferrogabbros) have fayalite. Olivine gabbros (Fig. 19*a*) and troctolites are less common than pyroxene gabbros. Olivine norites likewise are not so common as other norites. Grains of magnetite may be included in the olivine, and exsolved oriented needles and tablets of iron minerals may be very abundant. In olivine types the plagioclase usually is bytownite or more calcic.

Gabbroic rocks with primary hornblende are only locally abundant.

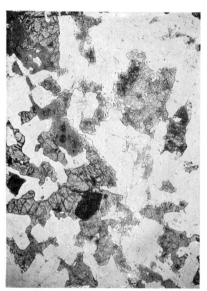

Secondary hornblende is common as a replacement of pyroxene and in fibrous rims around olivine. The color of the primary hornblende is commonly brown, less commonly green. Oriented microlites may also be present. Secondary amphibole is generally green to pale green. Primary hornblende is not common in olivine gabbros. Some gabbroic rocks contain hornblendes of two generations, differing in color and other optical properties.

Biotite occurs in some types as an accessory; in a few norites and gabbros it becomes an essential mineral. Quartz, likewise, may be present in traces, especially in norites and hornblende gabbros, and in a few quartz gabbros it is an essential constituent.

Fig. 19*c*. Norite, Wichita Mountains, Oklahoma. Labradorite, hypersthene, biotite, magnetite. Nicols not crossed, ×10.

The chief accessories are apatite, magnetite, ilmenite, and spinel (both picotite and pleonaste). Less common are pyrite, pyrrhotite, garnet, and sphene, and traces of feldspathoids in alkalic types. Chromite is accessory in some troctolites. Some more silicic gabbros contain accessory orthoclase or micropegmatite. Many norites also contain such accessories as sillimanite, andalusite, cordierite, and garnet believed to result from wall-rock contamination.

The plagioclase alters to saussurite, a mixture chiefly of albite and zoisite or other epidote-group minerals as well as varying amounts of chlorite, actinolite, orthoclase, and other minerals. The pyroxenes, which may be replaced by amphiboles, are also altered to chlorite, talc, and serpentine. Olivine is altered to serpentine plus magnetite.

Augite, hypersthene, and olivine may be accessory in anorthosites, and traces of quartz, myrmekite, micropegmatite, perthite, or anti-perthite may be present. Rutile, corundum, and pyrope are additional possible accessories. In pre-Cambrian anorthositic plutons the plagio-clase is usually labradorite or even andesine, whereas that in anortho-sites of layered lopoliths is bytownite.

Textures and Microstructures. Gabbros are normally coarse- to medium-grained, subhedral granular; pegmatitic types also occur but are not common. Norites tend toward anhedral-granular. Porphyritic types (plagioclase phenocrysts) are rare, but gneissoid and banded textures are not uncommon. Both plagioclase and olivine may show preferred orientations. A few orbicular gabbros are known. In some plutons the grain size, texture, and mineral composition vary markedly within short distances (autoinjection structure). Apatite and mag netite are euhedral; pyroxene, olivine, and plagioclase subhedral; any quartz and orthoclase are interstitial.

Corona structures (or "reaction rims"), particularly around olivine (Fig. 19a), but also around magnetite and pyroxene where these min-erals are in contact with plagioclase, are widespread and conspicuous. The central rounded olivine is surrounded by a rim of fibrous enstatite or hypersthene. This may in turn be enveloped by a second corona of fibrous actinolitic hornblende, in which pleonaste grains appear. Gar-net, tremolite, actinolite, anthophyllite, and cummingtonite also ap-pear in the rims, in which the fibers are set generally normal to the contacts. Deuteric overgrowths and replacements of augite and hy-persthene by nonfibrous hornblende (uralite) are also widespread; the hornblende in turn is replaced by biotite. Hornblende also forms very large, subhedral poikilitic crystals. In norites hypersthene may be rimmed by augite. Cataclastic textures, with fractured, bent, and marginally granulated crystals, may be well developed. Flaser gab-bros are also recorded. In anorthosites, flow and banded structures are common; cataclastic and even mylonitic textures locally are well de-veloped. Anorthosites are commonly coarse-grained (Fig. 20a). The mafic minerals may be strung in synneusis textures or clustered. Plu-mose myrmekite may form a conspicuous interstitial constituent.

Occurrence. Gabbros and norites occur (1) as minor marginal phases of batholiths; (2) as early bodies in complex batholiths (south-ern California); as individual plutons, which may be layered (Skaer-gaard, Greenland); and (3) as units in layered peridotitic lopoliths. Troctolites are associated with peridotites. Anorthosites occur either (1) as large pre-Cambrian plutons in which the plagioclase is labra-

dorite or andesine (Adirondacks, New York), associated with pyroxene granites, syenites, and monzonites (southern Norway), (2) as
units in peridotitic lopoliths, in which the plagioclase is bytownite
(Stillwater complex, Montana), or (3) as segregations of strictly limited dimensions in gabbro masses.

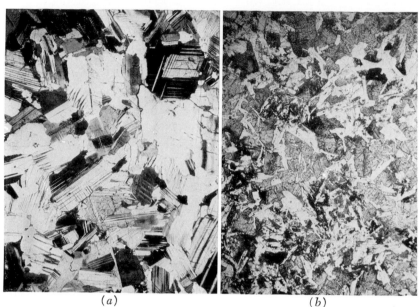

(a)   (b)

FIG. 20. (a) Anorthosite, San Luis Rey Quadrangle, California. Bytownite. Nicols
crossed, ×10. (b) Diabase, Dillon, Montana. Labradorite, augite, magnetite;
ophitic texture. Nicols not crossed, ×10.

Diabase

Definition. Diabase is intrusive, hypabyssal, normally holocrystalline, usually containing:

> Mafics (various pyroxenes, less commonly olivine)........ 65–25%
> Plagioclase (labradorite, less commonly bytownite)....... 30–70

Diabases differ from gabbros chiefly in their textural characteristics
and occurrences and to a lesser extent in the nature of the pyroxenes.
Dolerite is the English equivalent for diabase.

Mineralogy. The plagioclase laths usually are zoned, in some cases
normally, with cores of either labradorite or bytownite and margins
of labradorite, andesine, or even oligoclase. In other cases the zoning
is extremely variable, involving reversals, rhythmic layering, resorp-

tions, and repairs. Albite and albite plus Carlsbad twinning are typical; pericline twinning is not rare; and other twin types (Manebach, Ala) may also be present.

The pyroxenes are present in great variety and may show extreme ranges in composition: enstatite to hypersthene, magnesian pigeonite to ferroan pigeonite, diopsidic augite to subcalcic ferroan augite. The orthopyroxenes of the range Of_{15-35} may show fine-grained graphic intergrowths with exsolved clinopyroxenes, resulting in mottled extinction, for the entire grain, the cores, or the margins. This relationship is the same as in the plutonic gabbros, except that in diabases cooling was more rapid, and the exsolved units are smaller and less well segregated. Both pigeonite and augite may show zoning. Some augite is purple, owing to Ti; the mineral may be untwinned or very complexly twinned.

Olivine varies from magnesian types to near fayalite, which is not common. Not uncommonly there is a general range in composition in a single rock, or even thin section, the smaller olivine grains usually being richer in iron. Rarely normal-type zoning occurs in single crystals. Oxyhornblende, or hornblende, may also be present, and in slightly alkalic types hastingsite may occur. Uralitic hornblende is usually green. Biotite, which may be a titanian variety, can be accessory or essential. Accessories include titanian or chromian magnetite, ilmenite, picotite, apatite, analcite, quartz, and granophyre (quartz plus orthoclase or anorthoclase). Varieties with more than 5 per cent of quartz are quartz diabases and are not rare. Uncommon marginal phases of some diabase dikes contain small amounts of glass. Alteration products are saussurite after plagioclase, serpentine (including bowlingite), iddingsite and magnetite after olivine, serpentine and chlorite after pyroxene, and calcite and prehnite. In diabases associated with spilites the labradorite has been extensively albitized and the mafic minerals converted to various secondary constituents.

Textures and Microstructures. Textures are fine- to medium-grained and even-grained. Pegmatitic types occur as local facies. The texture typically is ophitic (Fig. 20b), with slender to broad plagioclase laths wrapped or molded by anhedral to subhedral pyroxene, the larger plates of which may also enclose the plagioclase. In the subophitic types this relationship is less well developed, and the pyroxenes tend toward subhedralism and form rounded smaller grains between feldspars. Very rarely phenocrysts of plagioclase or of augite appear as individuals or in clusters. The plagioclase laths may be seriate in size-range distribution. Rims of alkali feldspar are thin and not common.

Magnesian olivine forms large subhedral crystals, with gradations to small, rounded, subophitic grains at the fayalite end of the series.

The relationships among the various pyroxenes are complex. In addition to zoned augite and pigeonite, the two may occur together as separate individuals, with or without orthopyroxene. Augite and ferroan augite also may be present as individual grains, with or without pigeonite. For both pigeonite and augite magnesian varieties tend to form larger, more nearly euhedral individuals, whereas the ferroan types are ophitic to granular. Overgrowths are numerous:

Core of olivine, zone of pigeonite, zone of bronzite, rim of augite
Embayed core of pigeonite, rim of bronzite
Columnar core of pigeonite, rim of hypersthene
Columnar core of pigeonite, rim of augite
Columnar core of augite, rim of ferroan pigeonite

Olivines may have reaction rims of pigeonite or orthopyroxene; the pyroxenes have rims of hornblende or biotite.

Apatite forms euhedral prisms or needles. Magnetite is typically skeletal, molded between plagioclase or mafic minerals. Quartz or granophyre is interstitial. Vesicles filled with chlorite, calcite, and quartz may be present.

Occurrence. Diabases occur as sills, dikes, sheets, laccoliths, plugs, and less regular hypabyssal intrusive bodies, usually in swarms widespread over very large areas, as, for example, in the Karoo system of South Africa and in the pre-Cambrian areas of Montana, Wyoming, and Colorado. Some of the larger sills or sheets have been differentiated *in situ,* mainly through crystal settling, and also contain schlieren and veins of granophyre and diabase pegmatite. Other well-known United States occurrences include those in the pre-Cambrian of northern Minnesota, Wisconsin, and Michigan and in the Triassic of Connecticut and New Jersey.

Basalt

Definition. Basalt is volcanic and uncommonly hypabyssal intrusive, holocrystalline, hypocrystalline rarely vitreous, with matrix aphanitic, containing:

Plagioclase (labradorite).................... 40–60%
Mafics (clinopyroxene and olivine).......... 55–35

Mineralogy. The average composition of the plagioclase must be labradorite or more calcic for the rock to be classed as a basalt. Usually there is considerable variation in composition: phenocrysts are anorthite, bytownite, or commonly labradorite and not uncommonly are zoned normally with broad homogeneous cores and several thin marginal rims. More complex and irregular zoning may also occur. Smaller phenocrysts (Fig. 21b) are usually more sodic, and matrix plagioclase is still more sodic and may be andesine; for example:

Phenocryst core.............. An_{78}
Phenocryst border........... An_{62}
Microphenocryst............. An_{64}
Matrix plagioclase........... An_{56}

Plagioclase phenocrysts are of the high-temperature type. Glass inclusions, zonally arranged, and olivine inclusions are common, and albite, pericline, and Carlsbad twinning are well developed.

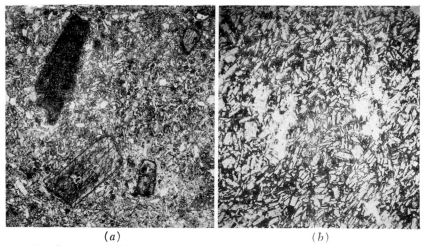

(a)   (b)

FIG. 21a, b. (a) Hornblende basalt, Tendoy Mountains, Montana. Oxyhornblende phenocrysts with resorbed margins in matrix of labradorite, augite, magnetite. Nicols not crossed, ×10. (b) Basalt, Modoc, California. Labradorite microphenocrysts in cryptocrystalline matrix containing some augite. Nicols not crossed, ×10.

In coarser-grained basalts the larger pyroxene crystals are diopsidic augite, whereas the smaller granules are pigeonite. In finer-grained types a single metastable pyroxene, subcalcic augite, is present. Like the plagioclase, the clinopyroxenes may be seriate in size distribution, with a gradation in composition from diopsidic augite in the larger phenocrysts, normal augite or subcalcic augite in the microphenocrysts, and pigeonite in the matrix granules. Phenocrysts that are zoned likewise have less calcic margins. Augite phenocrysts are neutral, brownish, light green, or light purple (Ti) in color; color zoning including the hourglass type is conspicuous, as are twinning and inclusions of apatite, magnetite, and glass. Hypersthene (very rarely enstatite) also forms phenocrysts, but less commonly than augite. Basalts with hypersthene phenocrysts may also carry clinopyroxene phenocrysts and pigeonitic matrix pyroxene.

Olivine (Fig. 21c) likewise may show compositional variation in single rock slices, the smaller grains becoming richer in Fe^2, and ranges as great as Fo_{76-54} have been reported. Some crystals are zoned, with narrow ferroan rims. Other mafic minerals are oxyhornblende as phenocrysts, with corroded and resorbed margins (Fig. 21a) and uncommon biotite as matrix scales, especially around magnetite grains. Quartz is accessory, but if present in amounts more than 5 per cent, the rocks are quartz basalts. Xenocrystic quartz pieces also may be abundant and are rimmed by shells of glass and augite laths. Cristobalite is widespread in the matrix of some basalts; tridymite is less common. Orthoclase, if present, is normally an accessory, but in some rocks it becomes an essential mineral.

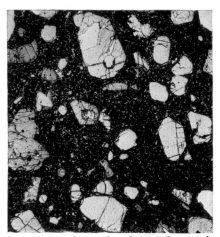

Fig. 21c. Olivine basalt, Modoc, California. Olivine and augite phenocrysts in fine-grained matrix of labradorite, augite, and magnetite. Nicols not crossed, ×10.

Trachybasalt is a term for an olivine basalt with some orthoclase, sodic amphibole, and biotite. Other accessories are apatite, titanian magnetite, picotite, and ilmenite; zircon is uncommon. Feldspathoids occur as accessories in alkalic types. Glass may be an essential or accessory constituent; it commonly contains iron oxide dendrites. Amygdular fillings consist of the normal rock minerals and zeolites, calcite, and quartz.

The pyroxenes alter to chlorite (including a fine-grained variety commonly called chlorophaeite), nontronite, serpentine, and carbonate; olivine mainly to iddingsite (rims or pseudomorphs) or to serpentine or nontronite. The feldspars are usually fresh, but may be kaolinized or chloritized. Mineralogical varieties are quartz basalt, olivine basalt, hypersthene basalt, and hornblende basalt. Melaphyre is an obsolete term for an older (Carboniferous-Permian) basalt. Tholeiite is widely used for the continental flood-type basalt. Picrite basalt is a poor name for an olivine-rich, mafic basalt. Spilites are basalts with albitized labradorite and augite altered to actinolite, chlorite, and epidote and serpentinized olivine.

Textures and Microstructures. Basalts show a great variety of textures from vitreous to holocrystalline types. The main ones are:

1. Vitreous. Chiefly light brown glass ($n = 1.505$ to 1.620, average about 1.575) with crystallites (globulites, trichites, etc.) and minor microlites. Called tachylite. Its altered or hydrous equivalent, composed of glass remnants, cryptocrystalline material, microlites of augite, olivine, and labradorite and secondary zeolites, carbonate, and chlorite, is palagonite.
2. Hypocrystalline
   a. A dominant vitreous matrix with subordinate phenocrysts—vitrophyric texture; rock is basalt vitrophyre.
   b. Variable amounts of rounded to irregular spherulites of radially arranged plagioclase microlites, in a matrix of dominant to nearly absent glass or cryptocrystalline material—variolitic texture; rock is a variolite.
   c. Matrix mainly microcrystalline, with subordinate triangular patches of interstitial glass between feldspar laths—intersertal texture.
   d. Matrix mainly of microcrystalline plagioclase laths, and augite granules in fluxion pattern. Glass is subordinate and in irregular areas—hyalopilitic texture.
3. Holocrystalline
   a. Matrix dominantly feldspar microlites—pilotaxitic texture.
   b. Matrix mainly pyroxene granules and minor interstitial plagioclase—granulitic texture.
   c. Matrix of plagioclase microlites "wrapped" by anhedral pyroxene—ophitic texture.

Most basalts are porphyritic or glomeroporphyritic, although holocrystalline nonporphyritic types occur rarely. The phenocrysts are plagioclase, olivine, augite, diopsidic augite, hypersthene, or various combinations of these. Some basalts contain marble- to head-sized nodules containing principally olivine and minor enstatite, chromian diopside, and picotite, regarded as dunite xenoliths. Basaltic explosive materials and rocks are common—cinders, lapilli, bombs, and tuffs (both glass and crystal) and agglomerates. Vesicular and cellular textures (basalt scoria) likewise are widespread.

Some plagioclase phenocrysts may be broken or corroded. Matrix plagioclase usually forms slender laths, which may be oriented in flow structures. Olivine shows considerable shape variation, from anhedral grains through skeletal laths to euhedral crystals. Embayed phenocrysts also occur, and in glassy types, olivine phenocrysts may be "hollow", i.e., frames of olivine and fillings of glass. Reaction rims of granular pigeonite, single hypersthene crystals, or hypersthene-vermicular magnetite mixtures may surround olivine. Reaction rims of augite or of augite plus subgraphically intergrown olivine have formed around hypersthene phenocrysts (believed to be xenocrystic) in some basalts.

Magnetite forms euhedral octahedra and cubes, skeletal crystals, and rounded grains. Ilmenite may appear as a hexagonal skeletal framework in magnetite.

Occurrence. Basalt is the most abundant of extrusive rocks, occurring chiefly as flows and also as pyroclastics. Three main geological associations are recognized:

1. Flood or plateau basalt ("tholeiitic" type)—quartz diabase association. Occurs in great thicknesses over very large areas, for example, the Keweenawan (pre-Cambrian) lavas of the Lake Superior region —15,000 ft thick; the Columbia River–Snake River plains of Washington and Oregon of Miocene age, with an area of 200,000 square miles; and the Triassic "traps" of New Jersey.

2. Olivine basalts of oceanic areas, usually associated with minor trachyte and phonolite. Example: the basalts of the Hawaiian Islands.

3. Basalt-andesite-dacite-rhyolite association of orogenic regions, such as the San Juan region of Colorado.

FOIDAL GABBRO–FOIDAL BASALT FAMILY

Foidal Gabbro

Definition. The mafic feldspathoidal rocks, which vary widely in mineralogy, can be divided conveniently into two major groups: one with essential calcic plagioclase, the other without essential calcic plagioclase. Both groups are mafic, in that ferromagnesian minerals equal or exceed light-colored constituents, and both carry essential feldspathoids. The rocks, which are intrusive and mainly holocrystalline, usually phaneritic, are very rare, but a multiplicity of minor mineralogical varieties have been described and named. Only the more prominent members of the family are considered.

Main Types. Because of their variable mineralogy, the chief representatives can be best described individually.

Types with essential calcic plagioclase

1. Theralites

Augite and olivine................ 45–80%
Labradorite...................... 35–15
Nephelene........................ 15–5
Accessories... Biotite, barkevikite, apatite, magnetite, ilmenite,
        analcite

2. Teschenites

Mafics (titanian augite, barkevikite).......... 45–75%
Labradorite... 30–10
Analcite................................. 15–10
Accessories... Olivine, biotite, apatite, magnetite, ilmenite, nephe-
        line, orthoclase

Textures are variable, medium to coarse subophitic, ophitic, and finely granular. Labradorite and augite are zoned. Augite is rimmed by barkevikite or aegirine; plagioclase is corroded by analcite and rimmed by orthoclase.

3. Essexites, in the intention of the original definition (not "Oslotype" essexites), vary from foidal monzonites to foidal gabbros. As here used, they contain

Labradorite.............................. 25–35%
Soda orthoclase, anorthoclase, sanidine........ 10–15
Nepheline............................... 5–10
Mafics (augite, hornblende)................. 50–35
Accessories... Apatite, analcite, biotite, olivine, sphene, titanian
        magnetite

Many essexites are fine-grained and trachytoid; alkali feldspar and nepheline are anhedral. Essexite porphyries are also known.

Types without calcic plagioclase

1. Melteigites

Nepheline............................... 20–45%
Aegirine and/or aegirine-augite............. 50–30

Some also have essential biotite, melanite, and barkevikite; accessories include cancrinite, apatite, sphene, perovskite, magnetite, pyrite, calcite. If the rock contains >50 per cent and <70 per cent nepheline, it is called ijolite; if >70 per cent nepheline, it is an urtite. The rocks are medium-grained, subhedral-granular. The augite is zoned, in subhedral prisms. Nepheline carries fluid inclusions and is replaced by cancrinite.

2. Monchiquites are dike rocks with olivine and titanian augite phenocrysts, less commonly phenocrysts of biotite and/or alkali amphibole too, in a matrix of analcite containing microlites of the phenocryst minerals. The analcite matrix, if unaltered, can easily be confused with glass, which it was originally called. The augite and amphibole are zoned. Limburgites have augite and olivine phenocrysts in a matrix of alkali-rich glass.

3. Alnoites are also dike rocks containing olivine, biotite, and some augite phenocrysts in a matrix of melilite tablets, titanian augite, biotite and accessory apatite, perovskite, magnetite, in some cases melanite, nepheline, and calcite. Less commonly the melilite is anhedral and shows peg structure. A rare type contains monticellite.

Occurrence. Rocks of this group are rare and occur as minor intrusions and differentiates in small intrusives—stocks, sills, sheets, laccoliths. Their associates are gabbros and peridotites of alkali affinities, syenites, nepheline syenites, and other feldspathoid-rich rocks. Theralite occurs in the Lugar sill at Lugar, Ayrshire, Scotland, together with teschenite. In the United States essexites were first described from Salem Neck, Massachusetts; melteigites are represented by occurrences at Magnet Cove, Arkansas, and Iron Hill, Colorado; and rocks of the monchiquite type by dikes in the Fourche Mountains of Arkansas (fourchite). The type locality for alnoite is the island of Alnö, Sweden.

Foidal Basalts and Related Rocks

Definition. Foidal basalts are extrusive, usually holocrystalline, with matrix aphanitic. As in the foidal gabbros, two main subdivisions are recognized on the presence or absence of essential calcic plagioclase:

I. With essential calcic plagioclase
    A. With essential olivine—basanites
        1. Olivine, augite, calcic plagioclase, nepheline—nepheline basanite
        2. Olivine, augite, calcic plagioclase, leucite—leucite basanite

B. Without essential olivine—tephrites
    1. Augite, calcic plagioclase, nepheline—nepheline tephrite
    2. Augite, calcic plagioclase, leucite—leucite tephrite
II. Without essential calcic plagioclase
  A. With essential olivine—foidal basalts
    1. Olivine, augite, nepheline—nepheline basalt
    2. Olivine, augite, leucite—leucite basalt
    3. Olivine, augite, melilite—melilite basalt
  B. Without essential olivine
    1. Augite, nepheline—nephelinite
    2. Augite, leucite—leucitite

The plagioclase is labradorite or bytownite of the high-temperature type. Zoning is common, but without marked compositional variation, although rims as sodic as andesine and oligoclase do occur. Very rarely sanidine armoring is seen. Plagioclase of the phenocrysts is generally a little more calcic than that of the matrix. Nepheline occurs rarely as porphyritic hexagonal prisms; usually it is confined to the matrix where it is either anhedral-interstitial and difficult to detect or in stubby euhedral prisms in rocks richer in nepheline (nephelinites, nepheline basalts). Kalsilite occurs in some rare types, usually with augite and olivine. Others contain kalsilite together with leucite. Leucite occurs both as phenocrysts and matrix crystals (Fig. 22*a*). The phenocrysts are typically eight-sided in section (icositetrahedra), somewhat rounded, and the larger ones show very weak birefringence and the characteristic lamellar twinning in several directions. Inclusions of augite microlites and granules and of glass are common and zonally arranged. Matrix leucite is isotropic, rounded, with outer zones of glass inclusions.

Melilite varies somewhat in composition: it is usually (−), but may be (+). Inclusions of augite, magnetite, and perovskite are usually centrally arranged. The mineral commonly displays Berlin blue interference tints. Other feldspathoids that may be present in variable amounts include haüyne (Fig. 22*b*), sodalite and analcite in tephrites and basanites, and haüyne, nosean, sodalite, analcite, and kalsilite in foidal basalts. The last two are anhedral matrix constituents, whereas the members of the sodalite group occur both as matrix euhedra and phenocrysts, the latter in some rocks as essential constituents.

The pyroxene of the phenocrysts is brownish, pale green, or lavender, zoned and hourglass diopside or augite, with common borders of aegirine-augite. Aegirine-augite also forms entire phenocrysts (Fig. 22*b*). Two differently colored augites may form phenocrysts in the same rock. Inclusions of biotite, magnetite, and glass may be present, and twinning on (100) is widespread. The matrix pyroxene is aegirine or aegirine-augite, as needles and rods. Olivine is intermediate to relatively rich in iron. Both serpentine and iddingsite rims occur. Some varieties of leucitites (wyomingite) contain essential phlogopite.

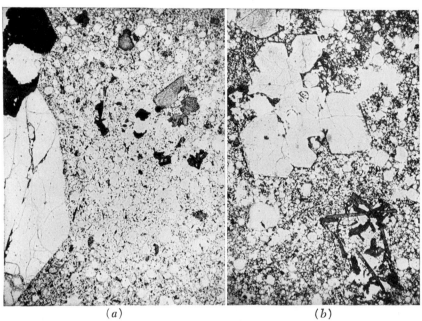

(*a*)   (*b*)

FIG. 22. (*a*) Leucite tephrite, Rome, Italy. Leucite and aegirine-augite phenocrysts in matrix of leucite, labradorite, aegirine. Nicols not crossed, ×11. (*b*) Leucitite, Rhenish Prussia, Germany. Haüyne phenocrysts, leucite, and aegirine-augite microphenocrysts in leucite-aegirine matrix. Nicols not crossed, ×11.

Accessories are basaltic hornblende and biotite (which show resorption and corrosion rims), sphene, perovskite, melanite, chromite, chromian spinel, magnetite, ilmenite, apatite, sanidine, and glass.

Alteration minerals are natrolite and other zeolites (particularly from nepheline), serpentine, iddingsite, nontronite, chlorite, calcite, and limonite.

Textures and Microstructures. Most of the rocks are porphyritic-holocrystalline; rare types are porphyritic-hypocrystalline. The glassy types are leucitic, and the brownish glass is potassic in composition. Phenocrysts are leucite, nepheline (rarely), nosean, haüyne, sodalite, melilite, calcic plagioclase, diopside, augite, aegirine-augite, olivine, biotite, phlogopite, and basaltic hornblende (uncommon). Many of the matrix constituents, nepheline, haüyne, nosean, aegirine, apatite, and perovskite, are also euhedral. Melilite appears as small irregular laths or as larger, broad plates poikilitically enclosing leucite, some magnetite, and pyroxene. Sanidine, analcite, nepheline, and kalsilite are anhedral-interstitial.

Occurrence. Foidal basalts occur as uncommon flows and minor intrusives (plugs and dikes) of very restricted extent, usually of Tertiary or Recent age, associated with each other and with sanidine basalts and hypersthene latites. Representative areas are the Leucite Hills of Wyoming and the Navajo-Hopi region, Arizona.

PERIDOTITE FAMILY

Definition. Peridotite is holocrystalline, phaneritic, plutonic, containing:

Mafics (olivine, pyroxene, hornblende)..........	85–95%
Ores (magnetite, ilmenite, chromite, etc.)....... ..	10–3
Calcic plagioclase ......, ...	<5

Types with essential olivine are peridotites. If olivine is absent or present in accessory amounts only, the rocks are perknites. With an increase in plagioclase the rocks grade into troctolites and gabbros.

Mineralogy. Peridotites and perknites are subdivided on the basis of the mafic minerals present with olivine. However, in practice their classification may be very difficult, owing to intensive serpentinization and to the formation of secondary amphiboles and phlogopite, which should not be confused with their primary counterparts. A widely accepted nomenclature of the main types is as follows:

Mafic mineral(s)	*Name*
Olivine.............................	Dunite (Fig. 23a)
Olivine + enstatite (or hypersthene).....	Harzburgite (very common) (Fig. 23b)
Olivine + clinopyroxene (usually augite)	Wehrlite
Olivine + orthopyroxene + clinopyroxene	Lherzolite
Olivine + hornblende (primary).........	Cortlandtite
Pyroxene (enstatite, hypersthene, augite)	Pyroxenite
Hornblende.........................	Hornblendite

The olivine is normally forsterite, usually not more ferroan than Fa_{20}, but in some differentiates intermediate olivine or manganoan olivine (hortonolite) is present. Negative crystals may form inclusions. In a very rare type of peridotite the olivine group is represented by monticellite. The clinopyroxene is diopside, diopsidic augite, or augite, some of which may be chromian and thus green in color. In rare alkali types, titanian augite with hourglass structure may be present, rarely jadeite. The orthopyroxene is usually enstatite, but hy-

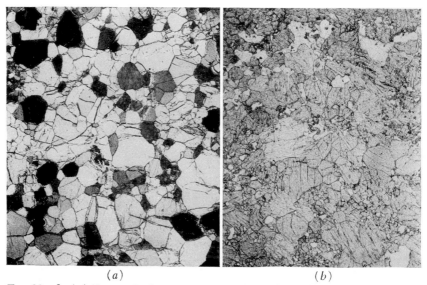

(a)   (b)

FIG. 23a, b. (a) Dunite, Jackson County, North Carolina. Olivine in mosaic aggregate. Nicols crossed, ×9. (b) Pyroxenite (harzburgite), Wolf Creek, Dillon, Montana. Enstatite and olivine. Nicols not crossed, ×9.

persthene is not uncommon. The amphiboles are brown or green hornblende; in sodic types barkevikite occurs. Edenite and chromian edenite also represent the amphiboles. It may be very difficult to separate magmatic from uralitic or hydrothermal amphibole. Schiller-type inclusions are common and abundant in both pyroxene and amphibole. Mica is colorless to pale red brown phlogopite. Accessories are numerous and varied: magnetite, ilmenite, chromite, picotite, pleonaste, pyrite, pyrrhotite, pentlandite, platinum, apatite, pyrope, perovskite, corundum, anorthite, or bytownite and rarely analcite or nepheline. Secondary minerals of deuteric or hydrothermal origin are numerous and may be intensively developed: tremolite, actinolite, cummingtonite, anthophyllite, phlogopite, chlorite, serpentine (antigorite and chrysotile), talc, clinohumite, magnesite, dolomite, calcite, sphene, magnetite, and hematite.

Mineralogical varieties include: Kimberlite, an olivine-phlogopite rock with accessory bronzite, chromian diopside, perovskite, pyrope, ilmenite, and chromite; some are diamond-bearing. Types of pyroxenite are enstatolite, hypersthenite, websterite (ortho- plus clinopyroxene). Picrite has been used for olivine-rich mafic gabbros of alkalic affinities, for peridotites of alkalic affinities, and for the supposed extrusive equivalents of peridotites. These rocks contain preponderant olivine, titanian augite, barkevikite, and either essential or accessory calcic plagioclase.

Textures and Microstructures. All of the constituents are generally anhedral. The olivine-rich types, especially dunites, show a mosaic texture—equigranular-anhedral (Fig. 23a). The grain size varies from medium-grained to very coarse grained; fine-grained varieties are rare. Porphyritic types are very rare, except in a few small intrusives, in which rare microphenocrysts of olivine or spinel are inconspicuous. A common fabric in pyroxene-olivine rocks is the pseudo-porphyritic-poikilitic texture in which large, irregular anhedra of pyroxene include rounded grains of olivine, magnetite, and spinel. The pseudophenocrysts of pyroxene may reach a length of over an inch. Amphibole likewise may be pseudoporphyritic-poikilitic. In some types the texture is pseudoporphyritic without the amphibole or pyroxene being poikilitic. Layered textures are common, particularly in peridotites of lopoliths, accentuated by chromite streaks. Olivine may be oriented in subparallel flow texture, and autoclastic structures are not uncommon. Olivine may show undulatory extinction, and translation lamellae appear in both olivine and enstatite.

Even the accessories are usually anhedral, magnetite and spinel being rounded. The rare sideronitic texture consists of interstitial magnetite "cementing" the essential mafics. Accessory plagioclase is also normally interstitial, but perovskite forms euhedral octahedra.

Overgrowth replacements are widespread, particularly of various amphiboles, especially anthophyllite and tremolite on pyroxene. Kelyphitic rims on rounded pyrope consist of radial-fibrous augite ± picotite, or enstatite, or hornblende or biotite and magnetite.

The replacements of olivine and pyroxene by chlorite, talc, phlogopite, and especially by serpentine give rise to a wide variety of secondary textural features (Fig. 23c)—rims, relicts, island-and-sea, pseudobreccia, pseudomorphs, veins, latticework, networks, and mesh.

Cataclastic structures are not uncommon in Alpine-type serpentinites.

Occurrence. Peridotites, along with gabbros and anorthosites, occur in differentiated lopoliths and thick sheets (Stillwater Complex, Montana; Laramie, Wyoming). Swarms of serpentinized peridotites occur as minor associates of granitic and granodioritic batholiths in folded mountain regions. These so-called Alpine types of peridotites

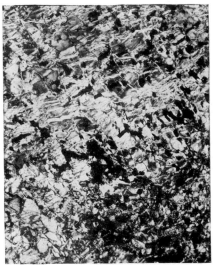

Fig. 23c. Serpentinite, Blacktail Range, Montana. Antigorite, chrysotile, magnetite. Nicols crossed, ×9.

are represented in the United States by the peridotite belt of the Appalachian Mountains and by the swarms of dikes, sills, and plugs in the Coast Range of Oregon and California.

PYROCLASTIC ROCKS

Definition. Pyroclastic rocks consist of detrital materials expelled from volcanic vents, transported aerially and deposited upon land surface, in lakes, or in marine waters. Exceptionally in some cases the material is carried as nuées ardentes—dense, hot volcanic clouds. The material deposited on land commonly is eroded and transported by running water and redeposited, together with sedimentary clastic and chemical material, in bodies of water. Thus many of these rocks are hybrid not only in the nature of their constituents, igneous and sedimentary, but also in the manner of their formation, igneous and sedimentary.

Classification. The following classification is based on grain size and shapes:

Grain size, mm	Unconsolidated	Consolidated
>32..............	Bombs Blocks (angular) Blocks + ash	Agglomerate Volcanic breccia Tuff breccia
>4 < 32..........	Lapilli Cinders (vesicular)	Lapilli tuff Cindery lapilli tuff
>¼ < 4..........	Coarse ash	Coarse tuff
< ¼..............	Ash or volcanic dust	Tuff

The coarser rocks, such as agglomerates, are not well suited for thin-section studies, except for any fine-grained matrix they may possess. Tuffs, which may be weakly indurated, commonly require impregnation prior to sectioning. Tuffs can be described on the basis of four factors: (1) the source of the materials, (2) the physical nature of

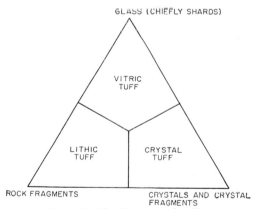

FIG. 24. Classification of tuffs.

their particles, (3) the mineralogical and chemical composition of their igneous part, and (4) the mineralogical (and chemical) composition of any contaminating sedimentary fraction.

Based on the source of the materials, tuffs are (1) essential, if the particles are of the same kind as any accompanying erupting lava, (2) accessory, if the particles consist of earlier pyroclastics and lava from the same source, and (3) accidental, if the particles are rocks unrelated to the source. On the nature of the particles (Fig. 24) tuffs are classified as (1) vitric, containing predominantly glass shards, (2) lithic, containing predominantly rock fragments, and (3) crystal, consisting chiefly of pyrogenic crystals and crystal pieces. Combinations may be termed vitric-crystal tuff, crystal-vitric tuff, etc. The igneous rock type (rhyolitic, andesitic, etc.) also serves to distinguish among tuffs—particularly those in which crystals are abundant. Reworked tuffs contain variable amounts of sedimentary material, and the nature of the predominating sedimentary material may be employed as an additional descriptive term. Thus such tuffs can be arenaceous, calcareous, or argillaceous.

Vitric Tuffs

Vitric tuffs are those in which pieces of igneous glass are the single most abundant constituent. Much volcanic ash and dust, if unaltered and not reworked, is in this category. Many vitric tuffs are of rhyolitic composition, but dacitic, trachytic, andesitic, and basaltic vitric tuffs also occur. Some idea of the general composition of the vitric material may be secured by measuring the refractive index of the glass, which may show little or only minor variation (0.003 to 0.007), particularly if the tuff is essential, unaltered, and not reworked. In some cases intergradations of vitric and crystal tuffs give some indication of the composition of the vitric material. In other cases a chemical analysis is required. The glass particles, or shards (Fig. 25a and b), are angular and sharp and in shape are of four main types: (1) curved, lunar, or Y-shaped, with usually four or more concave sides, (2) flat plates, (3) fibers or thin rods, and (4) dust. They represent the fragmented sides of gas bubbles and vesicles. The shards themselves may be clear, dusty, or nearly opaque with minute inclusions of magnetite. The glass is usually colorless, but basic types are tan to brown. Small vesicles may be present, shaped as spheres, discs, curved tubes, beaded aggregates, tapering funnels, pear-shaped cavities, etc. The glass may be unaltered and isotropic or devitrified to a faintly polarizing cryptocrystalline aggregate of unidentifiable materials. Most of the older tuffs (pre-Miocene) show some devitrification.

Palagonite tuff consists of devitrified basaltic tuff fragments, crystals of augite and olivine, and plagioclase microlites.

The particles range downward in size from 4 mm, and the average particle size normally decreases away from the source. In addition to shards, crystals and crystal fragments of different minerals may form a

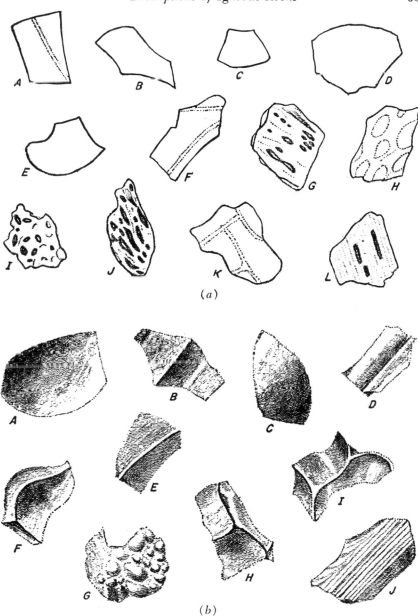

(a)

(b)

Fig. 25. (a) Shards from Kansas volcanic ash (transmitted light). A–F, Pliocene ash; G–L, Pleistocene ash. ×144. (*Courtesy of Kansas Geological Survey.*) (b) Shards from Kansas volcanic ash (reflected light). A–E, Pliocene ash; F–J, Pleistocene ash. ×144. (*Courtesy of Kansas Geological Survey.*)

minor to subordinate component. The crystal pieces are of the minerals of such rocks as rhyolites, andesites, etc. Pieces of various rocks may also be present in minor amounts. Fossils include seeds, insects, and vertebrate remains. Secondary minerals are calcite, montmorillonite, allophane, halloysite, celadonite, zeolites, cristobalite, opal, chalcedony, quartz, and iron oxides. One type of general alteration, to montmorillonite and cristobalite, results in the formation of bentonite. Replacement by opal, chalcedony, and cryptocrystalline quartz results in the formation of silicified tuffs ("porcellanites"), with flinty, crypto-crystalline textures. Some vitric tuffs, which were deposited in bodies of water, contain a cement of chemically or biochemically precipitated calcite.

Welded tuffs, or ignimbrites, are vitric tuffs in which shards have been fused together. In this process shards are flattened, vesicles are collapsed to curving dusty lines, and the pieces are tightly molded one to another. In some cases the glass pieces show crystallization of fibrous sanidine and tridymite inward from the shard margins, so that the rims consist of normally arranged crystalline fibers, and the cores remain hyaline and isotropic. In some welded tuffs containing sanidine crystals, new Na-rich sanidine has formed overgrowths on the intratelluric crystals.

Crystal Tuffs

In crystal tuffs, intratelluric crystals and crystal fragments, which under nonexplosive conditions would have formed phenocrysts in lavas, form the largest single component. The crystals are rarely complete, being usually cracked or broken and corroded; angular fragments of crystals are very common. For rhyolitic crystal tuffs the crystals are of quartz, sanidine, biotite, hornblende, and less usually augite. Some rhyolitic tuffs contain considerable tridymite which acts as a binder. For dacitic types the crystals are hornblende, pyroxene, sodic plagioclase, and quartz. In andesitic types (Fig. 26a) hornblende, hypersthene, andesine, and magnetite are the usual crystals. Sanidine and augite or aegirine-augite form most of the crystals in trachytes and sodic trachytes. Trass is a commercial term for trachytic tuffs and (nepheline) phonolitic tuffs in parts of Germany. Puzzolane is a commercial term for a trachyte or leucite phonolite tuff used in Italy in the manufacture of hydraulic cement. In basaltic tuffs olivine, augite, magnetite, and labradorite form the crystals and crystal fragments. Some tuffs have the composition of melilite basalts.

The crystals display the usual textural characteristics of phenocrysts, such as glass inclusions and zoning. Envelopes of glass may enclose the crystals. Crystal tuffs usually contain a variable amount of shards, and all gradations occur between crystal and lithic tuffs. A subordinate number of rock fragments may also be present. In some types spherulites of feldspar appear.

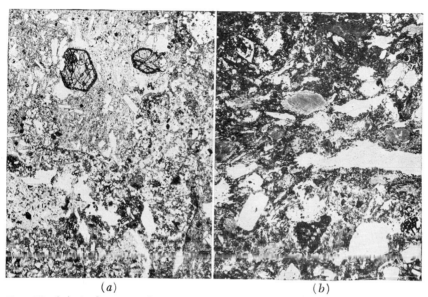

(*a*) (*b*)

Fig. 26. (*a*) Andesitic agglomerate, southwestern Montana. Hornblende, augite, andesine, magnetite crystals, glass shards, cryptocrystalline material. Nicols not crossed, ×9. (*b*) Basaltic lithic tuff, Big Belt Mountains, Montana. Labradorite and magnetite crystals, rock fragments, glass, cryptocrystalline material. Nicols not crossed, ×9.

Lithic Tuffs

If rock fragments constitute the most important fraction, the rock is a lithic tuff. The fragments may include pieces of older eruptives or throat rocks (accessory type), of the strata or other wall rocks through which the conduit extended (accidental type) or of flows and other pyroclastic rocks genetically associated with the tuff itself (essential type). Pumice, scoria, obsidian, various flow rocks (particularly andesite and basalt), granophyres, and fine-grained or porphyritic hypabyssal igneous types are common, but plutonic igneous, metamorphic, and sedimentary varieties may also be represented. Other components are glass shards and shattered pyrogenic crystals in subordinate amounts (Fig. 26*b*).

Hybrid Tuffs

Tuffs that have been eroded, retransported, and redeposited by running water usually contain admixed sedimentary material in various proportions—detrital quartz, clay, or both. Tuffs grade through argillaceous tuffs and tuffaceous clays into clays and likewise through

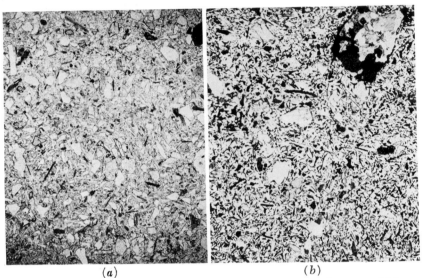

(a)   (b)

Fig. 27. (a) Hybrid tuff, Sweetwater Basin, Montana. Detrital quartz, feldspar, augite, garnet, biotite in matrix of glass shards. Nicols not crossed, ×10. (b) Hybrid tuff, Sweetwater Basin, Montana. Clastic quartz, feldspar, granite fragment, *upper right,* in matrix of glass shards (dark) and calcite (light). Nicols crossed, ×10.

arenaceous tuffs (Fig. 27a) and tuffaceous sandstones into sandstones. Intergradations between tuffs and graywackes also occur, and marine tuffs or tuffaceous sandstones are not uncommonly associated with graywackes. Some redeposited tuffs are cemented by calcite (Fig. 27b).

4

SEDIMENTARY ROCKS—GENERAL

ORIGIN AND CLASSIFICATION

The initial subdivision of sedimentary rocks is based upon the dominant mechanism of their formation; thus the main groups are:

1. *Epiclastic:* those resulting from the mechanical accumulation of rock and mineral pieces formed through physical processes
2. *Chemical:* those formed by the accumulation of minerals precipitated directly from aqueous solution by inorganic chemical processes or precipitated by reaction between minerals and aqueous solutions
3. *Organic:* those consisting of minerals and materials precipitated from aqueous solutions through the action of organisms or consisting in large part of organic remains (coal)
4. *Residual:* those formed *in situ* by advanced decomposition and not having undergone appreciable transportation.

Epiclastic or detrital sedimentary rocks consist of the physically weathered (disintegrated) and chemically weathered (decomposed) material from older rocks (igneous, metamorphic, or sedimentary), which has been transported and deposited by running water (streams, ocean currents), wind, or ice. In the main they consist of minerals not readily soluble—quartz, feldspars, and clay minerals, which are transported as particles. Epiclastic rocks have two prominent characteristics that are used as a basis for their further subdivision, namely, size and composition of the particles. In Table 2 are listed the generally accepted size-range subdivisions, the corresponding materials and rocks, and various adjectival terms.

In psephitic aggregates a distinction is also made if the particles are rounded (conglomerate) or angular (breccia). Psammitic and pelitic

Microscopic Petrography

TABLE 2. SIZE CLASSIFICATION OF EPICLASTIC SEDIMENTARY
PARTICLES AND AGGREGATES

Size, mm	Particle	Aggregate		
				(Grabau)
256 —	Boulder	Gravel	Psephite (psephitic)	Rudite (rudaceous)
	Cobble	Conglomerate		
64 —				
	Pebble			
4 —				
	Coarse sand	Sandstone	Psammite (psammitic)	Arenite (arenaceous)
2 —				
	Sand			
$\frac{1}{16}$ —				
	Silt	Siltstone		
$\frac{1}{256}$ —			Pelite (pelitic, argillaceous)	Lutite (lutaceous)
	Clay	Clay Shale		

rocks may be further subdivided on the basis of mineralogical composition, expressed in terms of the proportions of the three most common clastic minerals—quartz, feldspars, and clays (Fig. 28). It is necessary to remember, however, that there are other important epiclastic rocks that consist dominantly of minerals other than quartz, feldspars, and clays, notably the clastic limestones, in which the particles are calcite. These are commonly called calcirudites, calcarenites, and calcilutites, depending on their grain size. Rocks consisting of transported shell fragments are bioclastic rocks.

Rocks of chemical origin are subdivided on the basis of the chief component: siliceous (opal, chalcedony, quartz), calcareous (aragonite, calcite, dolomite), phosphatic (apatite), ferruginous (limonite, hematite, glauconite, etc.), and salines (halite, sylvite, carnallite, etc.). Organic rocks are categorized similarly on the basis of the nature of their materials: organic limestone, organic siliceous rocks (diatomite, etc.), organic phosphorite, and coal. Coal, because it does not consist of minerals and because its study requires special techniques, is not described here. Residual rocks include some clays and bauxite; soils are not described in this book.

Since the student seeks ultimately to determine the origin of the rock with which he is working, it is advantageous and purposeful to describe rocks of general compositional similarity together, despite profound differences in their origin. Thus, for example, chemically precipitated cherts are normally described in conjunction with spiculite cherts, calcarenites with chemically deposited and organic limestones, and transported clays with residual clays.

It is well to remember that the species pigeonholes of man's classifications are only rarely adopted by the natural representatives. Thus in sedimentary rocks, as well as in the other two major groups, gradations are common, and many rocks lie between two or more "end members" rather than near or at the extremes.

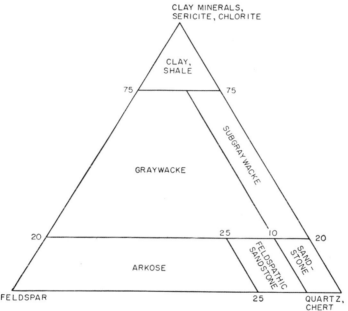

Fig. 28. Classification of epiclastic psammitic and pelitic rocks (excluding calcilutites and calcarenites).

Some degree of coherence is necessary before an aggregate of sedimentary minerals or particles is included as a rock. However, many unconsolidated sedimentary materials, particularly sands, may be advantageously studied either by the immersion method or by mounting in more permanent media.

Sedimentary materials become sedimentary rocks through consolidation, by the processes of cementation, compaction, and recrystallization. As consolidation proceeds, significant mineralogical transformations may also take place. New minerals are precipitated directly from solution; others are formed by reaction between solutions and minerals already present in the aggregate. These mineralogical and textural changes, taking place in the sedimentary environment during or shortly after lithifaction, are termed diagenetic. In some cases such changes may be difficult to distinguish from much later metasomatic or low-grade metamorphic transformations that affect the rock. Minerals formed within sediments during lithifaction or shortly thereafter by recrystallization or replacement are called authigenic minerals in contrast to those unchanged minerals that were brought into the sedimentary environment from outside—the allogenic or detrital species.

TEXTURES AND MICROSTRUCTURES

Textures of Epiclastic Rocks

In epiclastic rocks the texture depends on (1) size of the grains, (2) form of the grains, and (3) arrangement of the grains. Under size must be considered not only absolute size (Table 2) but also variation in size, i.e., degree of sorting. Sediments range from those that are very well sorted (some quartzose sandstones) to those in which sorting is very poor to absent (till). Some idea of the degree of sorting in sandstones may be secured from examination of thin sections, if one remembers that some apparent grain-size variation results from the fact that the section cuts grains at different "levels." Usually, however, in order to describe sorting at all quantitatively, the rock must be subjected to mechanical size analysis by screening or settling.

Grain form partakes of two qualities—sphericity (shape) and roundness. Sphericity measures the degree to which the particle approaches its ideal form, i.e., a sphere. In shape sedimentary particles are (1) tabular (platy, discoidal, oblate), (2) equant (blocky, spheroidal, equidimensional, equiaxial), (3) bladed (triaxial), and (4) rod-shaped (prismatic, roller-shaped, prolate). These classes are based on variations in the ratios of the three axes *a*, *b*, *c*—length, breadth, and thickness, respectively, thus requiring three-dimensional measurements. In a special shape category are shards—glass pieces or clay pseudomorphous after glass. Also of special interest are the crystallographically bounded, highly angular forms resulting from etching, noteworthy in some accessory detrital quartz, feldspar, garnet, augite, hypersthene, hornblende, and staurolite. Thin sections, since they provide only one section of a grain, must be used cautiously in assigning shapes to particles. Precise shape determinations are time-consuming and usually are not performed as part of an ordinary petrographic examination.

Roundness, which is not basically related to sphericity, measures the sharpness of the corners and edges of a particle. In thin sections the random sections of grains give a fair idea of the quality of roundness by comparison with a standard set of grain outlines (Fig. 29).

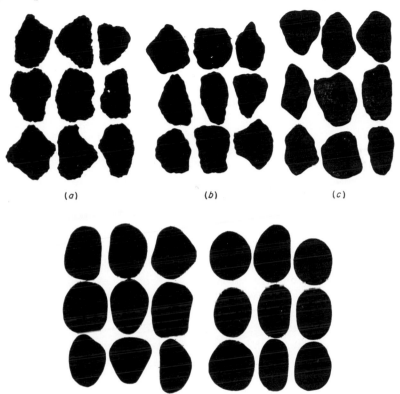

(a)   (b)   (c)

(d)   (e)

FIG. 29. Roundness. (a) Angular, (b) subangular, (c) subrounded, (d) rounded, (e) very rounded.

Angular: Little or no evidence of abrasion; sharp corners and edges. Sandstones with angular grains may be considered as having a microbreccia texture.

Subangular: Distinct evidence of abrasion; particles retain original form, with faces unmarked, but corners and edges have been worn off slightly; some interfacial angles may still be sharp.

Subrounded: Considerable abrasion in evidence; smooth curves characterize corners and edges, with corresponding reduction in areas of original grain faces; original shape persists.

Rounded: Original corners and edges smoothed to broad curves; original faces largely worn away.

Well-rounded: Entire surface consists of smooth, broad curves; all original corners, edges, and faces removed.

Quantitatively roundness is expressed by the ratio of the average radius of curvature of the various corners or edges to the radius of curvature of the maximum inscribed sphere. In practice the measurements are made on sections or projections of grains. Like the exact determination of sphericity, quantitative roundness values are not obtained in elementary or routine petrographic studies.

The arrangement of particles partakes of two factors—orientation (fabric) and packing. In sandstones the long axes of quartz grains, which normally coincide with the *c* and optic axes, may show a subparallel arrangement as the result of current flow during deposition. Platy minerals, muscovite, biotite, sericite, and chlorite are usually oriented parallel with the bedding. In shales a high degree of parallel orientation of platy clay minerals is common, to such a degree that aggregates may yield a diffuse interference figure. In some clastic limestones fossil shells and fragments display parallel orientation.

Banding or layering, which is usually on a scale not encompassed by thin sections, in some rocks, e.g., carbonaceous shales, siltstones, cherts, and chert-siderite rocks, is sufficiently fine to appear under the microscope. Other rocks, especially some clastic limestones and some clays, display a pellet texture, in which ovoids of material of one grain size are set in a matrix of a different grain size.

Packing refers to the three-dimensional contact pattern of a grain and its contiguous neighbors. If particles are so placed with respect to each other that the aggregate occupies the smallest possible volume, the space between particles (porosity) is at a minimum. Conversely, if the same grains are packed to occupy the largest possible volume, porosity is at a maximum. Some strongly compacted sediments have tightly packed grains that may even interlock. Porosity is defined as the percentage of open space (i.e., not occupied by solids) in the total rock volume. It is primary or secondary, primary porosity being determined during lithifaction (many sandstones), secondary porosity resulting from later changes (some dolomites). Original rock porosity is governed by (1) degree of sorting, (2) grain shape, (3) packing, and (4) degree of cementation. Secondary porosity, which may be either greater or less than the primary porosity, is affected chiefly by solution of cement or matrix or deposition of additional cement. The permeability of a rock is the property of permitting passage of fluids through its voids. Rocks are permeable if they possess pores or other openings that are more or less continuous or joined. Conjugate porosity is prerequisite for permeability. Sandstones and clays both may be porous, but clays are generally impermeable. Permeability, of course, is also a function of the type of fluid (fresh water, brine, petroleum, natural gas) and the hydraulic pressure or head.

The cements in epiclastic rocks fall into two general types: (1) clastic binders—clay minerals, muscovite or sericite, and chlorites; and (2) precipitated binders such as calcite, quartz, chalcedony and hematite. From a textural viewpoint cements are of four types:

1. Structureless (amorphous): opal, limonite, collophane
2. Interstitial-granular: chalcedony, calcite, clay minerals
3. Poikiloblastic, large anhedral crystals of cement enclosing numerous clastic grains: "sand" calcite, barite
4. Oriented overgrowths, deposited in crystallographic continuity on clastic grains: quartz in sedimentary ("ortho") quartzites, calcite in some calcarenites

A final textural feature of epiclastic sediments is the surface texture of the grains themselves. Some quartz grains show pitting or frosting; others are smooth and highly polished. Pebbles and coarser pieces may show striations.

Textures of Chemically Precipitated Rocks

The textures of chemically precipitated rocks result from the processes of crystallization from solution or gel, of recrystallization of amorphous, cryptocrystalline, or phaneritic material, and of replacement. The various results may be grouped into the following categories:

1. Equigranular
   a. Anhedral: limestone, rock salt, anhydrite, by direct precipitation; some chert by recrystallization
   b. Subhedral to euhedral: dolomite by replacement
2. Heterogranular
   a. Uneven-grained: some cherts and anhydrite-gypsum rocks by recrystallization; some dolomitic limestones by replacement
   b. "Porphyroblastic": some rock salt, dolomite, rock gypsum, rock anhydrite, polyhalite rock by recrystallization; quartz euhedra in salines

3. Fibrous: rock gypsum by replacement of anhydrite
4. Colloform
    a. Colloform banding (minute, closely spaced, scallopy bands): dripstone, travertine, some cherts
    b. Oolites and pisolites: oolitic limestones, some phosphorite
    c. Ovules (granules): phosphorite, glauconitic rocks
    d. Spherulites: chert, sphaerosiderite
5. Porous
    a. Primary: tufa, sandstone
    b. Secondary: microvugs in dolomite, dolomolds in chert and other crystal solution cavities—halite in clay, glauberite in dolomite
6. Miscellaneous secondary textural features
    a. Oriented overgrowths: calcite, dolomite, feldspar
    b. Marginal corrosion: chlorite and sericite on quartz
    c. Pseudomorphs: limonite after chamosite oolites, halite + anhydrite after gypsum, sylvite after anhydrite, chalcedony after calcite oolites
    d. Veinlets: calcite in limestone and dolomite, gypsum in rock anhydrite

Most of these textural types require no further description. Oolites consist of concentric layers of mineral material deposited successively around a center. The nuclei commonly consist of clastic grains or aggregates—quartz, calcite, clay, silt, microfossils, shell fragments, and even oolite fragments. Some oolites show both concentric and radial fibrous structures due to postdepositional recrystallization. Replacement may destroy the layered structure. Calcite and aragonite are common oolitic minerals; others, formed in some cases by replacement of oolites originally calcareous, are dolomite, siderite, chalcedony, quartz, hematite, limonite, glauconite, chamosite, collophane, analcite, barite, pyrite, sulfur, and the aluminum hydroxide minerals of bauxite. Some oolites are markedly irregular in shape, being attenuated, flattened, and indented; these are spastholiths. Ovoid bodies similar to oolites but without the concentric layering are called ovules (granules) and are represented by glauconite, greenalite, and collophane. Spherulites are ovoid bodies with a radially fibrous structure only; chalcedony and some siderite are typical; some other minerals that form them are barite, strontianite, anhydrite, and colemanite.

Textures of Organic Rocks

The texture of a rock containing dominantly organic remains is determined chiefly by:

1. The original fossil form

2. The extent to which the original form is preserved, if it was transported

3. The internal grain pattern of the fossil

4. The extent and type of replacement or recrystallization of the original material

5. The nature and texture of the binding agent

Most invertebrate fossils consist originally of calcite or aragonite, usually either one or the other, less commonly the two together. Examples are algae, foraminifera, molluscs, crinoids, corals, bryozoa, gastropods, and many brachiopods. Other fossils, including some brachiopods, coprolites, bones, and teeth, consist chiefly of collophane. Still other creatures, such as diatoms, radiolaria, and some sponges, build their skeletons of opal. Chitin forms the exoskeletons of arthropods and skeletal parts of graptolites, which usually are preserved as carbonaceous films.

Aragonite tends to invert to calcite; thus older calcareous fossils are largely calcitic. If the two forms of $CaCO_3$ occur in the same shell, they form separate layers. In many calcareous fossils, the carbonate appears as fibers or prismatic crystals, either nearly normal or parallel to the surface of the shell. In other cases the carbonate is in a granular mosaic; in echinoderms each plate is a single crystalline unit of calcite.

The original material may be replaced, particularly by chalcedony (chert) or dolomite, but also by hematite, siderite, collophane, pyrite, marcasite, carbon, and microcrystalline quartz. Fossils also are recorded as cavities (molds) and as casts. The latter type is abundantly illustrated by the glauconite internal casts of foraminifera.

The division between textural and structural features is gradational and is based to a large extent on the size of the feature, those on a microscopic and hand-specimen scale usually being classed as textural, and larger ones designated structural.

SPECIAL FEATURES

Insoluble Residues

In carbonate rocks and some salines study of minor constituents may be facilitated through concentration of an insoluble residue fraction by removal in solution of minerals forming the bulk of the rock.

In the process, however, some soluble accessory constituents may be destroyed. The residue once concentrated may then be studied advantageously by the immersion method, whereas thin sections of the untreated rock may not display any of these minor accessory constituents.

CARBONATE ROCK RESIDUES

Limestones and dolomites are treated with HCl; ordinary commercial HCl will suffice, diluted with H_2O to at least 50 per cent but not less than 10 per cent. However, if fossiliferous structures and delicate material are to be preserved, acetic acid should be employed. Ordinarily about 10 g of rock will yield ample residue for study. The carbonate can be dissolved in beakers; usually two acid applications, with H_2O washing between, will suffice. A final washing to decant fine silt and clay is followed by drying.

An effective analysis of the insoluble fraction should include (1) identification of minerals and substances, (2) description of the characteristics (principally form) of the individual species, (3) calculation of the weight per cent of the individual constituents.

In carbonate rocks the more widespread species of the insoluble residue fraction are quartz, chalcedony, clay minerals, anhydrite, and gypsum. Quartz occurs abundantly, in a variety of forms—as clastic grains or grain aggregates, as euhedral crystals, as drusy aggregates, and as oolites. Chalcedony forms oolites, clastic grains, lacy to granular aggregates, fossils and may contain rhomboid cavities (dolomolds) from which dolomite euhedra have been dissolved. The clay minerals are chiefly kaolinite and illite. Other less abundant constituents are sulfur, pyrite, marcasite, sphalerite, millerite, magnetite, hematite, limonite, maganese oxide minerals, adularia, albite, muscovite, chlorite, glauconite, barite, and celestite. Insoluble residues are an aid to correlation, especially in nonfossiliferous strata and with material from drill cores and cuttings. Although the insoluble-residue suite also changes laterally in facies variations, the changes are normally neither as abrupt nor as pronounced as vertical changes between strata.

SALINE RESIDUES

Some common evaporite rocks contain complex assemblages of insoluble-residue minerals, some of which are relatively rare and do not occur commonly outside of this association. Salines that may yield extensive residues include rock salt, rock gypsum, and rock anhydrite (both bedded and cap rock). Halite, of course, is water-soluble, and anhydrite and gypsum may be dissolved in sodium thiosulfate ("hypo" solution). The species obtained are listed in Table 3.

TABLE 3. MINERALS OF INSOLUBLE RESIDUES OF SALINE (EVAPORITE) ROCKS

Anhydrite	Kaolinite
Ankerite	Limonite (some after pyrite)
Aragonite	Lueneburgite, $Mg_3B_2(OH)_6(PO_4)_2 \cdot 6H_2O$
Barite	Magnesite
Boracite, $Mg_3B_7O_{13}Cl$	Magnetite
Brookite	Malachite (crystals)
Calcite	Malladrite, Na_2SiF_6
Celestite	Marcasite
Chalcedony	Opal
Chalcocite	Pinnoite, $Mg(BO_2)_2 \cdot 3H_2O$
Chlorite (crystals)	Pyrite
Danburite, $CaB_2Si_2O_8$	Pyrrhotite
Dolomite	Quartz
Fluorite	Rutile
Gibbsite	Sphalerite
Goethite	Sulfur
Gypsum	Sulfoborite, $Mg_6H_4(BO_3)_4(SO_4)_2 \cdot 7H_2O$
Hauerite, MnS_2	Sussexite, $(Mn,Mg)(BO_2)(OH)$
Hematite	Szaibelyite, $(Mg,Mn)(BO_2)(OH)$
Hilgardite and parahilgardite, $Ca_8(B_6O_{11})_3Cl_4 \cdot 4H_2O$	Talc
Hydroboracite, $CaMgB_6O_{11} \cdot 6H_2O$	Tourmaline
Ilmenite	Veatchite, $SrB_6O_{10} \cdot 2H_2O$
Kaliborite, $KMg_2B_{11}O_{19} \cdot 9H_2O$	Zircon

Among the accessories destroyed during solutions are bischofite, $MgCl_2 \cdot 6H_2O$, langbeinite, $K_2Mg_2(SO_4)_3$, and rinncite, NaK_3FeCl_6. The more common rock species, such as anhydrite, gypsum, sulfur, celestite, the carbonates, pyrite, and quartz, may show considerable variation in form, twinning, zoning, and inclusions, which should all be noted. Most of the rarer minerals are epigenetic, formed by diagenesis, postlithifaction reactions, or metasomatism.

Accessory Detrital Minerals

Epiclastic rocks such as sandstones and arkoses commonly contain a varied assemblage of accessory detrital constituents, usually referred to as the "heavy" accessories, although some noteworthy species have specific gravities lower than 2.85 (G of bromoform) rather than higher. Since these minerals are of varying degrees of stability in the sedimentary environment and since the presence of some betokens particular types or groups of source rocks, a study of the complete accessory suite is highly advantageous in determining the provenance of the host rock. Provenance includes not only the source rocks but also the weathering, transportational, and depositional environments.

To study the accessory detrital suite effectively, its minerals must usually be concentrated—by means of heavy liquids, magnetic separators, electrostatic separators, a Humphreys spiral, panning, or combinations of these and other devices. In studying the suite the following should be noted:

1. The total amount (weight per cent) of the entire group
2. The identities of the species and their individual abundances
3. Grain size (most "heavies" are in the 0.25- to 0.10-mm fraction)
4. Individual physical characteristics: shape (including habit and etching), roundness, color, zoning, fractures, inclusions, and fluorescence
5. Compositional variation in species as determined by variation in optical properties

In Table 4 is given a list of the most common heavy detrital accessory minerals of sands and sandstones. Species common in the light (G < 2.85) accessory fraction are albite, calcite, chalcedony, dolomite, microcline, muscovite, oligoclase, and orthoclase.

TABLE 4. COMMON HEAVY DETRITAL MINERALS OF SANDS AND SANDSTONES†

Actinolite	HYPERSTHENE
Anatase	ILMENITE
ANDALUSITE	KYANITE
APATITE	LEUCOXENE
AUGITE	LIMONITE
Barite	MAGNETITE
BIOTITE	Monazite
Brookite	RUTILE
Cassiterite	Siderite
CHLORITE	Sillimanite
Corundum	SPHENE
DIOPSIDE	Spinel
EPIDOTE-CLINOZOISITE	STAUROLITE
Fluorite	Topaz
GARNET	TOURMALINE
GLAUCONITE	Xenotime
Hematite	ZIRCON
HORNBLENDE	Zoisite

† Most common are shown in capital letters.

Minerals that occur very rarely or only locally as accessory detritals are feldspathoids, olivine, cordierite, calcic plagioclase, serpentine, talc, and enstatite. Accessories of high stability that can survive more than one cycle of weathering and transportation include rutile, zircon, tourmaline, leucoxene, and apatite. In Table 5 are listed detrital suites that are characteristic of specific groups of source rocks.

TABLE 5. DETRITAL MINERAL SUITES (BOTH HEAVY AND LIGHT) OF SANDS AND SANDSTONES CHARACTERISTIC OF SPECIFIC SOURCE GROUPS OF ROCKS

I. Pegmatites and hydrothermal veins

Microcline	Anatase
Albite	Brookite
Muscovite	Columbite-tantalite
Biotite	Cassiterite
Tourmaline (all varieties except dravite)	Apatite
Dumortierite	Hematite (specular)
Spodumene	Sphalerite
Topaz	Wolframite
Barite	Gold
Fluorite	

II. Granites, granodiorites, syenites, rhyolites, quartz latites, trachytes

Orthoclase	Zircon
Microcline	Monazite
Oligoclase	Xenotime
Biotite	Sphene
Apatite	Magnetite
Allanite	

III. Tonalites, diorites, monzonites, dacites, andesites, latites

Oligoclase-andesine	Sphene
Magnetite	Apatite
Ilmenite	Corundum
Hornblende	

IV. Basalts, diabases, gabbros

Augite	Apatite
Hypersthene	Pleonaste
Magnetite	Olivine
Ilmenite	Leucoxene

V. Peridotites, serpentinites

Magnetite	Leucoxene
Picotite	Serpentine
Chromite	Talc
Ilmenite	Chlorite
Anthophyllite	Pyrope
Enstatite	Magnesite

TABLE 5. DETRITAL MINERAL SUITES (BOTH HEAVY AND LIGHT)
OF SANDS AND SANDSTONES CHARACTERISTIC OF SPECIFIC
SOURCE GROUPS OF ROCKS (*Continued*)

VI. Contact metamorphic rocks

Andalusite	Dravite
Hypersthene	Tremolite
Diopside	Wollastonite
Corundum	Vesuvianite
Cordierite	Axinite
Scheelite	

VII. Low- to medium-grade regional metamorphic rocks

Muscovite	Tourmaline (black, blue)
Biotite	Albite
Chlorite	Actinolite
Epidote-clinozoisite	Talc
Chloritoid	Piedmontite

VIII. High-grade regional metamorphic rocks

Kyanite	Hornblende
Sillimanite	Oligoclase-andesine
Almandite	Magnetite
Staurolite	Zircon
Rutile	Glaucophane
Hematite (specular)	

IX. From sediments

Barite	Celestite
Glauconite	Collophane
Hematite (earthy)	Limonite

The accessories together rarely exceed 1 per cent and **not** uncommonly constitute less than 0.1 per cent. Older sediments normally contain a less varied suite than younger rocks, and sediments derived from older sediments carry a simpler suite than those from igneous and/or metamorphic rocks. The variety of minerals varies inversely as the distance from the source rocks. Tectonic movements result in rejuvenation of the suite.

Authigenic Minerals

An authigenic mineral is one formed *in situ* by sedimentary processes, prior to, during, or shortly after lithifaction (Table 6).

Adularia, albite, calcite, and quartz are those most commonly forming crystallographically oriented overgrowths on their clastic nuclei.

TABLE 6. COMMON AUTHIGENIC MINERALS

Adularia	Glauconite
Albite	Gypsum
Analcite	Hematite
Anatase	Illite
Anhydrite	Marcasite
Barite	Microcline
Brookite	Pyrite
Calcite	Quartz
Celestite	Rutile
Chalcedony	Sericite
Chamosite	Siderite
Chlorite	Tourmaline
Collophane	Zeolites (heulandite, laumontite, phillipsite)

Overgrowths of adularia on plagioclase also are recorded. Tourmaline may show colorless overgrowths on the negative pole of detrital dark tourmaline grains. Rare authigenic overgrowths have been reported on zircon, hornblende, and garnet.

5

DESCRIPTIONS OF SEDIMENTARY ROCKS

SANDSTONE AND RELATED ROCKS

Sandstone and Siltstone

Definition. Sandstone is composed predominantly of clastic particles with subordinate cement, the clastic pieces consisting chiefly of quartz, with no more than 25 per cent feldspar and no more than 20 per cent clay minerals (Fig. 28). If the rock contains between 10 and 25 per cent feldspar, it is usually referred to as a feldspathic sandstone. On the basis of the binding agent there are two major groups: one with a mineral cement, precipitated in voids between grains; the other containing interstitial detrital clay and micaceous minerals. Another suggested subdivision of sandstones is into impure sandstones, i.e., >10 per cent argillaceous material, or wackes; and pure sandstones, i.e., <10 per cent argillaceous material, or arenites.

Mineralogy. The chief detrital mineral is quartz, with an average content estimated to be about 65 per cent. Small amounts of clastic chert, chalcedony, or quartzite may also be present. Most of the clastic feldspar is usually of the potash type—orthoclase, microcline, or both, but sodic plagioclase may also be common. The feldspars may be fresh or altered in varying degrees to kaolinite and sericite. Both fresh and altered types may occur together. The clay fraction consists chiefly of sericite, illite, kaolinite, and chlorite. Montmorillonite may be present in younger sandstones. The accessory detrital constituents ("heavy" minerals and others) together rarely exceed 1 per cent of the volume of the rock and not uncommonly are less than a 0.1 per cent. Among the common and widespread mineral species in this group are andalusite, apatite, augite and diopside, biotite, chlorite, epidote and zoisite, garnet, hornblende, hyperthene, ilmenite, kyanite, leucoxene, limonite, magnetite, monazite, muscovite, rutile, sillimanite, sphene,

114

staurolite, tourmaline, and zircon. Usually much rarer and far less widespread are actinolite, anatase, barite, brookite, cassiterite, chloritoid, chrysotile, corundum, dumortierite, fluorite, hematite, siderite, spinel, and topaz. Clastic calcite, dolomite, collophane shell fragments and glauconite in particles may also be present not uncommonly.

Many varieties of sandstone are distinguished on the basis of the nature of the most abundant binding agent.

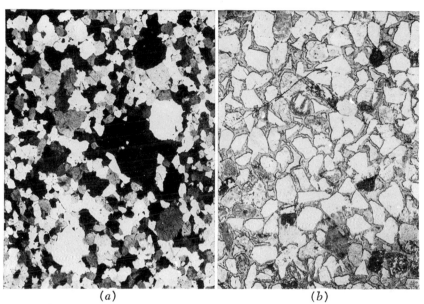

(a) (b)

FIG. 30*a, b.* (*a*) Sandstone, Flathead (Cambrian), Armstead, Montana. Chiefly quartz grains, well interlocked with quartz overgrowth cement. Moderate sorting. Nicols crossed, ×10. (*b*) Sandstone, Tertiary, Blacktail Range, Montana. Angular to subangular quartz and feldspar grains cemented by opal. Sorting good. Nicols not crossed, ×10.

1. Clastic binders
    a. Clay minerals—argillaceous sandstone
    b. Muscovite (including sericite)—micaceous sandstone
2. Precipitated cements
    a. Carbonate, usually calcite, rarely dolomite; ankerite and siderite are uncommon—calcareous sandstone
    b. Silica, usually quartz (Fig. 30*a*), less commonly chalcedony or opal (Fig. 30*b*)

   c. Iron oxide, limonite, goethite, and hematite—ferruginous sandstone

   d. Sulfate, gypsum, anhydrite, barite, celestite—sulfatic sandstone

   e. Others—pyrite, collophane, fluorite, manganese oxides, bitumen
(asphalt)

The most common cements are calcite and quartz. Sandstones with
quartz cement have been given various names—quartzitic sandstone,
sedimentary quartzite, and orthoquartzite (Fig. 30*a*).

Not uncommonly more than one mineral forms the cement, and as
many as four different species have been found occurring together.
Such combinations as quartz and calcite; quartz, dolomite, calcite;
quartz, dolomite, calcite, anhydrite were precipitated in the sequences
listed. Calcite cement also may precede quartz cement. A combination of calcite and iron oxides is not rare. Opal and chalcedony may
occur together, or quartz and chalcedony, clay-calcite, and clay-
limonite.

In addition to the secondary cement minerals, other authigenic constituents are adularia, illite, chlorite, glauconite, pyrite, and marcasite,
and uncommon tourmaline, zircon, rutile, brookite, anatase, and zeolites (especially heulandite and laumontite).

Other sandstone varieties include flagstone—a thin-bedded, usually
argillaceous or micaceous sandstone (also used less commonly for a
thin-bedded, sandy limestone); brownstone—a ferruginous sandstone
with quartz grains coated by iron oxide films; ganister—a compact,
highly siliceous sedimentary quartzite consisting of angular quartz
grains cemented by secondary quartz; grit—many grits are actually
graywackes, others are sedimentary quartzites in which the sharpness
of the quartz grains is a result of secondary enlargement by quartz
cement. Black sand is a placer sand, rich in magnetite and/or ilmenite.
Greensands are rich in glauconite, which, upon cementation, usually
by calcite, become glauconitic sandstones. Siltstones, which are finer-
grained than sandstones, are mineralogically similar, but may contain
a relatively high content of heavy accessory minerals.

Loess, a poorly consolidated eolian deposit, contains both silt- and
clay-size fractions. In the usually angular to subangular silt fraction
quartz predominates, with orthoclase, microcline, sodic plagioclase,
muscovite, biotite, chlorite, chert, calcite, dolomite, volcanic shards,
and carbonaceous material also present. Scattered quartz grains also
may be subrounded. Accessories are calcic plagioclase, sanidine, as
well as various combinations of the heavy minerals, including epidote
and zoisite, ilmenite, garnet, hornblende, leucoxene, pyroxenes, rutile,

sillimanite, sphene, staurolite, tremolite-actinolite, zircon, and others. In the clay fraction, montmorillonite, illite, quartz, dolomite, cristobalite, and volcanic shards are present, with some kaolinite. Much material designated adobe is clayey silt, similar in composition to loess.

Textures and Microstructures. The bulk of the clastic particles should fall in the sand-size range, $\frac{1}{16}$ to 2 mm, or, according to some usages, 0.1 to 2 mm. If the majority of the particles are in the silt-size range, i.e., $\frac{1}{256}$ to $\frac{1}{16}$ mm or 0.01 to 0.1 mm, the rock is a siltstone (Fig. 30c). Dune sands and eolian sandstones are of slightly finer average grade than water-deposited sandstones. The degree of sorting varies considerably, but for the highly quartzose types the degree of sorting is generally high. Beach and marine sandstones normally display very good sorting; eolian sandstones are nearly as well sorted; whereas outwash and river sandstones are much less restricted in the size range.

The textural characteristics of sandstones depend in large part upon (1) shape of the clastic particles, usually measured in terms of sphericity, (2) degree of roundness, usually expressed as angular, subangular, subrounded, rounded, and well rounded, (3) degree of sorting, (4) arrangement of particles and packing, (5) nature and amount of

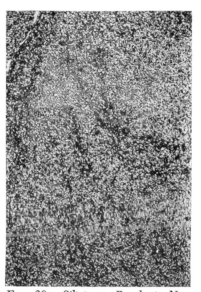

Fig. 30c. Siltstone, Rondout, New York. Chiefly silt-sized quartz particles with some carbonaceous shreds. Nicols not crossed, ×10.

cement. Both shape and rounding vary considerably in sandstones. In fact, no systematic characteristic differences in sphericity, rounding, sorting, or size can be used to distinguish in all cases among dune, beach, or river sands.

In some sandstones that contain elongated quartz grains, the axes of elongation tend to coincide with the *c* axes of the quartz, and the axes are arranged subparallelly. This parallel or subparallel orientation with bedding also characterizes detrital accessory micas and chlorites. Some siltstones, particularly those of lacustrine origin, show fine rhythmic banding. In some sandstones the quartz grains show frosting and pitting, which has usually been ascribed to eolian abrasion. The characteristics of the quartz have been used to determine its source. Undulatory extinction, fractures, biaxial character, and such inclusions as graphite, sillimanite, and kyanite indicate a metamorphic source. Relatively large subhedral inclusions of feldspar, zircon, apatite, magnetite, and mica also suggest metamorphic derivation. Planes of liquid–gas inclusions and inclusions of monazite, needle tourmaline, and rutile (sagenite) are more characteristic of igneous and hydrothermal quartz.

In sandstones with quartz cement, the cement may be fine-grained, interstitial, and clouded by fine dust. In other types it has been deposited as crystallographically (and optically) continuous overgrowths on clastic grains. The boundary between the two may be distinguished by a film of iron oxide, by a line of dusty inclusions, or by frosting and pitting of the nucleus. In other cases the distinction between the core and the rim is not marked. First the detrital quartz is enlarged to form subhedral to euhedral crystals, and with increasing silicification the pore space tends to be eliminated and an anhedral quartz mosaic is produced. In some rocks minor ragged relicts of calcite give evidence of replacement of an original calcitic cement by secondary quartz. Cryptocrystalline to feathery chalcedony may also be a cementing agent, some of it formed by crystallization of opal. Some of the chalcedony may be set in radial patterns around quartz grains. Opal cement is generally confined to geologically young sandstones.

Oriented authigenic overgrowths also occur on other minerals: (1) tourmaline, on which colorless feathery protuberances are deposited preferentially over the rounded negative pole of the more darkly colored detrital nucleus, (2) zircon with rare dentations attached to prism faces, (3) feldspar, usually cores of microcline, but also of other feldspars, including even calcic plagioclase, and authigenic rims normally of adularia and rarely of microcline or of albite. Several generations of overgrowths may be present. The rounded nucleus may be kaolinized or coated by iron oxide to distinguish it from the fresh overgrowths. The marginal feldspar tends to form euhedral faces and crystals of simple rhombic outline. Overgrowths have also been reported on garnet and hornblende.

Carbonate cement shows considerable variation in grain size, from very fine grained, nearly cryptocrystalline, through medium-grained, to very large interlocking poikilitic anhedra each of which enclose several to numerous quartz grains. Continued growth of such large poikilitic grains may lead to the development of euhedral "sand calcite" crystals. Barite cement shows similar development to form "sand barite" rosettes, and gypsum may be likewise developed. Rarely calcitic or iron oxide oolites appear. Some carbonate cement is formed by recrystallization of clastic calcite; some results from intrastratal solution of shell fragments. The calcite grains usually form an an hedral mosaic or an interlocking sutured aggregate. In dolomitic cements the grains tend toward euhedral rhombs. Another euhedral mineral is widespread pyrite, in cubes.

Various clastic minerals show marginal solution and etching— quartz, feldspar, garnet, augite, hypersthene, hornblende, and staurolite.

Glauconite occurs in subrounded, mammillary grains, colored light to dark green, and composed of cryptocrystalline aggregates. Some are internal casts of foraminifera; some show alteration to limonite.

Most sandstones contain voids or interstices between grains, unfilled or only partly filled by cement. This porosity may be primary, depending mainly on sorting, grain shape, and packing, or it may be secondary, depending largely on amount of resolution of cement. The voids usually are minute but may be sufficiently large to accommodate the formation of small quartz or calcite crystals or linings of chalcedony or drusy calcite.

Siltstones that are thinly bedded or fissile normally are grouped with shales, at least megascopically.

Occurrence and Origin. Highly quartzose sandstones occur as relatively thin but widespread blanket-type units, rarely thicker than a few hundred feet. Fossils usually are uncommon, and cross-bedding may be a conspicuous structural feature. The major varieties, quartz-rich sandstone, glauconitic sandstone, micaceous sandstone, and ferruginous sandstone, all can be found as part of a stable-shelf tectonic association, accompanied by clay shales and normal marine and fossiliferous limestones. The ferruginous sandstones not uncommonly occur in red-bed associations. Feldspathic sandstones characteristically are formed in unstable shelf environments. Sandstones are formed as the result of marine, littoral, alluvial, and eolian deposition. High-quartz sands may be formed (1) by intense chemical destruction of all original minerals except quartz, (2) by reworking of first-cycle quartzose sands, and (3) by local re-sorting of arkosic sandstones and graywackes. Well-known United States examples include the Flathead (Fig. 30a) and Potsdam (Cambrian), St. Peter (Ordovician), Berea (Mississippian), Dakota (Cretaceous), Tensleep or Quadrant (Pennsylvania).

Siltstones are principally products of fluvial, lacustrine, eolian, and glacial environments.

Conglomerate and Breccia

Although conglomerates and breccias, as units, do not lend themselves well to thin-section studies, their matrixes may usefully be studied by microscopic techniques. Conglomerates are clastic rocks with pebbles or subangular to rounded mineral or rock pieces larger than 2 mm in diameter. The term breccia is used if the fragments are not rounded. Generally the rock is called a conglomerate if about 10 per cent or more of the fragments are of pebble size; the matrix of sand or finer sizes normally predominates. Pebbly sandstone is intermediate between conglomerate and sandstone. Glacial conglomerates, or tillites, contain relatively few large pieces in a matrix of predominantly clayey material. The degree of sorting varies greatly, ranging from very well sorted types, such as quartz-pebble conglomerates, to tillites, which are characterized by an extreme range of size grades.

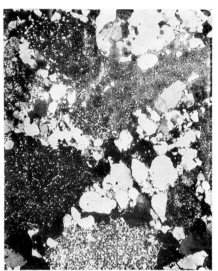

Fig. 31a. Jasper conglomerate, Buffalo Gap, South Dakota. Pebbles of chert, sandstone, and quartzite; grains of quartz, chalcedonic cement. Nicols crossed, ×10.

Many conglomerates show two distinct peaks in their size-distribution curves; i.e., they tend to be bimodal. These also tend to be lithologically homogeneous and usually contain pebbles of quartz, quartzite, or chert in a matrix of quartz sand bonded by a mineral cement (Fig. 31a). The pebbles in these (oligomictic) conglomerates are in the fine- to medium-pebble-size ranges, are well sorted, have a high sphericity, and are highly rounded. The matrix sand, which at least in some cases has been introduced into the interstices of the gravel after its deposition, is commonly a well-sorted quartz sand bonded by calcite or quartz. Such conglomerates are typically derived from marine gravels formed on a transgressive beach area, are associated with sedimentary quartzites, and form blankets that may be widespread, but are usually relatively thin and may pinch out locally.

In contrast are the (polymictic) conglomerates in which pebbles are of varied lithology and mineralogy, consisting not only of quartz, but also of granite and other plutonic rocks, as well as eruptive and even other sedimentary and metamorphic types. Fanglomerates belong in this group. Such conglomerates have particles that are usually coarse, poorly sorted, and show moderate sphericity and roundness values. The subordinate sand and silt matrix consists of quartz, fresh feldspar, mica, and the alteration products sericite, kaolinite, and chlorite, cemented by subordinate quartz or calcite. One variety is the granite pebble (arkosic) conglomerate, in which most of the pebbles consist of granite, aplite, or pegmatite. Another variety is graywacke conglomerate. Conglomerates of this type are thick and wedge-shaped, representing fluvial outpourings into marginal parts of geosynclines derived from adjacent, markedly uplifted source regions.

Intraformational conglomerates and breccias are formed by desiccation and cracking during temporary withdrawal of shallow waters and subsequent shifting during reflooding. Two types are common: shale-pebble breccia or conglomerate (flat-pebble conglomerate), consisting of thin shale pieces in a sandy matrix; limestone conglomerate or breccia, in which flat and relatively small pieces of usually sandy or oolitic limestone or dolomite are embedded in a matrix of limestone or sandy limestone and dolomite. The flat pieces may be packed together on edge to form the striking edgewise conglomerates.

Till and tillite are characterized by extreme heterogeneity of composition and lack of sorting. The larger pieces may be faceted and striated and are set in a greatly predominating matrix of clay and some sand, consisting of angular particles of quartz, fresh feldspar, calcite, dolomite, and other rarer minerals, and rock pieces in a still finer grained aggregate of illite, sericite, chlorite, and in some cases also montmorillonite and kaolinite. Older tillites contain little or no montmorillonite or kaolinite.

Conglomerates with limonite or hematite cement are not common. Cementing pyrite may also appear. In some examples cementing material penetrates pebbles along cracks. Silica cement may be deposited in crystallographic continuity over matrix quartz grains or may be cryptocrystalline to slightly coarser toward the center of interstices.

Sedimentary breccia varieties of special origin are talus breccias, collapse breccias, and bone breccias (bone beds). Breccias of cataclastic origin (fault breccias, friction breccias) are in this book considered to belong with metamorphic rocks; volcanic breccias are referred to under pyroclastic rocks, intrusion breccias under migmatites.

Arkose

Definition. Arkose is a clastic rock, with particles predominantly of sand size, containing 25 per cent or more feldspar and not more than 20 per cent clay, sericite, and chlorite (Fig. 28).

(*b*)   (*c*)

Fig. 31*b, c.* (*b*) Arkose, Belt series, Tendoy Mountains, Montana. Moderately sorted, subrounded particles of quartz, microcline, and orthoclase. Nicols crossed, ×10. (*c*) Arkose (brownstone), Portland, Connecticut. Poorly sorted, subangular to subrounded quartz and feldspar in matrix with some sericite and clay; tourmaline, *lower left*. Nicols not crossed, ×10.

Mineralogy. The main clastic minerals are quartz and feldspar. Among the feldspars potash (orthoclase, microcline, and perthitic variants) and soda types are most abundant, and several varieties may occur together (Fig. 31*b*). Entirely fresh feldspars may be mixed with altered varieties, or the feldspars may be generally altered or fresh. The presence of angular, kaolinized feldspars usually indicates alteration after deposition. Muscovite, biotite, chlorite, amphibole, pyroxenes, and epidote are present in minor amounts, and various other heavy minerals (rutile, zircon, garnet, magnetite, tourmaline, and apatite) occur as accessories. Minor amounts of small rock fragments, particularly of granite, aplite, shale, siltstone, chert, and some schists may also be present. The clay mineral is usually kaolinite, in some cases apparently illite (Fig. 31c). The common cement is calcite, in some cases limonite; silica is rare. Other arkoses contain little or no cement, being consolidated chiefly by pressure. Iron oxide concretions or carbonaceous material may be present. Some grits are really arkoses.

Textures and Microstructures. Much of the quartz is of igneous derivation and may show the characteristic inclusions. Oriented overgrowths are not common. The particle size is generally in the coarse-sand range; the sorting is moderate to moderately good, with some silt usually present. Particles normally are subrounded to angular, and sphericity is poor to moderate. Because of only partial cementation and fair sizing, the porosity may be high. The feldspars may show oriented overgrowths.

Occurrence and Origin. Arkoses are of two genetic types: (1) Basal or residual, thin and local blanket arkoses represent reworked mantle by seas encroaching on terrain underlain dominantly by felsic plutonic rocks. Such arkoses, which lie at the base of a sedimentary series and are associated with feldspathic and quartzose sandstones, in some cases have been misidentified as granite or granitized sediments, particularly where encountered in well cores and cuttings. An example is the LaMotte (Cambrian) formation of Missouri. (2) Tectonic arkoses are thicker wedge-shaped deposits, either areally extensive or of limited extent, which are mainly of fluvial and torrential origin, associated with coarse fanglomerates. Well-known examples occur in the Newark (Triassic) series of New England. Strong rapid erosion and rapid burial are characteristic environmental conditions, and fault troughs and rapidly subsiding basins are characteristic places of deposition.

Graywacke

Definition. Graywacke is a clastic rock with particles ranging from clay through silt and sand sizes to pebble or very coarse sand sizes. The graywacke field (Fig. 28) is bounded by 20 to 75 per cent clay, sericite, chlorite, 0 to 70 per cent quartz, 10 to 80 per cent feldspar. Subgraywackes are defined as containing less than 10 per cent feldspar. Generally the quartz content is 30 to 45 per cent, feldspar 10 to 50 per cent, clay-mica matrix must exceed 20 per cent, and rock fragments are 5 to 10 per cent.

Mineralogy. The conspicuous clastic minerals are quartz and feld-spar. Much of the former is probably derived from metamorphic rocks. In some graywackes the feldspar content is low; in others feld-spar exceeds quartz. The feldspars include microcline, orthoclase, and plagioclase, usually sodic, although more calcic types also occur. Both fresh and altered feldspars appear, and plagioclase exceeds alkali feld-spar in many cases. Normally the feldspars are somewhat altered,

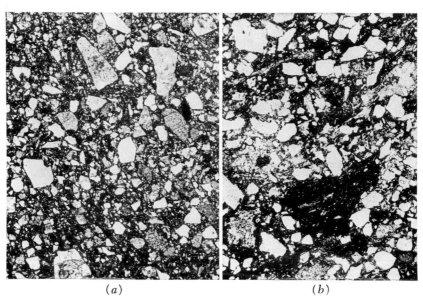

(a)   (b)

Fig. 32. (*a*) Graywacke, Fortune formation (Ordovician), Lawrence Harbour, Newfoundland. Angular to subrounded quartz, chert, and feldspar pieces, poorly sorted, in matrix of chlorite, sericite, biotite, clay minerals, and pyrite. Nicols not crossed, ×10. (*b*) Graywacke, Sansom formation (Ordovician), Snows Pond, Newfoundland. Angular to subangular, poorly sorted, quartz, feldspar, and rock fragments in chlorite-sericite-kaolinite matrix. Nicols not crossed, ×10.

either kaolinized by weathering or partly replaced by low-temperature minerals such as sericite and calcite. Rock types present as fragments include mainly phyllite, greenschist, slate, and chert, as well as minor basalt, siltstone, sandstone, and quartzite (Fig. 32*b*). Accessory heavy minerals usually are scanty, including such species as hornblende, augite, epidote, serpentine, biotite, magnetite, zircon, and tourmaline. Detrital muscovite is common in some subgraywackes.

The grains and fragments are set in an abundant pasty matrix (Fig. 32*a*) consisting of chlorite (which is largely responsible for the dark gray or gray green color of the rock), sericite, biotite, illite, some silty quartz, and locally, zeolites. Some of the sericite and chlorite is authigenic. Pyrite in cubes replacing matrix also is authigenic, and matrix carbonate, usually ankerite, as well as clusters of rutile needles, are probably of similar origin. Calcite, dolomite, and siderite also occur, and some secondary silica cement may be present. In subgraywackes chlorite may be a less abundant constituent, but carbonaceous shreds are common. Some graywackes contain carbonized wood fragments. Many grits are actually graywackes, and "salt-and-pepper" sandstones are quartzose graywackes with abundant detrital chert.

Textures and Microstructures. Sorting generally is very poor, with pebble to clay sizes abundantly represented. Thus permeability is low. Sphericity and roundness are very low to moderate. Thus texturally, the rocks are microbreccias. The quartz may be highly angular, even sliverlike, and feldspars and rock pieces are likewise angular. Usually the long axes of these minerals and of the micas as well are generally parallel with the bedding planes. The matrix is a microcrystalline to felted aggregate of the micas (both muscovite and biotite), illite, and chlorite, locally replaced by carbonate and pyrite cubes. Sericite, illite, and chlorite replace detrital quartz and feldspar, usually penetrating the grains marginally in a dentate pattern and entirely destroying the original clastic boundary. In some instances the chlorite-quartz intergrowth is restricted to the secondary quartz overgrowth, in other cases the micaceous minerals encroach even upon the original detrital nucleus.

Some graywacke beds are finely laminated with interbedded shaley layers. Subgraywackes are usually finer-grained, with poor to moderate sorting of subrounded to angular particles.

Occurrence and Origin. Graywackes are commonly associated with submarine lavas and tuffs (basalts and spilites), silty shales, siltstones, and bedded cherts. They may grade into mafic tuffs and may alternate rhythmically with shale. Dark siliceous limestones, jaspers, and manganiferous sediments are other associates. Their environment of formation requires rapid erosion, rapid transportation, and burial sufficiently rapid to prevent complete chemical alteration of mafic minerals. Most graywackes are of marine origin, but a few are nonmarine. They are very characteristic sediments of some orogenic belts, forming thick lenticular bodies in linear geosynclines. Density currents may aid in forming graywackes with graded bedding. Ripple marks are absent, and fossils are rare. Much of the chlorite, sericite, and pyrite has been produced diagenetically by reactions among the matrix materials, between matrix and clastic pieces and between matrix components and dissolved marine salts.

Subgraywackes, which are associated with silty shales, thin, nodular limestones, and in some cases even with quartzose sandstones, are indicative of moderate subsidence in unstable basins and of burial sufficiently rapid to prevent re-sorting.

The Timiskaming (early pre-Cambrian) of Ontario contains conspicuous graywackes. Other examples are the Tyler (pre-Cambrian) formation of Michigan and the Franciscan (Upper Jurassic) of California. Many "sandstones" of the Pennsylvanian coal formations are subgraywackes.

CLAY, SHALE, AND RELATED ROCKS

Clay

Definition. Clay is an unconsolidated or poorly indurated natural earth, containing an excess of particles of clay size ($\frac{1}{256}$ mm or less in diameter) which should consist dominantly of the clay minerals. In practice, however, the name clay is applied to material containing as little as 10 per cent clay minerals. Usually, because of their poorly consolidated nature, clays must be indurated before successful sectioning.

The mineralogy of clays reflects the complexity of the clay mineral group. Clays consisting of any of the clay minerals in nearly pure form have been described, and nearly all combinations of the various clay minerals also occur. The nomenclature of varieties of clay is mineralogically unsystematic, being based in part on mineralogy (diaspore clay), in part on occurrence (underclay), and in part on use (fuller's earth, china clay). In many cases microscopic techniques alone do not suffice to study and identify the clay minerals alone or in aggregate.

KAOLIN AND KAOLINITE CLAY

Kaolin (including china clay) consists chiefly of kaolinite (Fig. 33), with variable amounts of dickite or nacrite and in some cases halloysite. Other minerals are quartz, microcline, albite, muscovite, hematite, and in some types, fluorite, cassiterite, zircon, magnetite, rutile, topaz, and tourmaline. Varied rock fragments, such as granite, pegmatite, quartz-tourmaline rock, and others, may be present. Minor very fine grained gibbsite or spherical groups of radial gibbsite may be present, as well as diaspore and boehmite. The aluminum hydroxide minerals usually replace oolites, pisolites, or crystals of kaolinite.

Pseudohexagonal kaolinite plates, corroded quartz grains, and grains of accessory constituents are scattered at random singly or in interlocking masses through a very fine grained kaolinitic matrix. Some kaolinite pseudomorphs after plagioclase retain the relict twinning.

Quartzose kaolinite pellets may be common. Kaolinite in "soft" clays forms well-oriented sheets grouped in books or vermiform, accordionlike aggregates. In the "hard" and "flint" types, the finer-grained kaolinite may form compact colloform masses. Quartz grains are replaced by kaolinite. In some types irregular shard-like pieces of coarse kaolinite in a finer-grained matrix show irregular, wavy extinction bars and even "polarization crosses," similar to Bxa figures, but without conoscopic conditions.

Many of the so-called flint clays and fire clays are dominantly kaolinitic. Flint clays usually have some quartz and hydrated aluminum oxide minerals, too. Residual clays derived from pegmatites and granites and their transported derivatives are also kaolinitic. Some underclays contain kaolinite as the chief clay constituent; others contain it with illite or have illite with minor dickite. Even some fuller's earths

Fig. 33. Kaolin, Macon, Georgia. Vermicular (accordionlike) kaolinite crystals in two directions at right angles; tabular sericite replacing kaolinite; matrix of cryptocrystalline kaolinite. Nicols not crossed, ×72. (*After Paul Kerr and American Petroleum Institute.*)

are kaolinitic, as are some recent marine clays, particularly nearshore types.

Examples of kaolinite clays occur in the Spruce Pine district, North Carolina, residual after pegmatites. Transported types are typified by those of the Tuscaloosa formation (Cretaceous) of the Aiken area, South Carolina.

ILLITE CLAY

Micaceous minerals of the illite group appear to be common or to predominate in:

1. Many marine clays, especially deep-sea (abyssal) types. Other clay minerals are variable amounts of montmorillonite, kaolinite, and a chloritic constituent. Other minerals include quartz, iron and manganese oxides, calcite, glauconite, feldspar, collophane, and various accessories such as tourmaline, garnet, zircon, hornblende, hypersthene,

augite, epidote, biotite, muscovite, pyrite, and zeolites. Other particles consist of glass, remains of diatoms, foraminifera, radiolaria, sponge spicules, sharks' teeth, and carbonaceous material.

2. Underclays, which may consist of kaolinite-illite mixtures or, if they are calcareous, of illite alone. Partly altered or fresh feldspars may be present, also quartz in grains and lenses, muscovite, epidote, and other heavy accessories. Secondary calcite may form crystals, in some instances in vugs. Typical are the underclays of the Pennsylvanian cyclothems of Illinois and Pennsylvania.

MONTMORILLONITE CLAY

The chief representatives in which montmorillonite predominates are bentonites (Figs. 34*b,c*) and their slightly transported and reworked derivatives (Fig. 34*a*). Bentonite is altered volcanic ash,

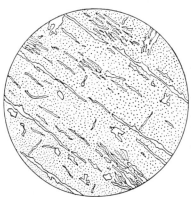

FIG. 34*a*. Montmorillonite clay, Jackson group (Eocene), Angelina County, Texas. Oriented-shred structure in montmorillonite, believed to result from pressure-packing. Nicols not crossed, ×12. (*Courtesy of A. F. Hagner.*)

which probably fell into water— marine, fresh, or even saline. It has the distinctive property of expanding to several times its original volume when immersed in water. The chief constituents are montmorillonite, cristobalite (as much as 30 per cent), glass relicts, grains of pyrogenic quartz, sanidine, oligoclase, biotite, hornblende, and zircon, and in some, carbonaceous shreds, calcareous foraminifera, opaline diatoms, gypsum crystals, hydromica, lepidocrocite, and pseudomorphs of zeolite (especially heulandite) after glass. Illite, kaolinite, and halloysite may be present in minor or subordinate amounts. The glass usually appears as relict, highly angular shards with concave walls, as fibrous fragments, as plates, and as Y-shaped pieces. It is replaced by montmorillonite marginally, or completely so that only "ghosts" remain, which may show secondary crenulations. The montmorillonite usually forms micaceous plates either parallel or normal to the glass surfaces. Very fine grained montmorillonite and vermicular crystals of it may also appear. Original layering may also be pseudomorphously preserved.

The montmorillonites vary considerably in composition—in the

Mg/Fe ratio and in the R_2O_3/SiO_2 ratio. Most are Ca montmorillonites, with a few containing exchangeable Na, K, H, or Mg. Very few bentonites are older than Cretaceous. The original bentonite occurs at Fort Benton, Wyoming, and is of Cretaceous age. Bentonites also occur abundantly in the Upper Cretaceous and Tertiary of the Gulf Coast. Some fuller's earth is montmorillonitic. Bentonites result from the devitrification of volcanic ash.

Transported clays derived from bentonites usually are mixtures of montmorillonite and kaolinite with some halloysite and allophane. Coarser clastic grains (as much as 25 per cent) are quartz, potash feldspar, plagioclase, muscovite, zircon, tourmaline, magnetite, glauco-

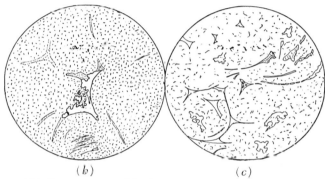

(b)   (c)

FIG. 34b, c. (b) Bentonite, Modelo formation (Miocene), Ventura Quadrangle, California. Glass shard partly replaced by montmorillonite. Nicols not crossed, ×60. (*Courtesy of Paul Kerr and Economic Geology.*) (c) Bentonite, same formation and locality. Glass shards in montmorillonite matrix. Nicols not crossed, ×60. (*Courtesy of Paul Kerr and Economic Geology.*)

nite, and chlorite. Other constituents are gypsum crystals and microrosettes, opal, limonite, pyrite lenticles and cubes, zeolites, organic fragments, and such fossils as diatoms and sponge spicules. Montmorillonite replaces quartz, feldspar, and glass. In some types the montmorillonite is shreddy and oriented parallel to subparallel. Coarsegrained patches and streaks of kaolinite-halloysite or kaolinite-halloysite-allophane are set in a granular or flaky montmorillonite base that also may contain kaolinite and some halloysite. Patches and veins of coarsely crystalline montmorillonite with undulatory extinction appear along cracks. Clays of this type occur in the Coastal Plain of Texas.

The so-called metabentonites consist of a mixed-layer clay mineral, usually montmorillonite-illite, along with minor chloritic clay material in some cases. Glass, biotite, apatite, and zircon of pyrogenic origin may also be present. Paleozoic metabentonites are known from Appalachian states.

Diaspore Clay

Diaspore clays are of two major types: those containing principally diaspore ± boehmite (diasporite) and those containing diaspore along with considerable or even predominating kaolinite. The first types, represented by the diaspore clays of Missouri, contain (1) diaspore alone, (2) boehmite alone, (3) diaspore + boehmite, or (4) diaspore +boehmite and subordinate kaolinite and a chloritic clay mineral Accessories are coaly material, wood casts, pyrite, and alunite. Some varieties contain boehmite-diaspore pisolites; others are massive-granular. The Mercer (Pennsylvanian) formation in Pennsylvania contains kaolinitic clays with diaspore, minor boehmite, iron oxide, siderite, pyrite, illite, and clastic zircon, tourmaline, and mica. The kaolinite forms a microgranular matrix, clusters of fine to coarse crystals, veins of minute to large vermicular crystals cutting the matrix and the diaspore aggregates. Diaspore clouded by iron oxide dust forms nodular aggregates resembling pisolites and scattered matrix grains. Second-generation clear diaspore caps older diaspore nodules.

Some fireclays are diaspore clays. The Missouri diaspore clays are also known as burley clay. The so-called high-alumina clays usually contain some diaspore or boehmite.

Other Clays

Halloysite clays that occur in Indiana at the base of the Mansfield (Pennsylvanian) sandstone are relatively pure or contain mixed alunite, allophane, and phosphatic material. Certain fuller's earths consist principally of attapulgite along with coarser detrital quartz, alkali feldspar, and accessory sphene, leucoxene, zircon, magnetite, and collophane. The clay particles are well oriented and yield aggregate biaxial figures.

Bauxite

Definition. Bauxites are residual rocks (or less commonly are transported for short distances), consisting chiefly of one or more of the aluminum hydroxide minerals, boehmite, diaspore, and gibbsite, usually with variable amounts of kaolinite and some iron and titanium oxides.

Mineralogy. The chief constituents are the aluminum hydroxide minerals, which may occur separately or in various combinations.

Some bauxites contain boehmite alone, others contain it combined with gibbsite or diaspore. Still other types consist dominantly of gibbsite or of diaspore; all three may occur together. Kaolinite not uncommonly is present in minor to large amounts, and in some varieties halloysite and nontronite have been detected. Hematite, goethite, and limonite normally occur in small amounts, but in bauxites derived from mafic rocks they may be very abundant. Anatase and leucoxene usually are present, and in some examples Mn minerals also appear. Other nonclastic constituents that occur locally are chalcedony, pyrophyllite, siderite, calcite, and pyrite. Other constituents, either residual or transported, are quartz, chlorite, apatite, zircon, tourmaline, and rutile.

Textures and Microstructures. The texture is highly variable. Main types are:

1. Pisolitic and oolitic
2. Massive-cryptocrystalline to microcrystalline-granular
3. Fragmental
4. Granitoid
5. Cellular
6. Stratified

Oolites and pisolites may be massive or concentrically layered, commonly with ramifying, radiating cracks. Color and grain-size variations differentiate the different shells. Gibbsite is the common mineral, but diaspore and boehmite (Figs. 35a,b) also form oolites. Pisolites may be set in a microcrystalline-granular or in an oolitic matrix. Some pisolites have cores of microcrystalline gibbsite pseudomorphous after feldspar. Gibbsite crystals also line cavities. In some varieties the chief aluminum mineral is stained by iron oxides and is cryptocrystalline, thus difficult to identify by microscopic means alone. Coarser boehmite forms irregular grains to euhedral spindles; coarse-grained diaspore also appears as grains, spindles, and crossed twins. Kaolinite forms residual patches, oolites, grains, vermicular and accordionlike crystals, and, in some cases, veinlets cutting both matrix and pisolites. Pyrite, which occurs locally, surrounds pisolites, veins them, and also forms pyritohedra. Siderite is in grains and nodules, some radial.

Granitoid bauxites, which have inherited their textures from parent plutonic rocks, consist usually of gibbsite pseudomorphous after feldspar in a matrix of iron-stained, nearly opaque cryptocrystalline gibbsite. Transported types show stratification and contain sorted pebbles, grains, and pisolites of bauxite.

Occurrence and Origin. Bauxite is formed from a variety of parent rocks, including mainly nepheline syenite, syenite, phonolite, trachyte, and granite pegmatite, but also aplite, diorite, diabase, gabbro, basalt, and even various gneisses, schists, phyllites, arkosic sediments, and clays. It is developed under tropical climatic conditions where rain water moves continuously for long periods through porous, well-

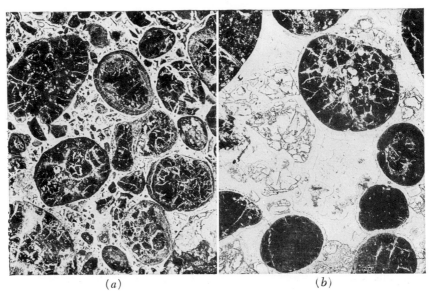

(a)   (b)

FIG. 35. (a) Bauxite, Banks, Alabama. Boehmite oolites in cryptocrystalline boehmite-gibbsite matrix. Nicols not crossed, ×9. (b) Bauxite, Floyd County, Georgia. Boehmite oolites (stained by limonite) in matrix of coarsely crystalline gibbsite and cryptocrystalline boehmite. Nicols not crossed, ×9.

drained aluminous rocks. Bauxites are either residual or, less usually, transported. Another subdivision is (1) terra rossa bauxites—associated with carbonate rocks and reportedly formed from clays; (2) lateritic bauxites—formed from and on crystalline rocks under tropical conditions.

Shale

Definition. Shale is a laminated or thinly bedded rock consisting either of clay-size particles, silt-size particles, or a combination of the two. Claystone or mudstone is an indurated clay that lacks the thin-bedded character of shale.

Mineralogy. The complete mineral composition of shales, as of clays, is not easily determinable microscopically. The coarser particles, which consist of quartz, feldspar (both potash and plagioclase), muscovite, chlorite, and accessory biotite, hornblende, epidote, magnetite, tourmaline, and zircon, are set in a "paste"—a microcrystalline to cryptocrystalline matrix of clay minerals, quartz, sericite, chlorite, limonite, rutile needles ("clay slate needles"), and carbonaceous

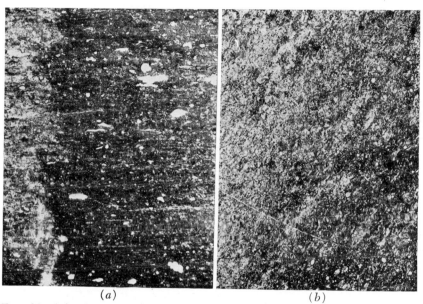

(a)   (b)

Fig. 36. (a) Shale, Monterey formation (Miocene), Los Angeles, California. Quartz particles in matrix silty quartz, clay, and bituminous material. Change in color is due to displacement along microfault. Nicols not crossed, ×9. (b) Shale, same formation and locality. Better sorted, less bituminous material, more calcite. Nicols not crossed, ×9.

material. Other constituents are pyrite, glauconite, collophane, and carbonate grains and euhedra. The clay minerals include illite (probably most widespread), chloritic clay minerals, montmorillonite (chiefly in Mesozoic or younger shales), and kaolinite. High-kaolinite shales usually are less thinly layered than other types.

The main mineralogical varieties are quartzose shale (Fig. 36a), with calcareous (Fig. 36b), ferruginous, carbonaceous, or even glauconitic material in the matrix; feldspathic shale, >10 per cent silty feldspar and with considerable matrix kaolinite; micaceous shale, with abundant detrital muscovite and considerable matrix sericite; and chloritic shale, with abundant silty feldspar and a chloritic matrix that may also be pyritic, siliceous, calcareous, or carbonaceous.

Carbonaceous or black shales are rich in macerated plant debris or carbonaceous shreds, as well as in pyrite, whereas bituminous shales contain their carbon principally in resins and pollen grains.

Oil shales are carbonaceous shales that yield, upon distillation, paraffins and olefins known collectively as kerogen. The organic material is mainly plant debris, including spores, spore and cuticle fragments, yellow to red globular algal remains, pollen grains, macerated shreds, and massive, homogenous substances. Some oil shales contain thin interlayered beds and seams of lacustrine saline minerals, including such types as trona, $Na_3H(CO_3)_2 \cdot 2H_2O$; gaylussite, $Na_2Ca(CO_3)_2 \cdot 5H_2O$; shortite, $Na_2Ca_2(CO_3)_2$; pirssonite, $Na_2Ca(CO_3)_2 \cdot 2H_2O$; northupite, $Na_3MgCl(CO_3)_2$; and bradleyite, $Na_3PO_4 \cdot MgCO_3$. Other minerals of these seams are quartz, dolomite, montmorillonite, analcite, apophyllite, and pyrite.

Phosphatic shales carry considerable collophane. Clay ironstones, which form thin seams and nodules in coal beds, are mixtures of clay minerals and siderite. Siliceous shales owe their high silica content to opal or cryptocrystalline quartz derived from opal and not from detrital quartz. Gypsiferous shales contain disseminated gypsum or anhydrite in grains or euhedra. Marls or marlstones are hybrid calcareous-argillaceous rocks, usually weakly indurated, either of lacustrine or marine origin. Anhydrite, gypsum, dolomite, barite, celestite, and glauconite may be present. The red color of some shales is due to limonite or hematite, whereas green shales owe their color mainly to the absence of ferric minerals plus the presence of illite and montmorillonite that contain ferrous iron.

Textures and Microstructures. Most shales contain a high proportion of silt-sized particles. In some shales this size predominates, but a few very fine grained shales have essentially no silt particles. The coarser clastic particles are normally subrounded to subangular, but the original shape may be obscured through marginal replacement. Shales generally show a marked parallel arrangement, not only of the matrix constituents, but also of the coarser detritals. Small-scale banding, laminations, or varves are common, resulting from deposition of varying amounts of such materials as quartz, calcite, chlorite, or carbonaceous shreds, or from deposition of particles of different grain size. The parallel orientation of clay minerals in shales can be tested in some cases by observing a diffuse optic figure from the matrix aggregate. Many oil shales are microscopically laminated, the darker seams containing concentrations of euxinic organic material.

Occurrence and Origin. Shales of stable shelf associations are primarily clay shales (Maquoketa shale, Ordovician), whereas on unstable shelf areas silty shales predominate. Shales composed chiefly of silty materials are characteristic of sediments deposited in intracratonic basins. Shales associated with tectonic arkoses are micaceous and feldspathic. Black shales are formed in restricted basins of low oxygen and high H_2S content (euxinic environment). Typical are the Utica (Ordovician) shales of New York, and the Chattanooga shale (Devonian-Mississippian) of Tennessee and other nearby states. The Mowry shale (Cretaceous) exemplifies the siliceous shales. Red shales are prominent constituents of red-bed series, as in the Chugwater (Triassic) of Wyoming.

CHALCEDONIC AND RELATED ROCKS

Chert

Definition. Chert is composed predominantly of fine-grained chalcedony, of cryptocrystalline quartz, or of combinations of the two (75 per cent or more). Flint is synonymous with chert.

Mineralogy. The silica takes the form of (1) feathery chalcedony, (2) cryptocrystalline quartz, (3) microcrystalline quartz, (4) opal, or (5) rarely as cristobalite. Clastic quartz grains may also be present in subordinate numbers. Older cherts or somewhat metamorphosed cherts contain little or no chalcedony or opal, being characterized by microcrystalline quartz. Many cherts are relatively impure, containing abundant calcite, also dolomite or siderite. Such rocks, poorly termed porcellanites, grade into cherty limestones. Porcellanite also has been applied (1) to rocks composed of clay and silt with large amounts of opal or chalcedony, which grade into siliceous shales, and (2) to silicified tuffs.

Other constituents that may be abundant are carbonaceous material (Fig. 37a), bitumen or graphite (sapropelic chert), detrital quartz (silty chert), pyrite, chlorite, siliceous sponge spicules (spiculite chert), and radiolarian capsules (radiolarian chert). Other microscopic fossils, which may be abundant locally, are usually conodonts, foraminifera, graptolites, ostracods, and spores. Less abundant constituents are limonite, sericite, feldspar, glauconite, and clay minerals.

Jasper consists of cryptocrystalline quartz, formed by recrystallization from chalcedony, stained brown, yellow, and red by iron oxides.

It is associated with iron ores. Tripoli is a light-colored, porous, rough aggregate consisting chiefly of fine-grained silica, believed to represent the residue of partly silicified carbonate rocks from which carbonate was leached. Siliceous sinter, which is deposited from hot springs, is a lightweight, soft, porous, light-colored aggregate composed mainly of a delicate network of minute fibers or concretions of opal. Geyserite is the same material deposited by geysers. Limonite and manganese oxides are common impurities.

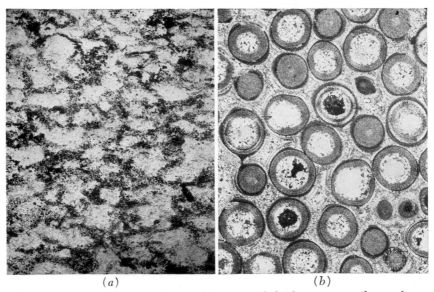

(a)   *(b)*

FIG. 37. (*a*) Chert, Teton County, Wyoming. Chalcedony, iron oxides, and carbonaceous material. Organic structures partly preserved. Nicols not crossed, ×10. (*b*) Oolitic chert (siliceous oolite), State College, Pennsylvania. Chalcedony and quartz, pseudomorphous after calcareous oolites and matrix carbonate. Nicols crossed, ×10.

In Continental European usage chert designates siliceous rocks with abundant organic remains, especially sponge spicules; the terms pthanite, silexite, and lydite are generally synonymous with American and British usage of chert.

Textures and Microstructures. The grain size and textural variability of cherts largely reflect the degree of crystallinity of the silica mineral. The rocks consist of mixtures in various proportions of essentially isotropic silica with scattered polarizing specks, chalcedony, and cryptocrystalline to microcrystalline quartz. Two types represent in a general way the limits of compositional and textural variations: (1) a variety consisting of microcrystalline, polyhedral, equant, uniformly sized quartz grains and (2) a type consisting of irregularly grained, fibrous, locally radiating chalcedony. Many minute quartz grains show wavy, irregular extinction. Irregular patches are made up of coarser, mosaic quartz. Geodal structures contain cores of coarser quartz that grade outward into feathery chalcedony and thence into cryptocrystalline quartz. Veinlets of relatively coarse quartz or chalcedony or of both are not uncommon, and colloform aggregates and ovoids of chalcedony are locally common. Vugs are lined with quartz, chalcedony, calcite, and chalcedony plus calcite. Some cherts show color banding or irregular lamination, with alternations of carbonaceous material, cryptocrystalline quartz, and clear, coarser chalcedony.

Novaculites are cherts consisting of mixtures of isotropic silica (not opal) and cryptocrystalline to microcrystalline quartz, but little or no chalcedony. Chitinous and siliceous microfossils are abundant in some layers. Some novaculites show pronounced cataclastic effects, including deformed fossils, brecciated, granulated, and schistose streaks and zones, microfaults, contorted quartz veinlets, and microaugen. Some types are thoroughly brecciated with angular pieces of light brownish cryptocrystalline quartz cemented by granular quartz.

Spiculite cherts consist of packed, siliceous sponge spicules in a cryptocrystalline quartz matrix. Recrystallization of the spicules results in ragged, obscured margins. Cherts of this type, in which spicules predominate greatly, also have been called spiculites. In some impure cherts calcite (or dolomite) forms grains, rhombic euhedra, veinlets, streaks, and irregular aggregates. The carbonate may show widespread replacement by silica. Pyrite and glauconite occur, usually as minor accessories. Other fossil remains include those of foraminifera, radiolaria, diatoms, echinoderms, and molluscs.

Oolitic cherts (Fig. 37b), chiefly of replacement origin, have calcareous oolites replaced by chalcedony and microcrystalline quartz in concentric patterns. Some of the oolites contain nuclei of detrital quartz separated from the concentric quartz by a zone of carbonate specks; others have cores of quartz pseudomorphous after dolomite. Between the oolites fine-grained quartz forms the matrix. Superficially similar to some cherts are silicified tuffs which may contain relict glass shards or their replaced "ghosts."

Occurrence and Origin. Chert occurs as continuous strata interlayered with shales and limestones (bedded cherts) and also as nodules, concretions, and stringers, chiefly in limestone, dolomite, and chalk, that normally constitute only a small part of the formation. The latter type is commonly of replacement origin, and examples retain structures of the carbonate rock they replace—oolites, fossils, and grain-size variations. Some chert concretions may, however, be primary precipitates. Bedded cherts are believed to have formed either by direct precipitation of silica or by diagenesis and silicification of diatomaceous and radiolarian earths. The silica for novaculites, which are bedded cherts, is believed to have been obtained through submarine alteration of volcanic ash. Some bedded cherts may represent silicified ash beds. Bedded cherts, which are associated with dark siliceous shales, sapropelic black shales, and dark siliceous limestone, are typified by the Arkansas novaculite (Devonian-Mississippian), the Monterey chert (Miocene) of California, and the Rex chert (Permian) of Idaho, Montana, and Wyoming, which is associated with phosphorite.

Diatomite and Radiolarite

Diatomite is composed principally of the accumulated tests of diatoms, which are made of opal. Radiolarite consists of the opaline skeletons of radiolaria. By some these two terms are used for both the consolidated and unconsolidated varieties, whereas others restrict their usage to consolidated types and employ diatomaceous earth and radiolarian earth for the unconsolidated equivalents. Kieselguhr and infusorial earth are other names commonly applied to diatomite. Tripoli or tripolite has also been applied to diatomaceous earth.

Diatoms—prolific, minute, unicellular aquatic plants—have bivalved, siliceous shells in the shape of discs, boats, ladders, crescents, needles, and many other forms. The surfaces are complexly ornamented with spines, ridges, knobs, and punctures. Some ten thousand species are recognized, both fresh- and salt-water forms. Thus diatomite can be subdivided into marine and fresh-water types. Water temperature, salinity, and other factors govern the predominance of species in the deposit. Many fresh-water diatomites are formed from skeletons of small, thick-walled, barrel-shaped types. Some diatomites consist mainly of only a few species, whereas others have numerous species. Other materials that may be present are clay minerals, detrital quartz, pumice and other rock pieces, volcanic shards, dolomite, detrital zircon, tourmaline and garnet, sponge spicules, radiolaria, and organic debris. The maximum dimension of the diatom shells ranges from about 1 to 100 μ; some very large diatoms measure 300 to 400

μ. Small diatoms are considered to be less than 20 μ; medium-sized diatoms measure 20 to 80 μ; large ones exceed 80 μ.

Marine diatomites are characteristically laminated with darker streaks $\frac{1}{16}$ to $\frac{1}{4}$ in. apart, parallel with the stratification, and are normally less well indurated, whereas fresh-water types are massive, commonly more thoroughly consolidated, and may be lighter in color. Beds of clay and cherty or opalized layers are common associates. Major occurrences are in California (Upper Miocene), in Nevada, Oregon, and Washington.

Radiolarite consists of the complex skeletons or tests of radiolaria, usually spherical or elongated, with latticework structures, spines, and other ornamentations. Other constituents of radiolarite are diatom shells, sponge spicules, detrital clay, quartz, feldspar, augite, hornblende, and magnetite, some calcite, and fragments of pumice and other volcanic rocks. Siliceous (abyssal) ooze includes some types of radiolarite.

LIMESTONE AND RELATED ROCKS

Limestone

Definition. Limestones are sedimentary rocks that contain 95 per cent or more of calcite; magnesian limestones contain 90 to 95 per cent calcite and from 5 to 10 per cent dolomite. Dolomitic limestones have from 50 to 90 per cent calcite, 10 to 50 per cent dolomite. The carbonates together should constitute at least 50 per cent of the rock. The calcite may be precipitated chemically, organically, or both, or be detrital in origin. Thus limestones may be grouped as (1) chemical, (2) accretionary or fossiliferous, (3) clastic.

Mineralogy. In addition to the carbonates, the chief remaining constituents are clastic quartz, chalcedony or chemically precipitated quartz, clay minerals, and glauconite. The principal clay mineral is illite, although kaolinite is not uncommon, and montmorillonite occurs rarely. The various accessories, usually included in the insoluble-residue fraction, are, in addition to those listed above, detrital ilmenite, leucoxene, magnetite, zircon, tourmaline, garnet, muscovite, biotite, microcline, orthoclase, and plagioclase. Authigenic constituents include collophane, marcasite, pyrite, chalcedony, quartz, glauconite, iron oxides, adularia, microcline, albite, carbonaceous material, some clay minerals, and local fluorite.

Some organisms have shells that consist wholly or in part of aragonite, which may persist in younger sediments but gradually inverts to calcite. It may be impossible to distinguish shell aragonite from shell calcite by microscopic means alone, and a staining test may be required (Kraus, Hunt, and Ramsdell, *Mineralogy*, 4th ed., pp. 225–226, McGraw-Hill Book Company, Inc., New York, 1951). In organic and biochemical limestones as well as in some clastic types, shells or shell fragments of various organisms may be abundant. In addition to calcite and aragonite, shells may consist of opal (some sponges), chitinous material (certain crustaceans), and collophane

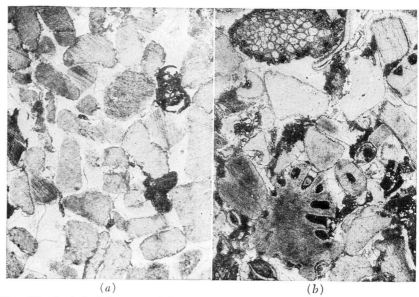

(*a*)   (*b*)

Fig. 38*a, b.* (*a*) Calcarenite (clastic limestone). Oriented overgrowths of clear calcite on rounded, turbid, clastic calcite grains. Two Mile Canyon, Boulder, Colorado. Nicols not crossed, ×10. (*b*) Fossiliferous (encrinal) limestone, Lockport, New York. Nicols not crossed, ×10.

(some brachiopods, sharks' teeth). The original fossil material may be replaced in varying degrees by pyrite, marcasite, glauconite, silica, limonite, and hematite.

Major mineralogical varieties are argillaceous limestone, which grades into shale or marl; cherty limestone; arenaceous limestone, which grades into sandstone; glauconitic limestone; ferruginous (hematitic) limestone; sideritic limestone; dolomitic limestone, which grades into dolomite; asphaltic or bituminous limestone; phosphatic limestone, which may grade into phosphorite; and pyritic limestone. Cement rock, or cementstone, is an argillaceous limestone in which the proportion of clay to calcite (about 1:3) approximates that required for the manufacture of portland cement.

Some limestones, particularly dark, carbonaceous types, yield the odor of H_2S from fresh surfaces (fetid limestones).

Textures and Microstructures; Origin. Marine limestones formed by direct chemical precipitation from sea water without the assistance of organisms are believed to be rare, although some fine-grained, even-grained, unfossiliferous types that are commonly grouped with the clastic limestones (calcilutites) may have originated in this manner.

Oolites are chemically precipitated, but most oolitic limestones are reworked and are of clastic derivation. Some fresh-water limestones, which are not common, are chemically precipitated.

The biochemical limestones show a wide variety of textures and considerable range in grain size. Three main types usually are distinguished: (1) biohermal or reef limestone (klintite), composed of algae, coral, crinoid, brachiopod, etc., remains, mound-like or discoid in shape, with irregular structures and uneven textures; (2) biostromal limestone (coquina), bedded, tabular limestones, composed chiefly of the remains of such animals as brachiopods, bryozoans, molluscs,

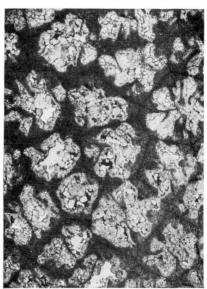

Fig. 38c. Coral limestone, Clark County, Indiana. Nicols crossed, ×10.

gastropods, crinoids, and corals (Fig. 38c); (3) pelagic limestone, composed mainly of the tests of floating (pelagic) organisms, principally foraminifera and pteropods. These creatures are usually microscopic; thus such limestones are normally fine-grained. Chalk, a white, fine-grained, porous, and weakly indurated limestone composed chiefly of very fine grained calcite, foraminiferal and molluscan remains, with minor sponge spicules and radiolarian tests, belongs to this group.

For study purposes, biochemical limestones may also be divided conveniently into microfossiliferous and macrofossiliferous types. The former includes such types as calcareous (abyssal) ooze, chalk, foraminiferal limestone (including fusilinid and nummulitic limestone), and ostracod limestone. In macrofossiliferous types ("shell" limestones) corals, crinoids, brachiopods, gastropods, algal colonies, and molluscs are represented. Bedded biochemical limestone composed predominantly of shells and shell pieces of the larger organisms is called coquina; those consisting mainly of microorganisms can be called microcoquina. Many planar fossil shells or pieces show parallel or subparallel arrangement with the bedding, if the force of bottom currents was appreciable, and curved shells not uncommonly lie convex upward. Most biochemical limestones contain predominating granular calcite, derived from fossil debris, which serves as fine- to coarsegrained cement. The calcite grains of fossil shells show a variety of patterns—layered, concentric, comb, radial, tangential, or combinations; fibrous, columnar, and lamellar. Some are dusty to opaque; others are clear.

Clastic limestones may be divided, on the basis of grain size, into calcarenites (Fig. 38a), containing predominantly sand-sized calcite particles ($\frac{1}{16}$ to 2 mm diameter), and calcilutites, composed chiefly of clay-sized calcite particles. Some calcilutites that are unusually fine and even grained are known as lithographic limestones from their former use in lithography. Lime muds contain particles originally precipitated by bacterial activity and also derived by destruction of fossil shells. Calcarenites contain three main types of calcitic particles: detrital calcite grains, fragments of fossil shells, and oolites. Some calcarenites and calcirudites (particles over 2 mm) are coquinas (or microcoquinas), consisting predominantly of transported shells and shell debris (bioclastic limestones). Crinoidal coquinas (encrinites) (Fig. 38b) are particularly common.

In addition to carbonate material, other clastic minerals, particularly quartz, clay minerals, collophane, and glauconite, occur. Clay minerals may be disseminated or concentrated in patches with detrital quartz. The glauconite forms rounded, lobate to mammillary grains of green microcrystalline aggregates. It also fills fossils and forms interstitial cryptocrystalline aggregates. Some glauconite grains are peppered with minute pyrite specks. Clastic grains, particularly quartz, may be very well rounded and well sorted. The common cement is calcite, which may appear as oriented overgrowths on clastic calcite particles and fossil fragments. The new calcite usually is clear, in contrast to the dusty detrital calcite. Calcite also forms large poikilitic crystals and fringelike overgrowths. Oriented overgrowths also occur on quartz and feldspar, resulting in the formation of small euhedra. The feldspars, albite, microcline, or orthoclase, appear as crystals of simple rhombic outline and unusual twinning (Roc Tourné twins) and are usually free of alteration, although zones of carbonaceous inclusions are common. Clastic limestones with less than 10 per cent quartz and consisting chiefly of oolites, fossil fragments, and detrital calcite have been called spergenites.

Oolites and the larger pisolites are spheroidal, ellipsoidal, or even elongate-curved and discoidal aggregates of calcium carbonate layers about a nucleus, formed in shallow, agitated waters (Fig. 39a). The carbonate may originally be precipitated as aragonite, which inverts to calcite, forming radial fibers that extend across the original layers and yield, in the aggregate, a pseudo interference figure. The nuclei are varied: detrital quartz grains, glauconite grains, clay pellets, calcite grains, grain aggregates or rhombohedra, shell fragments, and microfossils. Oolites may be partly replaced by quartz or by calcite crystals formed as secondary overgrowths on detrital nuclei of these minerals. In some pisolitic limestones associated with evaporites, detrital pisolites are partly replaced and cemented by anhydrite.

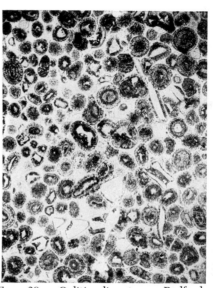

Fig. 39a. Oolitic limestone, Bedford, Indiana. Nicols crossed, ×9.

In many so-called normal marine limestones the textures are such that it is difficult to decide if clastic or biochemical processes predominated in their formation. Such limestones, even-grained, usually fine-grained, and poor in fossils, consist of fine- to medium-grained calcite in a homogeneous mosaic or saccharoidal aggregate. Overgrowths usually are not distinguishable.

Not uncommonly limestones also display secondary calcite veinlets and solution cavities.

In dolomitic or magnesian limestones (or sideritic limestones) the dolomite or siderite is secondary and forms rhombohedra that transgress the calcitic fabric. Biohermal and biostromal limestones are extensively dolomitized. Cherty limestone contains lenses, nodules, or concretions of chert or disseminated smaller spheroids of radial-fibrous chalcedony.

Some limestones have a nodular appearance in which irregular, fine-grained calcite pods (pseudo-oolites) are set in a coarser calcitic matrix (pellet limestones). Others show pseudobreccia textures in which films and flakes of calcite originally precipitated on plant surfaces are enclosed in a limey mud matrix. Still others reveal algal structures or shrinkage cracks.

Occurrence. Normal marine limestones, usually without conspicuous fossils, are abundant in sedimentary series deposited within tectonically stable shelf areas. Typical is the Niagara (Silurian) of the upper Mississippi Valley. Here also occur some coquinas (fragmental) and biohermal types. Argillaceous limestones are more characteristic of unstable shelf series and some intracratonic basin associations. Geosynclinal limestones are usually thin, dark, siliceous types; rarely they are thick normal or fossiliferous marine types (Mission Canyon, Mississippian, Montana). Many calcarenites are associated and intergrade with quartzose sandstones. A well-known example of an oolitic clastic limestone is the Salem ("Bedford") (Mississippian) limestone of Indiana. The Arbuckle (Ordovician) limestone of Oklahoma is a calcarenite. The best-known chalk beds are of Cretaceous age (Selma chalk, Texas, Niobrara chalk, Kansas).

Fig. 39*b*. Travertine, Suisun, California. Nicols crossed, ×9.

Travertine and Related Rocks

Travertine (Fig. 39*b*) and tufa (calcareous sinter) are formed by precipitation of calcite as the result of evaporation of springs, hot springs, streams, and ground water. Tufa is porous to cellular, containing plant remains and impressions. Some of it shows fibrous structures microscopically, in which rods are coated by minute calcite spines, normal to their axes. Travertine is more dense and usually thinly and crinkly banded. Coarse radial fibers of calcite may be conspicuous locally. Dripstone (cave onyx), deposited in caverns from ground waters, is a variety of travertine. Stalactites, stalagmites, columns, and other $CaCO_3$ cave forms are built of dripstone and show concentric structures in cross sections.

Caliche is a calcitic crust ($\pm$ gypsum) produced on and near ground surface of some semiarid regions by evaporation of ground water drawn upward under capillary action. The term also has been used for the soda niter rocks of northern Chile.

Dolomite

Definition. The term dolomite is usually applied to rocks in which 50 per cent or more of the carbonate is the mineral dolomite and in which the total amount of carbonate is in considerable excess over other constituents. Some geologists would restrict dolomite to those rocks in which the mineral dolomite is 90 to 100 per cent of the carbonate and would use calcitic dolomite for the range 50 to 90 per cent $CaMg(CO_3)_2$. In general in the limestone-dolomite series, the intermediate types, i.e., those in which both calcite and dolomite are abundant, are much less common than the end members of the series.

FIG. 39c. Dolomite, Eifelgebirge, Germany. Dolomite subhedra and euhedra (zoned), some secondary porosity. Nicols not crossed, ×9.

Mineralogy. The chief mineral is dolomite, usually with varying but minor calcite. Since most dolomites form by replacement of limestones, other minerals originally present in limestones may be preserved, including detrital quartz, chert, feldspar, clay, some heavy accessories and authigenic feldspar, chalcedony, hematite, limonite, anhydrite, gypsum, barite, celestite, and halite. It is not always easy to distinguish between calcite and dolomite in thin section. Measurement of ϵ' on crushed grains is helpful, but for quantitative estimates staining tests are very useful (Kraus, Hunt, and Ramsdell, *Mineralogy*, 4th ed., pp. 226–227, McGraw-Hill Book Company, Inc., New York, 1951).

Textures and Microstructures. Dolomite shows a very strong tendency toward euhedral development (Fig. 39c), occurring commonly as rhombic euhedra in a matrix of anhedral-granular calcite. With complete conversion of the rock, a medium- to coarse-grained aggregate of interpenetrating dolomite subhedra is produced. The rhombohedra commonly are zoned, with cores crowded with dusty inclusions, and clear margins, or with alternating Fe^2-rich (ankeritic) and Fe^2-poor zones. The ankeritic zones weather to a red brown color. In a few cases rhomb cores consist of calcite, whereas margins are dolomite. Small grains of clastic quartz may be included in dolomite crystals. Dolomitization involves destruction of the original limestone fabric, and such features as fossils or clastic carbonate grain outlines are obscured or obliterated. Dolomite replaces calcite (including fossils and oolites), quartz, and chert. Dolomolds (rhomboid cavities) in chert are a common constituent of insoluble residues. In some rocks dolomite euhedra are rather uniformly disseminated; more commonly, however, the dolomitized parts are irregular in shape and distribution. In some limestones dolomitization has affected only selected layers, resulting in alternating bands of calcite and dolomite. Some dolomites show later silicification, containing chert pseudomorphs after dolomite rhombohedra. Volume-for-volume replacement of calcite by dolomite results in no porosity changes, but if the conversion takes place on a molecular basis, secondary porosity may result. Veinlets of secondary calcite, of dolomite, or of quartz and other minerals such as anhydrite are not uncommon.

Occurrence and Origin. Most dolomites originate by postdepositional replacement of limestone, but some, particularly those associated with evaporites, may represent primary chemical precipitates. Probably dolomitization can take place in various environments: (1) in the environment of marine limestone deposition prior to burial, (2) in the marine environment after burial, (3) in the terrestrial environment after uplift, either by ground waters or hydrothermal solutions. Dolomitization of biostromal and biohermal limestones is common, but other types may also be replaced. Dolomites are in general more common among older sedimentary rocks than among more recent. Many so-called primary dolomites, which display little textural evidence of replacement of limestone, are associated with beds of anhydrite and halite. A few clastic dolomites have also been recognized. Examples of well-known dolomites in the United States include the Bighorn (Ordovician) of Montana and Wyoming and the Niagara (Silurian) of the Great Lakes region.

PHOSPHORITES

Definition. Phosphorite (rock phosphate or phosphate rock) consists mainly of phosphate minerals, the most abundant of which is apatite. With an increase in various other constituents phosphorites grade into such rocks as phosphatic limestones or phosphatic shales. The main types are:

1. Primary bedded phosphorites (Fig. 40*a*)
2. Secondary residual phosphorites
3. Secondary transported phosphorites
4. Bone phosphorites (Fig. 40*b*)
5. Insular phosphorite or guano

Mineralogy. The most abundant and widespread minerals are varieties of apatite: carbonate-fluorapatite (francolite) and carbonate-hydroxyapatite (dahllite). In many cases these varieties are cryptocrystalline and essentially isotropic and are called collophane, much of which is yellow to light brown in color. Both anisotropic and isotropic francolite may occur together. Other authigenic constituents include calcite, chalcedony, pyrite, anhydrite, gypsum, and uncommon glauconite. Among the detritals quartz, muscovite, and clay minerals may be well represented. Other materials include bitumen, shell and bone fragments, sponge spicules, diatoms, radiolaria, and fossil fish and sharks' teeth. Secondary fluorite is not uncommon in some varieties. Variscite, $AlPO_4 \cdot 2H_2O$, appears in some leached residual phosphorites. Other phosphates that may be abundant locally include metavariscite, $AlPO_4 \cdot 2H_2O$; wavellite, $Al_3(PO_4)_2(OH,F)_3 \cdot 5H_2O$; and strengite, $(Fe,Al)PO_4 \cdot 2H_2O$. In insular phosphorites, brushite, $CaHPO_4 \cdot 2H_2O$; monetite, $CaHPO_4$; and whitlockite, $Ca_3(PO_4)_2$, are present; nitrates, sulfates, and oxalates of calcium and ammonium also occur.

Some uncommon rock phosphates consist mainly of iron aluminum phosphates of the orthorhombic variscite-strengite series or of its monoclinic equivalent, the metavariscite-phosphosiderite series; apparently orthorhombic and monoclinic pairs may occur together. Many of these deposits are secondary, formed by the replacement of various igneous and sedimentary rocks.

Textures and Microstructures. Many phosphorites have an oolitic to pisolitic texture, the oolites being either concentrically layered or massive (ovules) (Fig. 40a), with cores of clastic mineral grains (particularly quartz), pyrite crystals, or fossil fragments. Central parts may be massive, with most of the zoning confined to marginal parts. The banding usually results from color variations, with the central units

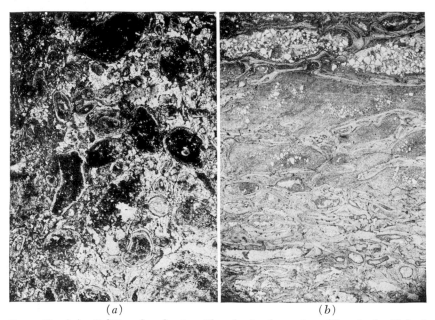

(a)   (b)

Fig. 40. (a) Oolitic phosphorite, Phosphoria formation (Permian), Hoback Canyon, Wyoming. Oolites of collophane in collophane-francolite matrix. Nicols not crossed, ×10. (b) Bone phosphorite, Morrison formation (Jurassic), Gros Ventre Creek, Wyoming. Silty and calcareous material filling cavities. Nicols not crossed, ×10.

normally darker. Many oolites show bleaching. Other types have alternating collophane and francolite zones or collophane and calcite zones. The oolites are well to poorly sorted and may show some abrasion and fracturing. Many are not rounded but are ellipsoidal, flattened, or with rather straight sides or even with marked indentations. Calcite veins them or selectively replaces cores or zones, which may also be replaced by chalcedony. Quartz, muscovite, and shell pieces are commonly irregularly included.

The matrix for the oolites is variable: in some cases it is chiefly collophane, or francolite, or both; in others it is mainly calcitic, and in still others it consists primarily of clay minerals and silty quartz. Quartz pieces are enveloped in comb-structure francolite. Irregular patches or hairlike to dentritic pieces of carbonaceous material may be common. Shell fragments are abundant locally, and some rare types consist dominantly of fragmented phosphatic fossil debris. Minute vugs lined with apatite, calcite, and fluorite are present. Some phosphatic beds lack the oolitic structure and are massive, very finely granular.

Phosphorite is also widely distributed as a subordinate constituent in other sedimentary rocks, occurring as concretions, nodules (in limestones and chalk), and as cement (in sandstone and glauconitic sandstone). The concretions display colloform banding or cryptocrystalline to euhedral-granular textures. Usually much foreign material is included: shell fragments, carbonaceous material, calcite, quartz, glauconite, muscovite, pyrite, gypsum, and limonite. Insular phosphate may be highly porous and vesicular; some is granular, some oolitic.

Occurrence and Origin. The Phosphoria formation (Permian) of Montana, Idaho, Utah, and Wyoming represents the primary, chiefly oolitic type of bedded marine phosphorite, formed by the slow precipitation of colloidal phosphate under anaerobic conditions, with close control of the water temperature and pH. Phosphates accumulate where deposition of clastic and other sedimentary minerals is minor. Francolite forms by recrystallization of the original collophane. Some sediments, originally lean in phosphate, are converted to phosphorites through leaching of the nonphosphatic constituents, principally calcite. These secondary phosphorites are partly residual ("land-pebble phosphate" of Florida) and partly transported ("river-pebble phosphate" of Florida). Some of the phosphate of the residual nodules and "pebbles" is redissolved and reprecipitated, or the nodules may serve to initiate precipitation of new phosphate from sea water. Considerable collophane is of organic derivation, from bones, teeth, some invertebrate shells, and fecal pellets; some also is diagenetic in origin, replacing mainly calcite.

FERRUGINOUS AND MANGANIFEROUS ROCKS

Included in this category are rocks with 10 per cent or more of iron or 15 per cent Fe_2O_3 or its equivalent. Major subdivisions are (1) iron carbonate (siderite) rocks, (2) iron oxide (hematite, limonite) rocks, (3) iron sulfide (pyrite, marcasite) rocks, (4) iron silicate (chamosite, glauconite, etc.) rocks. Also included are the manganese-rich sedimentary rocks. Most rocks of this group are best studied by a combination of thin sections and polished sections.

Iron Carbonate Rocks

Definition. Iron carbonate rocks consist of siderite in association with (1) chert—the cherty iron carbonate rocks, (2) clay minerals—the clay ironstones, and (3) calcite—the sideritic limestones. Clay ironstones are also known as siderite mudstones, and two well-known varieties occurring in Great Britain are called black-band ironstone and sphaerosiderite rocks. In iron carbonate rocks siderite is the main iron-bearing mineral, but variable amounts of chamosite or limonite may also be present.

Varieties. Cherty iron carbonate rocks are composed of thinly and rhythmically interlaminated chert (cryptocrystalline to microcrystalline quartz) and siderite in various proportions. Very few other constituents are present, although a little detrital quartz or clay, probably illite, may occur. The layers range in thickness from $\frac{1}{8}$ in. to about 6 in. In one type the cherty bands are thicker; in another the sideritic bands are thicker. Some chert beds are oolitic, in which original siderite oolites have been replaced by relatively coarse quartz. Fine-grained quartz forms scattered rhombic pseudomorphs after siderite. Siderite and at least some of the chert are generally believed to be primary precipitates formed without much assistance from organisms. Parts of the Ironwood and Negaunee (pre-Cambrian) formations of Michigan and Minnesota are representative.

In sideritic mudstones one variety consists of oolites, euhedra or granules of siderite set in a matrix of fine-grained quartz, feldspar, sericite, and clay minerals with or without chamosite, which forms shreds and plates. Some siderite oolites are zoned with brown cores and pale marginal zones. Also present locally are calcite, dolomite, abundant shell fragments replaced by siderite rhombs, fish teeth, worm castings, wavy carbonaceous bands, and plant debris. With an increase in chamosite, sideritic mudstones grade into iron silicate rocks.

Another type contains oolites of iron oxide in a mosaic matrix of mainly fine grained siderite. The sphaerosiderite type contains siderite spherulites in clay. The spherulites, which consist of narrow to broad radial fibers of siderite that end in irregular, angular terminations may include some clastic quartz. The clay matrix becomes subordinate to interstitial in some varieties, and the closely packed spherulites are polygonal in outline. Some spherulites are color-zoned and include clay particles. Sideritic mudstones are well represented in the Lower Jurassic of Great Britain.

In some sideritic limestones (Fig. 41*a*) medium-grained subhedral siderite replaces calcite to a varying extent. Siderite grains or rhombs may contain minute nuclei of pyrite. Other siderite limestones consist mainly of an aggregate of shell fragments (unaltered or sideritized) cemented by calcite and siderite. Dolomite and ankerite may also be present.

Siderite apparently is precipitated in a shallow marine environment, under weakly oxidizing conditions. Sideritic rocks are relatively uncommon, usually forming thin nodular beds or concretionary masses in shales, in some cases arranged in nearly continuous bands. Many of the concretions have fossil nuclei, such as ferns, insects, fish scales, or rarely mollusc shells. The pre-Cambrian sid-

Fig. 41*a*. Siderite ironstone, Siegen, Westphalia, Germany. Siderite and interstitial calcite. Nicols not crossed, ×9.

erite-chert rocks are exceptional in their thickness and extent.

Iron Oxide Rocks

Definition. Iron oxide rocks are those whose principal iron-bearing minerals are hematite or limonite or both. In some types chamosite, glauconite, and siderite are accessory to important constituents. The chief varieties are (1) oolitic hematite rocks, (2) fossiliferous hematite rocks, (3) oolitic limonite rocks, (4) bog iron ores, (5) gossans.

Varieties. The oolitic hematite rocks (Fig. 41*b*) contain oolites of hematite in a cement of hematite and calcite, and in some types also of quartz and siderite. The oolites, which are rounded to flattened ("flaxseed ore"), consist of hematite alone, less usually of hematite-calcite or hematite-chamosite. The structure is normally concentric, with very thin shells, rarely radial, and quartz grains may be included.

A few calcite oolites may also be present. Most of the oolites have clastic quartz nuclei, although some contain cores of cryptocrystalline quartz, chalcedony, shell particles, and oolite fragments. Thin coronas of dendritic hematite and quartz surround some oolites. The hematite may be of two types—a reddish brown type and a steely gray variety, with the oolites usually the red variety and the matrix the gray variety, although reversals and combinations also occur. Other

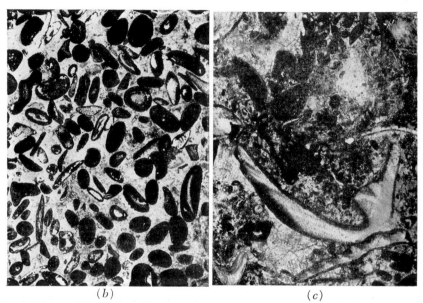

(b)   (c)

Fig. 41b, c. (b) Oolitic hematite rock, Clinton formation (Silurian), Wayne County, New York. Nicols not crossed, ×9. (c) Fossiliferous hematite rock, same formation and locality. Nicols not crossed, ×9.

matrix constituents are quartz, calcite, siderite, limonite, glauconite, chamosite, collophane, and fossil fragments. Accessories include feldspars, muscovite, magnetite, clay minerals, and various heavy detritals. The quartz is mainly detrital, but some may be authigenic. Some grains are partly replaced by matrix hematite. Most of the glauconite shows rounding or abrasion. Veinlets of hematite transect oolites, grains of quartz, glauconite, and carbonate matrix. Calcite veinlets transect hematite oolites. The hematite oolite rocks are of primary marine origin.

Fossiliferous hematite rocks (Fig. 41c) consist of flattened and elongated shell fragments in subparallel arrangement, which are coated, peripherally replaced, or entirely replaced by hematite and are cemented by calcite, hematite, and in some cases also by quartz and chalcedony. The fossil pieces include chiefly bryozoa and crinoid remains. The Clinton (Silurian) ores of the Appalachian region contain both oolitic and fossiliferous types. The hematite appears to be diagenetic in origin.

Oolitic limonite rocks contain closely or loosely packed, rounded to elongated and flattened oolites of limonite, usually with a concentric structure but in some cases a radial fibrous structure. Films of chamosite may coat the oolites. The matrix is sandy to clayey and may contain in addition chamosite, siderite, dolomite, calcite, and organic debris. Some of the oolites have a delicate skeletal framework of fine-grained quartz.

Bog iron ores consist chiefly of soft, porous limonite with admixtures, in varying amounts, of clay minerals, sandy quartz, siderite, manganese oxides, and organic debris such as leaves, roots, twigs, and seeds, which may be partly replaced by limonite. Rarer constituents are vivianite and iron sulfates. The limonite may be in spongy masses, with a vesicular or tubular texture or in pisolites and concretionary masses. Bog iron ores are deposited chemically and bacteriologically in lake margins and bogs, particularly in the glaciated northern parts of Europe and North America.

Gossans are iron-rich, residual, surficial deposits formed by weathering of veins and other ore deposits that contain such primary iron minerals as pyrite, pyrrhotite, chalcopyrite, bornite, covellite, and chalcocite, all of which are replaced by limonite. By x-rays the limonite can be distinguished as mainly hematite and goethite, although some lepidocrocite may be present too. Limonite also replaces carbonate, kaolinite, and various rock silicates. Other common constituents are jarosite, siderite, quartz, chalcedony, kaolinite, halloysite, allophane, beidellite, and nontronite. Less common are alunite, gibbsite, plumbojarosite, and scorodite. The texture is usually spongy and cavernous with skeletal, boxwork, and botryoidal limonite.

Iron Sulfide Rocks

Pyrite and marcasite, which are common minor authigenic constituents of many sedimentary rocks, including black shales and some limestones, and are also associated with glauconite and phosphatic nodules, appear very rarely as the main constituents of sedimentary rocks. Certain pyritic limestones grade into beds of granular pyrite. Examples occur in the Tully (Devonian) of New York and the Green-

horn (Upper Cretaceous) of Wyoming. In the Wabana area of Newfoundland occur Ordovician beds of oolitic pyrite with both pyritized
and unaltered fossil fragments (graptolites) set in a very fine grained
quartzose matrix. Nodules and concretions of pyrite and marcasite
are common in limestone and also occur in shales, some sandstones,
and in coals.

Iron Silicate Rocks

Definition. The principal sedimentary iron silicates are chamosite
and glauconite. Iron silicate rocks include the varieties (1) chamositic mudstones, (2) chamosite-siderite mudstones, (3) oolitic ferric

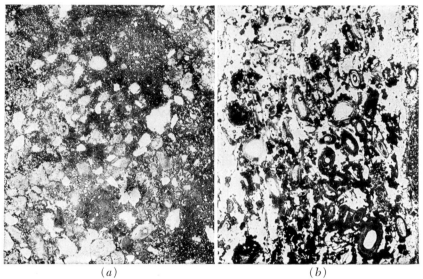

(a)   (b)

Fig. 42. (a) Glauconite sandstone, Haylet, New York. Glauconite and quartz in
a clay-glauconite matrix. Nicols not crossed, ×9. (b) Oolitic chamosite rock.
Clinton formation (Silurian), Franklin Springs, New York. Oolites of chamosite,
some with nuclei of quartz grains, in carbonate-clay matrix. Nicols not crossed,
×9.

chamosite rocks, (4) glauconite rocks, and (5) greenalite rocks. Each
of these must contain one or more of the iron silicates as the principal
iron mineral in order to be placed in this group.

Varieties. The chamositic mudstones (chamosite ironstones) consist
of a fine-grained aggregate of green, cryptocrystalline to isotropic
chamosite. Chamosite oolites (Fig. 42b) occur in some types in a
chamositic matrix, and in others (chamosite-siderite mudstones) sid-

erite is the dominant matrix constituent as rhombohedra or grain clusters, commonly corroding or replacing the oolites. In many cases chamosite oolites, which have a marked concentric structure and also show a pseudo interference figure, have formed by replacement of fossil fragments. Nuclei are grains of quartz, calcite, silt or chamosite or shell pieces. Oolites may be flattened or irregularly deformed (spastoliths). Other matrix constituents include quartz, feldspar, sericite, kaolinite, pyrite, collophane, dolomite, ankerite, and organic debris. Another variety consists of chamosite oolites in a matrix of calcite or of calcite plus disseminated chamosite. Complex chamosite-pyrite oolites are also found. Chamosite rocks are regarded as resulting from chemical deposition in shallow marine waters and complex diagenetic changes.

The ferric chamosite rocks are hybrids of chamosite and hematite. These are typified by the Wabana, Newfoundland, ores. The oolites consist of hematite or of chamosite or of alternate layers of the two. The matrix contains hematite, chamosite, and local siderite, as well as some quartz, collophane, and calcite. Other ferric chamosite rocks contain limonite or magnetite, with complex chamosite-magnetite-hematite oolites in a chamosite-rich matrix that may also contain magnetite, hematite, quartz, calcite, dolomite, and apatite. Many oolites have quartz-grain nuclei. In other rocks these complex oolites occur in a sideritic matrix or even a magnetite-rich matrix. Much of the magnetite apparently results from recrystallization during shearing and folding, by which means some stilpnomelane may also be developed.

Glauconitic ironstones (greensands) consist of glauconite granules, which may have been transported, mixed with detrital quartz, calcite, shell pieces, and other minerals (Fig. 42a). These may be cemented by calcite. Glauconite forms pellets, thin tablets, vermicular crystals, and internal casts of foraminiferal shells. Most of it appears to be of authigenic origin.

Greenalite rocks, found in the Lake Superior iron district, contain ovoid granules of isotropic or cryptocrystalline greenalite in a crypto- to microcrystalline matrix of quartz (chert) or quartz and calcite. Siderite may also be present.

Manganiferous Rocks

Manganese oxide minerals, principally as concretions, coatings, cements, and dendrites, occur in shales, sandstones, and other rocks. Rhodochrosite also forms concretions in shales. Sedimentary beds that consist predominantly of manganese minerals are rare. Examples are the manganiferous strata of Svabovce in Slovakia, where two types, a carbonate and a combined oxide carbonate type, are associated. Both types contain cryptocrystalline quartz, opal, pyrite, and organic debris. In addition the carbonate beds carry rhodochrosite, calcite, and pyrite, and the oxide-carbonate layers contain manganocalcite, pyrolusite, manganite, marcasite, and dolomite. Detrital constituents are quartz, feldspar, muscovite, and biotite. The carbonate rock shows an oolitic texture; the oxide-carbonate rock is cryptocrystalline. At Conception Bay, Newfoundland, shaley beds contain concentrations of rhodochrosite, collophane, and pyrite.

SALINES (EVAPORITES)

Rock Salt and Related Rocks

Definition. Rock salt is rock in which the principal chemically precipitated constituent is halite. The amounts of other components, mainly anhydrite or sylvite, may vary widely.

Mineralogy. Some varieties contain halite alone, but commonly some anhydrite is also present. The main mineralogical types are:

1. Halite rock (rock salt)
2. Halite-anhydrite ± polyhalite rock
3. Halite-sylvite ± carnallite rock (sylvinite, sylvinhalite, halito-sylvine)
4. Salt clay and silty halite rock

The accessory suite varies considerably; species that may be detected in thin section include magnesite, dolomite, boracite, rinneite, lueneburgite, kieserite, kainite, hematite, pyrite, quartz, and talc. A more complex assemblage can commonly be found in insoluble residues.

Textures and Microstructures. In form halite varies from irregular-equidimensional to parallel-elongate and even platy. Variations in grain size may be extreme, ranging from fine grains to recrystallized single grains with foot-wide cleavage faces. A common banded structure consists of thin dark layers of anhydrite alternating with thicker halite bands. Not all the anhydrite, however, is confined to the dark bands, which owe their color to minute dusty inclusions. The marginal anhydrite of the bands commonly is coarser-grained than the interior. Anhydrite also occurs in more irregular streaks and patches, rarely in radial aggregates. More complex layering also occurs, such as halite-polyhalite bands, halite-kieserite bands, lenticles of anhydrite-dolomite, anhydrite-magnesite bands, silty or clayey seams, anhydrite-clay-bitumen layers, pyrite–carbonaceous material layers, carnallite layers, and sylvite layers. Some halite crystals contain randomly oriented cavities partly filled with liquid (bubble inclusions, vacuoles). These inclusions are also arranged in dodecahedral zones or in curvilinear manner. Halite also includes minute thin hematite rods and plates, which may be concentrated in zones parallel with the cleavage or in irregular wavy bands. In rock salt that contains much sylvite the

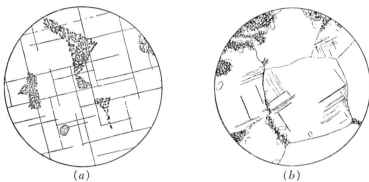

(a)   (b)

FIG. 43. (a) Halite-anhydrite-carnallite rock (Permian), Eskdale, East Yorkshire, England. Rounded carnallite grain (stippled) and small anhydrite crystals in angular patches outlining former halite grain pattern, all enclosed in single large, recrystallized halite unit. Nicols not crossed, ×8. (*Courtesy of F. H. Stewart, Mineralogical Magazine.*) (b) Halite-talc-quartz rock, same locality. Talc plates along halite cleavages and grain boundaries. Euhedral quartz crystals and patches of angular clastic quartz grains. Nicols not crossed, ×7. (*Courtesy of F. H. Stewart, Mineralogical Magazine.*)

hematite usually is restricted to the potash minerals, except where halite has replaced sylvite and inherited the inclusions. Other minerals included by halite are talc plates along cleavages (Fig. 43b); doubly terminated quartz crystals, which also occur along contacts between halite and anhydrite or magnesite and project into the halite; irregular or rounded carnallite grains (Fig. 43a); and minute rods or rounded plates of polyhalite. Some halite crystals show hopper-shaped phantoms with cubic overgrowths of clear halite.

Halite crystals may be fringed by a lacy network of anhydrite, anhydrite-polyhalite, or by magnesitic clay expelled during halite recrystallization. Solution cavities in halite are bordered by crystals of talc, celestite, or dolomite, and carnallite may fill rectangular "cleavage" cavities in halite. Some varieties of rock salt contain pseudomorphs after gypsum, with either halite or anhydrite as the replacing mineral. Not uncommonly however, they replace gypsum together, with anhydrite marginal and halite central. A peculiar coarse-grained intergrowth called "pegmatite" anhydrite consists of halite with large parallel or divergent anhydrite streaks.

Sylvite forms irregular grains, typically colored marginally or throughout by hematite flakes. Both anhydrite and sylvite are replaced by halite. Sylvite may contain halite inclusions and also shows interlocking contacts with halite. Some sylvite is tabular, pseudomorphous after anhydrite. Polyhalite replaces both anhydrite and halite. Carnallite appears in seams or as rounded to irregular grains in halite, less commonly in sylvite or along contacts of the two. Some magnesite and quartz are commonly associated with clay streaks, and magnesite also occurs in anhydrite bands.

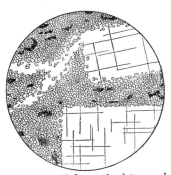

Fig. 44a. Halite-anhydrite rock (Permian), Eskdale, East Yorkshire, England. Halite veinlets transect granular anhydrite aggregates with carbonaceous material. Nicols not crossed, ×8. (*Courtesy of F. H. Stewart, Mineralogical Magazine.*)

Occurrence and Origin. Rock salt occurs in many periods in strata ranging in thickness from a few inches to several hundreds of feet. Commonly it is associated with other salines such as anhydrite, gypsum, and potash salts in series of beds that may be over a thousand feet thick. These evaporite groups occur either with limestones and dolomites or with red-bed sediments. Important rock salt strata of Silurian age occur in New York, Ohio, and Michigan; Mississippian-age salt is found in Virginia, Pennsylvania, and Michigan. Cyclic evaporite strata occur in the west Texas Permian where basal shale is overlain in succession by dolomite, anhydrite, and salt.

Halite is precipitated by evaporation of sea water. The banding has been described as seasonal, with dark anhydrite layers forming in warmer months and halite in cooler periods, and the pair representing the annual deposition. However, washing may reveal other colorless anhydrite bands in the apparently pure halite layers. Uncommon ripple marks demonstrate the presence of local detrital salt. Some rocks were halite-gypsum aggregates originally with gypsum altered to halite and/or anhydrite. Polyhalite is secondary. The rocks give much evidence of recrystallization, as well as diagenetic and later metasomatic changes.

Sylvite-Halite Rocks

Definition. In sylvite-halite rocks sylvite predominates over halite, but complete gradations occur to rock salt with minor sylvite.

Mineralogy. Sylvite commonly is colored red by hematite, in some cases only marginally, whereas halite is colorless. Other usually minor constituents include magnesite, anhydrite, kieserite, carnallite, kainite, polyhalite, langbeinite, leonite, quartz, clay, talc, and pyrite. Kieserite varies considerably in amount and may become a major constituent.

Textures and Microstructures. Sylvite is usually anhedral, halite anhedral to euhedral. Anhydrite, magnesite, and quartz are euhedral; carnallite appears as rounded inclusions in halite (Fig. 44*b*). Anhydrite forms uncommon rectangular crystals and may show marginal replacement by fibrous poly-halite. Clay patches are fringed by hematite flakes. Where kieserite is minor, it is interstitial, but some rocks contain considerable kieserite (3 to 50 per cent) and less halite. This is the "Hartsalz" of the German deposits, in which kieserite may appear as ellipsoids in a sylvite matrix. This variety grades into one characterized by coarse flakes of sylvite in a predominant, fine-

Fig. 44*b*. Halite-sylvite-carnallite rock, same locality. Carnallite (heavy stipple) along halite (*upper*)–sylvite (*lower*) grain boundary and enclosed in halite. Nicols not crossed, ×4. (*Courtesy of F. H. Stewart, Mineralogical Magazine.*)

grained kieserite matrix. Kieserite usually displays twinning, either paired or multiple. Both kieserite and langbeinite effloresce and alter to epsomite.

Occurrence and Origin. Sylvite-halite rocks occur with the various potash rocks, rock salt, and other salines, notably in the Permian Stassfurt deposits of Germany and in the Permian basin of west Texas and New Mexico. They are formed by evaporation of sea water. "Hartsalz" is secondary, formed by alteration of carnallitic rocks.

Carnallite Rocks

Definition. In carnallite rocks carnallite is a major constituent and may predominate over the total of other minerals, the amounts of which vary widely.

Mineralogy. The several major types are:

1. Carnallite with some halite, kieserite, sylvite, kainite, sand, and clay
2. Carnallite-kieserite with bischofite, halite, and anhydrite
3. Carnallitic marl with accessory halite, anhydrite, sylvite, rinneite, magnesite, quartz crystals, hematite, and clay

Boron salts as accessory minerals are particularly characteristic: boracite, pinnoite, kaliborite, hydroboracite, szaibelyite, and sulfoborite.

Textures and Microstructures. Carnallite is fine- to coarse-grained, rounded, and shows multiple lamellar twinning. Some has been recrystallized, and the orientation of trains of inclusions reveals the old grain boundaries. Margins of grains show corrosion by interstitial sylvite. Vertically elongated masses of carnallite in halite appear to have formed through replacement. Some of the Stassfurt, Germany, deposits contain carnallitic rocks with abundant kieserite. Carnallitic marl from Yorkshire, England, contains about 10 per cent carnallite, 17 per cent halite, sylvite, anhydrite, magnesite, rinneite, polyhalite and clay minerals, quartz, hematite, mica, and probably chlorite. Numerous ramifying veinlets, chiefly of halite, carnallite, and sylvite, cut the rock. Some veinlets contain quartz pseudomorphous after halite and halite-anhydrite pseudomorphous after gypsum. Some carnallitic rocks are layered with bands and streaks of carnallite, halite, and keiserite. Others are brecciated, containing angular to rounded fragments of halite, kieserite, anhydrite, and clay in a predominantly carnallitic matrix.

Occurrence and Origin. Carnallite rocks are prominent in the German bedded salt deposits. At Stassfurt the carnallite zone ranges in thickness from 15 to 40 ft, and the kieserite-carnallite zone below it varies from 20 to 40 ft. Carnallite rocks are precipitated by evaporation of sea water. Vein structures and other textural features indicate that considerable recrystallization and rearrangement of the minerals have taken place. In some rocks, such as the carnallitic marl, carnallite is a secondary constituent that has been introduced by brines.

Polyhalite Rocks

Definition. In polyhalite rocks polyhalite is an essential constituent; some varieties consist chiefly of polyhalite, whereas others contain a varied assemblage of other constituents to the total of which polyhalite may be subordinate.

Mineralogy. Three major types occur:

1. Rocks consisting mainly of polyhalite with accessory dolomite, anhydrite, halite, and kieserite
2. Polyhalite-anhydrite rocks; accessory minerals magnesite, langbeinite, kieserite, leonite, and pyrite
3. Polyhalite-halite rocks with variable amounts of magnesite, dolomite, kieserite, langbeinite, and bischofite

Polyhalite shows a wide variety of forms including fine-grained irregular groups, equidimensional grains, elongated crystals with random orientation, fibrous and spherulitic masses, spear-shaped crystals, rods and plates, and fibrous veinlets. In a single rock polyhalite may appear in several forms, as, for example, fibers mixed with granular material, or it may grade from fine-grained to coarse-grained. It is characteristically twinned, either in pairs or in sectors, and alters readily to gypsum.

Textures and Microstructures. Polyhalite replaces principally halite and anhydrite. Some rocks have anhydrite-halite pseudomorphs after gypsum arranged in layers, with polyhalite corroding the secondary anhydrite. Anhydrite that occurs as platy rectangular crystals is also corroded by polyhalite. Layers of coarse, subparallel polyhalite grains, with their long axes vertical, rest on thin seams of magnesite in anhydrite. "Blebby salt" is a miner's term for a rock with coarse-grained polyhalite aggregates in a halite matrix. The relations to kieserite vary; some rocks contain kieserite that replaces polyhalite and includes it; in others euhedral polyhalite crystals are associated with corroded kieserite.

Occurrence and Origin. Polyhalite rocks form beds as much as 8 ft thick in the New Mexico–Texas field, and in the German Stassfurt region the polyhalite zone is 40 to 60 ft thick. They are associated with kieserite and carnallite rocks, rock salt, and anhydrite-dolomite rocks. Most polyhalite is secondary, formed by the replacement of preexisting minerals by natural brines. Polyhalite rocks are formed by the replacement of such varieties as rock salt, halite-gypsum rock, and anhydrite-dolomite rock. Every gradation occurs between anhydrite-dolomite rocks with minor accessory polyhalite to polyhalite rocks with subordinate relict anhydrite.

Rock Gypsum

Definition. Rock gypsum consists either nearly entirely of gypsum or with gypsum as the major essential constituent.

Mineralogy. Some anhydrite is also commonly present, and gypsum-anhydrite rocks grade into rocks containing mainly anhydrite. Other minerals include calcite, dolomite, halite, sulfur, barite, quartz, and clay. Many strata are relatively impure. Doubly terminated quartz crystals, some with a pseudocubic habit and included hematite, have been found in cavities in massive gypsum.

Textures and Microstructures. The texture is fine- to coarse-grained, bedded or massive, equigranular or heterogranular. Gypsum forms

(a)   (b)

Fig. 45. (*a*) Rock gypsum, Grand Rapids, Michigan. Tabular to fibrous gypsum (twinned) replacing anhydrite. Nicols crossed, × 10. (*b*) Rock anhydrite, Sun City, Kansas. Vein of granular gypsum replacing radial anhydrite. Nicols not crossed, ×13. (*Courtesy of D. MacGregor.*)

large prismatic crystals in fine-grained anhedral gypsum, large plates enclosing small gypsum euhedra, parallel fibrous aggregates (Fig. 45*a*), spherulitic groups, and cross-fiber veins. Typically it shows replacement relations to anhydrite; the converse is rare. A single gypsum grain usually replaces several grains of anhydrite. Anhydrite may appear in radial aggregates.

Occurrence and Origin. Rock gypsum occurs in bedded deposits, individual strata of which vary from a few feet to hundreds of feet in thickness. Rock gypsum occurs alone or with anhydrite; rock salt, limestone, and shale are common associates. Important gypsum beds of Silurian age occur in New York, and others of Mississippian age are found in Michigan. In the western Great Plains region gypsum is interlayered with red beds of various ages. It also occurs in the cap rock of salt domes associated with anhydrite, limestone, and sulfur.

Gypsum may be deposited directly from sea water by evaporation. In many rocks, however, it has formed by replacement of anhydrite, which gives rise to a 30 to 50 per cent volume increase, resulting in intense, tight folding of remaining anhydrite layers. In many beds gypsum grades downward into anhydrite. Gypsite, a weakly consolidated efflorescent material, forms in arid regions over outcrops of gypsiferous strata.

Rock Anhydrite

Definition. In rock anhydrite anhydrite is the chief constituent, usually predominating markedly over other minerals.

Mineralogy. Although some anhydrite rocks contain no other essential mineral, anhydrite usually occurs with some other important constituent. The main associations are:

1. Anhydrite; minor calcite, aragonite, dolomite, celestite, halite, sylvite, quartz, pyrite, sulfur, and clay minerals

2. Anhydrite-gypsum; accessory calcite, dolomite, and clay

3. Anhydrite-halite; accessory dolomite

4. Anhydrite-carbonate (calcite, dolomite, magnesite, or dolomite-magnesite); accessory halite, celestite, talc, pyrite, hematite, sulfur, quartz, and carbonaceous material

5. Anhydrite-polyhalite ($\pm$ halite or dolomite); accessory magnesite, and langbeinite

Anhydrite-gypsum rocks grade into rock gypsum. Similarly anhydrite-halite rocks pass into rock salt. Anhydrite-polyhalite rocks pass into rock salt. Anhydrite-polyhalite rocks are transitional types between anhydrite-halite (Fig. 46*a*) or anhydrite-dolomite (Figs. 46*b*, *c*) rocks and polyhalite rocks.

Textures and Microstructures. Anhydrite displays a variety of forms: irregular interlocking grains, equidimensional to elongate; bladed to fibrous fans with curved cleavages (Fig. 45*b*); rectangular or tabular euhedra and rectangular crystals with steplike boundaries. Combinations of various habits occur together. Likewise anhydrite rocks can be equigranular or heterogranular. Large euhedra of anhydrite occur in fine-grained sugary anhydrite, polyhalite, and magnesite. The mineral may show the effect of considerable recrystallization, especially where associated with halite. In the layered types anhydrite bands are separated by films of carbonaceous material, by thin layers of dolomite granules, lenticular wisps of fine-grained magnesite, or layers of gypsum. Massive types are characterized by subhedral to euhedral anhydrite in a "pile-of-bricks" texture.

Dolomite is typically in rounded, clustered, brown granules with minute dark inclusions that may be concentrated either marginally or centrally. Some finely granular dolomite is interstitial to anhydrite blades. Euhedral dolomite appears in single crystals or groups of

(a)   (b)

Fig. 46a, b. (a) Coarse anhydrite-halite-magnesite rock (Permian), Eskdale, East Yorkshire, England. Blocky secondary anhydrite crystals across radial anhydrite; network of magnesite plates across a halite cavity, *upper right*. Nicols not crossed, ×6. (*Courtesy of F. H. Stewart, Mineralogical Magazine.*) (b) Anhydrite-dolomite-magnesite rock, same locality. Granular dolomite aggregate, cut by magnesite plates and enclosed in granular anhydrite. Nicols not crossed, ×12. (*Courtesy of F. H. Stewart, Mineralogical Magazine.*)

*r*hombohedra. Magnesite appears as basal plates with ragged edges (Fig. 46b) and flat lensoid cross sections. Some plates are in radial groups that are transected and offset by younger plates. Other plates have small irregular anhydrite inclusions centrally arranged. Some granular magnesite is disseminated or concentrated in stringers and patches, and similar material surrounds secondary acicular anhydrite crystals. Halite forms stringers and irregular patches or is recorded only by rectangular cavities into which other minerals such as talc, dolomite, anhydrite, celestite, and sulfur project. Together with anhydrite it forms pseudomorphs after gypsum. Anhydrite replaces dolomite, magnesite, and gypsum and is replaced by halite, magnesite, polyhalite, and sulfur.

Many anhydrite rocks show cataclastic effects and are metamorphic rocks in the strict sense, as evidenced by strained, bent, or broken crystals, transected layers, and breccia structures. One such type contains rounded to angular fragments and streaks of anhydrite-dolomite rock in a matrix of anhydrite with dusty inclusions. Another type displays extreme brecciation and flowage with dense fine-grained anhydrite pieces in a matrix of coarser anhydrite. Veins cutting these broken rocks contain, for example, halite, sylvite, and limonite (after rinneite); calcite and gypsum or gypsum alone.

Occurrence and Origin. Anhydrite is a very common evaporite, forming beds hundreds of feet thick associated with rock salt, gypsum, potash salts, dolomites, and clay. Notable occurrences in the United States are in the Silurian of the Michigan Basin, in the Mississippian of the Williston Basin, in the Permian of central Texas and south-central New Mexico, and in the Cretaceous of Florida. Metamorphosed anhydrite-gypsum beds are interlayered with tremolite marble, quartzite, and schist in some Jurassic rocks of California. Anhydrite is derived by evaporation from sea water above 42°C or at lower temperatures when the salinity is 4.8 times normal. However if halite

Fig. 46c Anhydrite-dolomite rock, same locality. Radial anhydrite in granular dolomite. Nicols not crossed, ×6. (*Courtesy of F. H. Stewart, Mineralogical Magazine.*)

is formed first, anhydrite and not gypsum is precipitated. Anhydrite formed by the dehydration of gypsum may later be rehydrated. Some anhydrite-dolomite rocks result from the diagenetic alteration of dolomites by sulfatic brines.

Anhydrite Cap Rock. Anhydrite cap rock on salt domes contains gypsum in various amounts, together with accessory calcite, dolomite, aragonite, sulfur, pyrite, sphalerite, quartz, chert, celestite, barite, kaolinite, and fluorite. The rock forms on top of a salt stock by cementation of anhydrite that accumulated after solution of rock salt by ground water. Subsequently anhydrite was replaced in varying degrees and patterns by gypsum, and in some parts of the cap rock gypsum has reverted to anhydrite. As the result of movements of the stock, the cap rock is sheared, fractured, faulted, and mylonitized, resulting in lenticular, braided, or granulated fabrics. Some shattered anhydrite has recrystallized into new larger crystals.

The undisturbed rock consists of equant, well-fitted anhydrite grains. Replacement by gypsum leaves corroded relicts of anhydrite in a gypsum matrix. Regenerated anhydrite tends to form spindle-shaped grains. Dolomite appears in rhombohedra, some with calcite envelopes. Calcite also forms equant grains and spindles. Much aragonite appears as residual skeletons in gypsum. Native sulfur occurs in veinlets and along shears and fractures in gypsum-rich cap rock and as disseminated coarse crystals in both primary and recrystallized anhydrite cap rock, replacing anhydrite and associated with abundant calcite. Quartz appears in minute, euhedral, doubly terminated crystals.

Kainite Rocks

Kainite rocks contain principally kainite, $KMg(SO_4)Cl \cdot 3H_2O$, and halite, commonly accompanied by such water-rich minerals as epsomite, $MgSO_4 \cdot 7H_2O$; bloedite, $Na_2Mg(SO_4)_2 \cdot 4H_2O$; leonite, $K_2Mg(SO_4)_2 \cdot 4H_2O$; and picromerite, $K_2Mg(SO_4)_2 \cdot 6H_2O$. Large inclusions of gas and of lithium-rich residual cognate water are common. Kainite rocks are secondary, formed as cappings on some potash rocks.

Barite Rocks

Barite is a rather widespread mineral in limestone, dolomite, marl, clay, siltstone, and sandstone, appearing in crystal groups, nodules, concretions, lenses, veins, cavity fillings, and as cement. It originates either from hypogene or meteoric solutions or may be authigenic. By weathering of these rocks it is concentrated in residual deposits. Sedimentary manganese nodules in shale are accompanied by barite in some localities. The barite is massive, platy, fibrous, earthy, or well crystallized. Microscopically some appears in prismatic or granular pieces that may be nearly cryptocrystalline. It may also be laminated, in convergent or curved fashion, or spherulitic.

Strontium Rocks

Strontium rocks contain celestite or strontianite. Celestite is more widespread, but both are usually only accessory constituents. Celestite forms geode crystals, nodules, layers, veins, and disseminations in limestone, marl, rock anhydrite, rock sulfur, and in shale and sandstone with halite and gypsum. Strontianite rock from near Barstow, California, contains strontianite masses, lenses, and layers as much as 3 ft thick in clay. Microscopically the strontianite is in fan-shaped or spherulitic aggregates, with minute spherulites interfingering to form a mosaic of polygonal pieces. Banding is faint. The strontianite is pale brownish yellow, with irregularly distributed color. Accessory material includes angular particles of quartz and feldspar, rare fragments of brown vitrophyre, calcite and celestite grains, and calcite spherulites. The rock is considered to have been formed by the replacement of limestone by meteoric waters.

Rock Borates

Definition. Borates occur in brines of saline lakes, as incrustations around saline lakes and playas, as deposits of hot springs, as disseminations in carnallite rocks, and as concentrations or strata in lake-bed strata. Only the last type is of petrographic and economic significance. The principal borate minerals are colemanite and kernite.

Mineralogy. The two main associations are (1) colemanite-ulexite, (2) kernite-borax. The first is more widespread. Minerals found with colemanite are howlite, probertite, calcite, gypsum, and celestite. Accessory minerals with kernite are tincalconite, ulexite, kramerite, probertite, calcite, realgar, and stibnite. The bedded deposits of Turkey contain priceite ("pandermite") as the principal constituent.

Textures and Microstructures. The colemanite masses display finely granular to radial fibrous structures, and bands of colemanite show cross-fiber structure. Some fibers are length-fast, but most are length-slow. Euhedra of colemanite occur in geodes with gypsum and celestite. Colemanite alters to calcite. Ulexite forms "cotton balls"—loosely coherent masses of acicular crystals, which show varying degrees of alteration to colemanite. The balls have a core of random fibers and an outer zone of subparallel fibers normal to the surface. Ulexite also forms individual layers several feet thick.

Kernite occurs as cross-fiber seams and veins, abundantly disseminated crystals in clay, and irregularly bounded crystals in massive borax. In the larger masses a fibrous or bladed structure is simulated by the development of the perfect (100) cleavage.

Occurrence and Origin. Colemanite and its associates form masses, nodules, lenses, and layers in clays, loosely indurated shales, and rock gypsum, associated with basalt, arkosic sandstone, fanglomerate, volcanic ash, tuff, and porous limestone. The chief deposits in the United States are in the southwestern corner of the Great Basin in California and Nevada.

Colemanite has been derived principally by meteoric alteration of ulexite originally formed in playa deposits. In the United States the boron is believed to have come from hot springs and solfataras associated with Tertiary vulcanism. The kernite deposit in the Kramer district of California is thought to have been formed by contact meta-morphism of a lake borax deposit.

Soda Niter (Caliche)

From the quantitative petrographic viewpoint nitrates form unim-portant rocks. The principal occurrences are in the Atacama and Tarapaca deserts of northern Chile. Here the main mineral is soda niter, $NaNO_3$, with variable amounts of anhydrite, gypsum, halite, glauberite, bloedite; niter, KNO_3; darapspite, $Na_3(NO_3)(SO_4) \cdot H_2O$; and a variety of borates, chromates, and iodates. Soda niter is usually massive granular, showing a perfect ($10\bar{1}1$) cleavage, extreme bire-fringence, and "twinkling" ($\epsilon = 1.337$, $\omega = 1.585$). The caliche beds may be as much as 12 ft thick locally and are overlain by thin gravel, sand, and gypsum. It is generally agreed that the nitrates have been deposited by evaporation of ground water, but the source of the nitro-gen has been much disputed. Physiographic and climatic factors have been the main controls in localizing the deposits.

Rock Sulfur

Native sulfur, which is as a constituent of tufa, volcanic ash, tuff, coal, clay, limestone, rock gypsum and other evaporites, and cap rock, may form layers of lenses of considerable thicknesses. The Sicilian de-posits lie below marl and over rock gypsum. Associated are calcite, celestite, aragonite, gypsum, and bituminous material. The sulfur varies from anhedral-granular to euhedra in cavities. Some of the rock is banded with alternations of sulfur and limestone or of limestone, coarsely crystalline calcite, and sulfur. In the bedded Russian deposits near Kuibyshev, sulfur forms layers in gypsum and in calcite and nodules in bituminous limestone. Some of it is oolitic; some has been recrystallized. The cap rock deposits of Louisiana and Texas consist of granular calcite, sulfur, anhydrite, gypsum, celestite, aragonite, and dolomite. The sulfur forms layers, lenses, pods, and veins. Sulfur and calcite replace anhydrite. Some of the rocks are brecciated. The sulfur of these deposits is considered to have been formed by the reduction of gypsum and anhydrite or of hydrogen sulfide by hydrocarbons, which process may be assisted by sulfur bacteria.

Analcite Rocks

Analcite is a prominent and characteristic mineral of some argil-laceous sedimentary beds, occurring in oolites with concentric struc-ture, as cement, as crystals, and in veinlets. Oolites may be present as individuals or as coalesced clusters with sutured contacts. Clusters of quartz grains of silt size are cemented by spherical analcite aggregates. Other minerals are calcite in grains and as dusty inclusions in analcite, clay particles, chalcedony, apophyllite, and limonite. The analcite is believed to have been precipitated by reaction of clay minerals with Na-rich marsh and lacustrine waters. Analcite has been reported from the Popo Agie member of the Chugwater (Triassic) formation of Wyoming, from the Chinle (Triassic) formation of Utah, and from the Green River (Tertiary) formation of Wyoming, Colorado, and Utah.

6

METAMORPHIC ROCKS—GENERAL

ORIGIN AND CLASSIFICATION

Introduction

Metamorphic rocks are mineralogically and texturally the most varied and complex of the three major groups. This complexity results from the following genetic features:

1. Metamorphic rocks may have any other rock type as a parent—igneous extrusive or intrusive, sedimentary, or even another metamorphic rock.

2. Because different factors or agents contribute singly or together to metamorphism, there are several distinctly different *kinds* of metamorphism.

3. Because the agents may vary in intensity, there are various degrees or *grades* of the different kinds of metamorphism.

4. Metamorphic rocks may be developed under conditions in which materials are removed from and added to the system, thus changing the composition of the initial parent material—*metasomatism*.

5. Not all metamorphic mineral assemblages achieved equilibrium. This may be true also if the rock is polymetamorphic in origin, i.e., subjected to two different kinds or grades of metamorphism.

Metamorphic rocks demonstrated to have been derived from igneous parents may be given the prefix *ortho-* (orthoamphibolite, orthogneiss), whereas those shown to have been formed from sedimentary rocks may be designated by the prefix *para-* (paragneiss). The use of the term orthoquartzite for a sandstone with a cement of crystallographically oriented overgrowth quartz (sedimentary quartzite) is inconsistent with this more general usage of *ortho-* and *para-*.

A metamorphic rock is one formed by textural, mineralogical, and in some cases chemical as well, transformations of preexisting rocks in geological environments within the lithosphere and excepting environments on the surface of the lithosphere. During metamorphism a mineralogical assemblage, which attained chemical equilibrium under one set of physical conditions, attempts to reachieve equilibrium when placed in a new physical environment.

Chemical Classes

Metamorphic rocks may be assigned to several large groups on the basis of their bulk chemical compositions, which reflect, to a large extent, the nature of the parent material, provided no significant metasomatism has intervened:

1. Quartz-feldspar rocks; parents: sandstones, arkoses, cherts, rhyolites, aplites, granites, granodiorites. Examples: quartzites, quartzose gneisses, felsic granulites.

2. Aluminous (pelitic) rocks; parents: clays, shales. Examples: slates, mica schists, andalusite hornfelses, sillimanite gneisses.

3. Carbonate rocks; parents: limestones and dolomites, commonly with quartz, chalcedony, and clay minerals as additional constituents. Examples: marbles, calc schists, calc-silicate gneisses.

4. Basic rocks; parents: andesites, diorites, basalts, diabases, gabbros, and their tuffs; marls, some graywackes. Examples: chlorite schists, actinolite schists, hornblende gneisses, eclogites.

5. Magnesian rocks; parents: peridotites, pyroxenites, serpentinites; chloritic sediments. Examples: talc schists, anthophyllite gneisses.

6. Ferruginous (and managaniferous) rocks; parents: ferruginous (and managaniferous) sediments. Examples: jaspilite, grunerite schists, eulysites.

Types of Metamorphism

The factors or agents of metamorphism are:

1. Heat
2. Pressure
   a. Confining (hydrostatic) pressure
   b. Directed pressure or stress
3. Fluids

Various combinations of these result in the different types of metamorphism:

1. *Cataclastic metamorphism,* also called kinematic or dislocation metamorphism
   Factor: stress ± confining pressure

Processes: mechanical breakdown of particles or grains

Examples: breccia, mylonite, phyllonite

2. *Pyrometamorphism,* also called optalic metamorphism, thermal metamorphism, caustic metamorphism

Factor: heat

Processes: recrystallization, minor reaction between minerals, inversion of minerals, melting

Examples: fritted sandstone, buchite

3. *Contact metamorphism,* also referred to as pyrometasomatism

Factors: heat, fluids largely of magmatic descent ± confining pressure

Processes: recrystallization, reaction between minerals, between minerals and fluids, ± removal and addition of material

Examples: hornfels, contact marble, skarn

4. *Regional metamorphism,* also called dynamothermal metamorphism

Factors: heat, stress, confining pressure, ± fluids of magmatic and juvenile descent

Processes: recrystallization, reaction between minerals (and fluids), orientation of minerals into parallel fabrics resulting in foliation

Examples: slates, mica schists, kyanite schists and gneisses, granulites, glaucophane schists

5. *Metasomatism,* also called hydrothermal metamorphism

Factors: fluids of magmatic descent, confining pressure, ± heat

Processes: recrystallization, reactions between minerals and fluids, replacement

Examples: pyrophyllite schists, some cordierite-anthophyllite rocks, greisen, aluminous (secondary) quartzites, topaz rocks, saussurite rocks; metasomatic rocks as a group have been called diabrochites

6. *Migmatization* or injection metamorphism

Factors: confining pressure, heat, igneous silicate fluids

Processes: recrystallization, introduction or generation of granitic material, reaction with granitic material, assimilation

Examples: injection gneisses, some augen gneisses, eruptive breccias, arterites ·

Intensity of Metamorphism

Early ideas on variation in intensity of metamorphic processes are reflected in the depth-zone classification of Grubenmann, who distinguished three zones, the uppermost or epizone, the intermediate or mesozone, and the lowermost or katazone. Temperature and confining pressure were regarded as increasing from epi- to katazone, whereas stress was considered as generally decreasing with depth.

Another means of expressing intensity variations is by metamorphic grade, which indicates the degree or stage of metamorphism that a rock has attained. In practice one chooses a rock unit of nearly fixed composition and observes the successive appearance of certain index minerals at different places in the formation. In aluminous (pelitic) rocks the diagnostic minerals, in increasing intensity order, are chlorite, biotite, garnet, staurolite, kyanite, sillimanite, under regional metamorphic conditions. Analogous sequences are available for other rock groups, e.g., chlorite, chloritoid, actinolite, hornblende in basic rocks, and increase in the Ca content (anorthite) of plagioclase in feldspathic rocks. By joining points on a map that mark the initial appearance of each of the diagnostic minerals, mineral isograds (biotite isograd, sillimanite isograd, etc.) may be defined, which represent the intersection of the margins of a metamorphic equal-intensity zone with the surface of the earth. In many cases, at least, isograds correspond to isothermals, which increase in value toward an area or focus of highest intensity. Although the device has been applied largely to areas underlain by regional metamorphic rocks, similar zonal relations were earlier shown to exist in some contact metamorphic aureoles, where in pelitic rocks the key minerals in increasing grade sequence are sericite-chlorite, andalusite-cordierite, and sillimanite. Similarly in carbonate rocks increasing intensity sequences, such as tremolite, diopside, wollastonite, larnite-spurrite, are known.

The concept of metamorphic facies is an attempt to extend recognition of specific metamorphic environments for all metamorphic rocks, irrespective of their composition. A metamorphic facies includes all rocks of the same or varying chemical composition that have achieved equilibrium in a given geological environment or, as usually expressed, under a specific combination of temperature-pressure conditions. Rocks belonging to the same facies may be considered as having attained the same grade of metamorphism. The assignment of a rock to a particular facies depends upon recognition of specific mineralogical assemblages, which are regarded as diagnostic of the facies. A facies is named after some rock (preferably common) that belongs to it. For purposes of rock identification, however, which, after all, must precede any attempted assignment of the genetic environmental conditions, it is not practical to describe rocks initially according to facies groups. The facies designation can be given only after the mineralogy, texture, field relations, and associations of the rock have been studied

TABLE 7. METAMORPHIC FACIES

Facies	Pressure-temperature conditions	Type of metamorphism	Mineralogical assemblages					
			Quartz-feldspar rocks	Aluminous (pelitic) rocks	Carbonate rocks	Basic rocks	Magnesian rocks	Ferruginous rocks
Greenschist	P moderate to low, T low, + stress	Regional, metasomatism	Quartz, Albite, Epidote, Muscovite (Microcline)	Quartz, Albite, Muscovite, Chlorite	Calcite, Dolomite, Quartz, Epidote, Tremolite	Albite, Chlorite, Epidote, Calcite, Actinolite, Glaucophane, Lawsonite, Pumpelleyite	Carbonate, Talc, Serpentine, Chlorite, Actinolite	"Chert", Hematite, Siderite, Stilpnomelane, Minnesotaite, Chlorite
Albite-epidote amphibolite	P moderate, T moderate, + stress	Regional	Quartz, Albite, Epidote, Microcline, Muscovite, Biotite	Quartz, Albite, Chloritoid, Muscovite, Biotite, Garnet	Calcite, Quartz, Epidote, Tremolite, Diopside, Vesuvianite	Albite, Epidote, Actinolitic hornblende, Lawsonite, Glaucophane, Diopside, Garnet	Chlorite, Actinolite	Quartz, Specular hematite, Magnetite
Amphibolite — Cordierite-anthophyllite subfacies	P moderate, T moderate, − stress	Contact	Quartz, Albite-oligoclase, Microcline, Biotite, Muscovite	Quartz, Oligoclase, Muscovite, Andalusite, Cordierite, Biotite	Calcite, Quartz, Diopside, Grossularite, Wollastonite	Plagioclase, Quartz, Anthophyllite, Cordierite, Biotite, Hornblende	Actinolite, Anthophyllite, Cummingtonite, Biotite (± metasomatism)	
Staurolite-kyanite subfacies	P moderate to high, T moderate to high, + strong stress	Regional	Quartz, Oligoclase, Microcline	Quartz, Oligoclase, Microcline, Muscovite, Biotite, Staurolite, Kyanite, Garnet, Rutile	Calcite, Quartz, Diopside, Grossularite, (Clino)zoisite, Phlogopite	Andesine, Hornblende, Epidote, Quartz, Biotite, Sphene, Garnet		Quartz, Magnetite

174

Facies	Conditions		Biotite Muscovite	Quartz Oligoclase Biotite Sillimanite Almandite Orthoclase Cordierite (±metasomatism)	Calcite Quartz Diopside Phlogopite Anorthite	Andesine Hornblende Diopside Almandite	Anthophyllite Cummingtonite Almandite-pyrope	Grunerite Garnet
Sillimanite-almandite subfacies	P high T high + stress	Regional						
Granulite	P very high T very high + stress	Regional	Quartz Orthoclase Oligoclase Kyanite (Sillimanite) Almandite Hypersthene	Quartz Orthoclase Oligoclase-andesine Sillimanite Almandite	Calcite Quartz Diopside Scapolite Phlogopite Anorthite	Andesine Diopside Hypersthene Garnet	Anthophyllite Enstatite-hypersthene Garnet Olivine (?)	Fayalite Hypersthene Diopside-hedenbergite Garnet
(Eclogite*)						Omphacite* Pyrope-almandite		
Pyroxene hornfels	P moderate T high − stress	Contact	Quartz Orthoclase Plagioclase Biotite	Quartz Orthoclase Biotite Andalusite Cordierite Sillimanite	Calcite Wollastonite Grossularite Vesuvianite Calcite Forsterite Periclase Diopside	Labradorite Diopside Hypersthene Biotite Olivine	Enstatite-hypersthene Forsterite Spinel	Fayalite Hypersthene Diopside-hedenbergite Garnet Cordierite
Sanidinite	P low T very high − stress	Contact; pyrometamorphism	Tridymite Glass	Cordierite Sillimanite (Mullite) Spinel Corundum Anorthite Glass	Calcite Spurrite Larnite (calcitic) Calcite Monticellite Melilite Diopside Merwinite (dolomitic)			

Sillimanite-almandite subfacies row assemblages: Biotite Muscovite; Quartz Oligoclase Biotite Sillimanite Almandite Orthoclase Cordierite (± metasomatism); Calcite Quartz Diopside Phlogopite Anorthite; Andesine Hornblende Diopside Almandite; Anthophyllite Cummingtonite Almandite-pyrope; Grunerite Garnet.

* Usually separated as a special "eclogite" facies; eclogites are the sole representatives and are also regarded as forming under very high pressure and temperature.

175

and correlated. Not all proposed facies are well established, nor are the temperature-pressure conditions definable except in a very general way. The generally accepted facies, their mineralogical criteria, and their environmental conditions are presented in Table 7.

In this book an attempt has been made to group metamorphic rocks into mineralogical groups, in so far as possible. From the standpoint of genesis this results here and there in some unusual bedfellows. Conversely, however, if the rocks are grouped by means of facies, mineralogical mesalliances are the rule, and the beginning student may experience considerable difficulty in rock identification.

TEXTURES AND MICROSTRUCTURES

Cataclastic Textures

Cataclastic textures and features result from the mechanical disruption of mineral grains or grain aggregates. Individual grain characteristics include wavy or irregular extinction (Fig. 49a); anomalous 2V in uniaxial minerals (quartz, calcite); bent, broken, or microfaulted cleavage and twin planes; and internal or marginal granulation. Quartz may show Böhm lamellae, which are fine lamellae with minute inclusions, formed apparently by gliding along surfaces subparallel with (0001).

Quartzose or quartz-feldspar rocks may show mortar structure, in which grains are girdled by a much finer grained marginal aggregate. Further cataclasis may proceed along sets of subparallel planes resulting in very fine grained zones or streaks (Fig. 49c). This leads in ultimate development to rocks that are completely pulverized to cryptocrystalline and even optically isotropic material (mylonite, pseudotachylite).

Crystalloblastic Textures

Crystalloblastic textures and microstructures result from the growth of mineral grains and aggregates in solid media. *Blasto*, used as a suffix, indicates the feature is metamorphic in development; used as a prefix it indicates that the feature occurs in metamorphic rocks but is partly residual in origin. If the crystalloblastic grains are anhedral they are xenoblastic; if euhedral, idioblastic. Xenoblastic grains in an equidimensional mosaic pattern have a granoblastic arrangement (Fig. 52a). If xenoblastic rocks are highly interlocking, as in a jigsaw puzzle, they are sutured (Fig. 52b). Some minerals show more marked tendencies to be idioblastic than others, and a general crystalloblastic series has been developed in which higher listed species tend to show idioblastic faces against those listed lower in the column.

Rutile, spinel, magnetite, sphene, pyrite
Garnet, staurolite, andalusite, tourmaline, chloritoid
Clinozoisite-epidote, zoisite, forsterite, chondrodite
Wollastonite, amphiboles, pyroxenes
Biotite, muscovite, chlorites, talc
Dolomite, calcite
Cordierite, scapolite
Feldspars, quartz

With little difficulty one can find numerous exceptions to this generalized scheme. The series is a function of the crystal structures of the minerals, at least in part.

In decussate textures the grains, particularly platy or prismatic minerals, lie crisscross. Parallel or subparallel orientations of platy or flaky minerals are lepidoblastic in texture; similar arrangements of prismatic or fibrous minerals are nematoblastic (see under Foliation).

Porphyroblasts

One widespread crystalloblastic texture is that in which relatively large metamorphic crystals or porphyroblasts of one or more species occur in a matrix of smaller grains. A single species may be represented both in the matrix and as porphyroblasts. In many cases porphyroblasts have idioblastic outlines (Figs. 59b, 61a) (staurolite, andalusite, ottrelite), but some are xenoblastic (hornblende, albite, and cordierite). In many cases they are crowded with inclusions of other minerals, one or more species, which may be zonally distributed (chiastolite, garnet, cordierite). This is the poikiloblastic or sieve structure, characteristic of some cordierite and staurolite (Fig. 61a). Poikiloblastic structure is, however, not confined to porphyroblasts. Some porphyroblasts (albite, chloritoid) contain inclusions that are at an angle to the foliation, and others have inclusions arranged in spiral pattern (helical or snowball garnet), both of which indicate rotation at one or several growth stages. Not uncommonly porphyroblasts may show zoning.

Porphyroblasts result from:

1. The superior crystallizing ability of minerals high in the crystalloblastic series
2. Two stages or kinds of metamorphism
3. Metasomatic introduction of certain elements

Some petrologists would confine porphyroblasts to crystals resulting from the rearrangement of elements available in the rock and
would use metacrysts for large, generally idioblastic grains resulting
from the introduction of materials. Only in some cases, from the chemical nature of the large crystals and the field relations of the rock, is
it possible to decide if the crystals have been formed as the result
of metasomatism (i.e., that they are metacrysts rather than porphyroblasts)—microcline in schists adjacent to granite plutons; tourmaline in
schists adjacent to pegmatites (Fig. 58*b*).

Relict Textures

Relict (residual or palimpsest) textures may survive in rocks that
have undergone relatively little recrystallization or internal differential
movement. A relict porphyritic texture is blastoporphyritic, with
phenocrysts perhaps marginally granulated or partly or pseudomorphously replaced. Some augen are metaphenocrysts. A blastophit-
ic texture is a relict diabasic fabric usually with pyroxene uralitized
and some other mineralogical changes and rearrangements. Amygdaloidal structures may also remain outlined. In some metamorphosed
clastic sediments, the textures may be referred to as blastopsephitic
(stretched-pebble gneiss), blastopsammitic (fritted sandstone), and
blastopelitic (argillite). Bedding may also be partly preserved, not
uncommonly at some angle to the foliation (slates, some phyllites, and
schists), but in many areas of strongly folded, medium- to high-grade
metamorphic rocks much of the foliation is parallel with original
layering.

Some rocks show textures inherited from metamorphic rocks formed
either under a different type or a different grade of metamorphism.
Some schists show traces (in the position of inclusions of porphyroblasts; earlier foliation-plane remnants) of a previous different metamorphic fabric. In some cases pseudomorphs (platy garnet after
chlorite, sillimanite after kyanite) indicate that a lower-grade rock
has been transformed to one of higher grade. In more cases, however,
lower-grade minerals replace higher-grade ones (chlorite after garnet; serpentine after forsterite; saussurite after plagioclase; hornblende
and glaucophane after omphacite; sericite after andalusite, staurolite,
and cordierite; talc after tremolite; brucite after periclase), indicating
that retrograde metamorphism (retrogressive metamorphism or di-
apthoresis) has occurred.

Maculose, Phacoidal, and Related Textures

Some metamorphic rocks have a spotted appearance, in some cases owing to strong development of porphyroblasts of such minerals as cordierite, andalusite, staurolite, or garnet or of graphitic segregations The contact spotted slates typify this kind of maculose texture (Figs. 51b,c) (Fleckschiefer—spotted slate; Fruchtschiefer—spots resembling wheat grains; Knotenschiefer—spots resembling knots or clots; Garbenschiefer—spots resembling carraway seeds).

Phacoidal textures characterize rocks having lensoid or ellipsoidal mineral aggregates in a matrix, either finer-grained or of distinctly different composition. In some augen gneisses the "eyes" consist of

Fig. 47. Pressure shadow of feather quartz around pyrite metacrysts in slate, Mariposa formation (Jurassic), Mother Lode belt, California. Nicols crossed. (*After A. Knopf, U.S. Geological Survey.*)

granular quartz, feldspar, or quartz-feldspar aggregates. Flaser gneisses, gabbros, marbles, and stretched-pebble gneisses show phacoidal textures. Some low-grade micaceous schists have small lenses of relatively coarse radiating chlorite or mica generally parallel with the foliation.

Pressure shadows are relatively coarse mineral fringes that form chiefly on those two opposing sides of porphyroblasts (or metacrysts) that parallel the foliation. They form around crystals of such minerals as chloritoid, magnetite, and pyrite (Fig. 47) and consist chiefly of quartz or of chlorite and quartz, which may appear in fibers more or less normal to the surfaces of the porphyroblasts. In some cases the fibers show some twisting or curvature indicating post- or syncrystallization rotation. Calcite pressure shadows may fringe fossil relicts in some marbles. The structures are ascribed to crystallization in areas of low pressure developed in the "shadow" of resistant crystals or to deposition in open spaces formed by rotation of the porphyro-blasts.

Rosette structures, consisting of fibrous or prismatic crystals ar-ranged in radiating aggregates, are conspicuous textural elements in some metamorphic rocks, formed in some contact and metasomatic rocks where stress was largely absent or even in some regional meta-morphic rocks after stress had dwindled. The list of minerals that ap-pear in rosettes and sheaflike groups includes anthophyllite, cumming-tonite, grunerite, sillimanite (Fig. 62c), tourmaline, wollastonite, clinozoisite, zoisite, tremolite-actinolite, stilpnomelane, chlorite, min-nesotaite, and, less commonly, hornblende, diopside, and vesuvianite. Similar structures (spherulites) are formed by albite in adinoles.

Some metamorphic rocks have foliations characterized by the parallel orientation of ellipsoidal nodules composed of an aggregate of minerals different or in different proportions from those of the matrix. The nodules range in length from less than an inch to several inches. Quartz-sillimanite nodules in micaceous sillimanite schists and leptites are the best examples, but quartz-tourmaline nodules in schist have also been described. The origin of the sillimanite nodules has been ascribed both to original segregations (clayey concretions) and to metamorphic differentiation. Segregations of plagioclase-epidote and hornblende-biotite in amphibolites; of garnet-diopside, of garnet-clinozoisite, of phlogopite, of diopside, of scapolite, and of scapolite-diopside in calc-silicate gneisses and similar rocks; of quartz-mus-covite in granite gneiss; and of quartz-calcite ± muscovite and pyrite in slate are other examples.

Symplectites and Other Semiregular Intergrowths

Symplectites are intimate secondary intergrowths of two minerals, one a single-crystal host, the other a guest appearing in vermicular, plumose, or micrographic units, which although either separate or connected, are usually crystallographically continuous (Fig. 48). Some symplectites result from metasomatism; others are formed by reactions between adjoining different minerals. In pattern, symplec-tites resemble many primary graphic to vermicular intergrowths, and in many cases in metamorphic rocks it is not possible to decide whether the intergrowths are syngenetic or epigenetic. Table 8 lists examples of these intergrowths.

Other noteworthy intergrowths are those termed diablastic, in which two or more minerals are interlaced as semiregular radiating or parallel laths—garnet-quartz, garnet-axinite. Kelyphitic rims of py-

Fig. 48. Symplectite of muscovite (gray) and quartz (clear) in biotite gneiss, Cuffey district, Colorado. Nicols crossed, ×170. (*Courtesy of J. E. Bever.*)

TABLE 8. GRAPHIC AND VERMICULAR INTERGROWTHS IN METAMORPHIC ROCKS (PRIMARY AND SYMPLECTITIC)

Host	Guest	Rock examples
Plagioclase........	Quartz (myrmekitic)	Many quartz-feldspar gneisses
Plagioclase........	Orthoclase	Quartz-feldspar gneiss
Plagioclase........	Muscovite	Biotite gneiss and schist, granite gneiss
Plagioclase........	Augite	Granulite
Plagioclase........	Hornblende	Granulite
Orthoclase........	Quartz (micrographic to granophyric)	Fritted sandstone
Orthoclase........	Muscovite	Biotite gneiss
Microcline........	Garnet	Calc schist
Biotite..........	Muscovite	Biotite gneiss, sillimanite gneiss
Calcite..........	Dolomite	Calc schist
Chondrodite......	Calcite	Marble
Scapolite........	Quartz	Marble
Epidote.........	Quartz	Gneiss, calc schist

roxene, hornblende, actinolite, biotite, plagioclase, magnetite, or various combinations of these occur around garnets in eclogites and pyroxene granulites. Sphene overgrowths on magnetite or ilmenite are not rare in some metamorphic rocks, and uralitic marginal replacements by amphibole of pyroxene are widespread.

Foliation

Foliation designates all parallel structures in metamorphic rocks of metamorphic genesis, as the result of which the rocks can be broken along nearly parallel surfaces. Some petrologists use schistosity as the equivalent of foliation, others subdivide foliation into various kinds, on the basis of the degree of perfection of the parallel surfaces that can be obtained:

Slaty cleavage (most perfect)
Schistosity
Gneissic structure (least perfect)

The European term S surface includes all types of foliation as well as other surfaces in metamorphic rocks that are of nonmetamorphic origin—relict surfaces and postmetamorphic fracture cleavage. Foliation results from (1) parallelism or subparallelism of tabular, prismatic, and fibrous minerals (lepidoblastic and nematoblastic arrangement of micas, amphiboles, etc.); (2) crystallographic orientation of xenoblastic minerals (quartz, calcite); (3) mineralogical banding.

Banding is of three genetic types: (1) relict sedimentary layering (stratification) or relict igneous layering (flow structure, primary layering in peridotites); (2) banding resulting from metamorphic diffusion (metamorphic differentiation); (3) banding formed by lit-par-lit injection of igneous material (usually granitic).

Not uncommonly in some direction within foliation planes there exists a parallelism of linear units, including such elements as prismatic or fibrous crystals of hornblende or sillimanite; elongate rods or "pencils" of grain aggregates, e.g., quartz or sillimanite; stretched pebbles; crests of microfolds or plications; and intersection of relict bedding and foliation. This structure is lineation. Not all types of lineation originate in the same way. Microfolds or corrugations may be essentially drag folds, whereas elongate minerals in most cases apparently crystallized with their long dimensions parallel with the axes of folds formed during compression.

Foliation in many instances has been formed parallel with the surfaces of differential movement in the rock, and in such cases mineral lineation typically is oriented normal to the direction of differential motion. Where foliation results from simple compression the foliation planes are normal to the direction of the compressive force; where it results from a couple the foliation planes are at an angle to the directions of the forces.

The detailed delineation of the fabric of metamorphic rocks includes determination of the directions of crystallographic orientation of such xenoblastic minerals as quartz, feldspar, and calcite. The techniques and interpretation of the results fall in the field of petrofabrics, which is an extensive subject by itself, involving use of the universal stage, beyond the scope of this work.[1]

[1] Some basic references and books on petrofabrics in English include J. C. Haff, Preparation of Petrofabric Diagrams, *Am. Mineralogist.,* **23:** 543–574, 1938; E. B. Knopf and E. Ingerson, Structural Petrology, *Geol. Soc. Amer. Mem.* **6,** 1938; H. W. Fairbairn, *Structural Petrology of Deformed Rocks,* Addison-Wesley Publishing Company, Cambridge, Mass., 1949; F. J. Turner and J. Verhoogen, *Igneous and Metamorphic Petrology,* pp. 517–564, McGraw-Hill Book Company, Inc., New York, 1951; P. Niggli, *Rocks and Mineral Deposits,* pp. 280–304, W. H. Freeman and Company, San Francisco, 1954.

7

DESCRIPTIONS OF METAMORPHIC ROCKS

CATACLASITES AND RELATED ROCKS

Metamorphic rocks formed principally by mechanical deformation or cataclastic metamorphism are a group in which the various types are related through textural rather than mineralogical characteristics. This group may be subdivided conveniently as follows:

Brecciated rocks
Phacoidal rocks
Mylonitic rocks
Vitrified rocks

Brecciated Rocks

Metamorphic breccias (also called friction breccias) are characterized by angular units consisting in the main of rock fragments, not uncommonly of varying size, set in a normally subordinate matrix made up of smaller rock pieces and mineral fragments and powder. Many breccias are so coarse grained that thin-section studies of anything but the matrix are impractical. If the particles are of smaller size and inconspicuous in hand specimen, the term microbreccia may be employed. In such rocks the individual elements are usually sharply angular to only slightly rounded (Fig. 49a). Many of the pieces show internal fracturing, and some of their component mineral grains may show strain, cleavage rupturing, and bent cleavage or twinning planes. If considerable rotation of the particles has occurred, the corners become rounded off through mutual abrasion, producing subangular to rounded pieces and supplying considerable additional finer rock and mineral powder for the matrix, which may thus predominate. Such cataclasites have been referred to as crush conglomerates. In some types breccia pieces are surrounded by numerous subparallel shear

184

surfaces along which the rock has been much more intensely granulated, resulting in a fragmented and streaked texture. Some recrystallization may take place along the shear planes (kakirite).

Brecciation affects a wide variety of rocks including such types as sandstones, limestones, plutonic igneous rocks, quartzites, marbles, and gneisses. Some of the so-called schistose grits may also be included in this group. These arenaceous sediments, well represented in the Highland Border of Scotland, show varying degrees of trans-

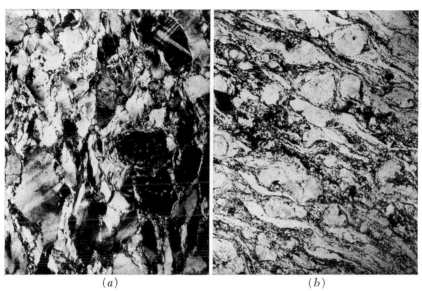

| (a) | (b) |

FIG. 49*a*, *b*. (*a*) Brecciated arkose; microcline, orthoclase, quartz. Hot Springs, Arkansas. Nicols crossed, ×9. (*b*) Biotite gneiss, cataclastically deformed; quartz, orthoclase, biotite. Neihart district, Montana. Nicols not crossed, ×9.

formation, from cataclastic to higher-grade regional metamorphic effects. In the former quartz grains may be rotated, strained, fractured, and attenuated. The pelitic matrix is sheared and altered to fine-grained sericite, or to a fine-grained sericite-chlorite-albite aggregate with some quartz, epidote, and sphene.

Phacoidal Rocks

In phacoidal rocks the characteristic textural feature consists of ellipsoidal or lensoid units in a finer-grained matrix that is brecciated and sheared. Some augen gneisses that belong to this category are quartz-feldspar rocks in which ellipsoidal single-crystal "eyes" of feldspar represent abraded relict phenocrysts set in a granulated matrix. In other rocks called augen gneisses the structure is gneissoid and of primary origin, and in still others the feldspar units may be metasomatic in origin. The (unacceptable) term porphyroid has been applied to acid volcanics in which blastoporphyritic quartz and feldspar grains spot a fine-grained, sheared quartz-sericite matrix. Cataclasites that show some recrystallization effects have been termed blastocataclasites.

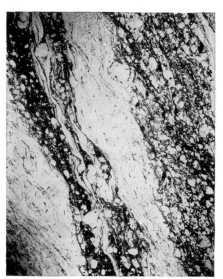

FIG. 49c. Sheared granodiorite; quartz, feldspars, mica, cryptocrystalline material. Bitterroot Mountains, Montana. Nicols not crossed, ×9.

In some types the eyes are not single-crystal units but consist of aggregates of minerals in grains coarser than those of the same species in the matrix and represent partly crushed relict patches. Some marbles display such textures, as may gabbros and granites, which are referred to as flaser gabbros and granites. The coarser patches also may be polycrystalline aggregates of hard minerals different from those of the matrix. Flaser gneiss is a general name for such rocks, although the poorer term mylonite gneiss has been used. This texture is not in all cases strictly of mechanical derivation. In some examples solution of minerals under stress and subsequent recrystallization have aided in shaping new grain patterns. This is particularly true in some deformed limestones, marbles, and even quartzites. Some mechanically metamorphosed conglomerates also possess the phacoidal texture, the pebbles being attenuated and deformed—"stretched-pebble" gneisses.

Mylonitic Rocks

Phyllonites (phyllite-mylonites) are fine-grained, highly schistose rocks whose fine texture results from the destruction of coarser-grained units and whose foliation in many cases results from closely spaced shear planes developed along the limbs of innumerable small microfolds. Phyllonites resemble phyllites and commonly contain low-grade metamorphic minerals, including sericite, chlorite, fine-grained graphite, and quartz. If the original rocks were also metamorphic, relict grains of higher-grade minerals may survive, including garnet, biotite, staurolite, kyanite, and andalusite, which will display marginal alteration to chlorite or sericite. Many phyllonites display remnant microfolds of curved mica flakes at various angles to the pronounced schistosity.

Mylonites have been formed by extreme milling and complete pulverization of rocks along major fault zones under strong confining pressure. The grain size usually is exceedingly fine, but thin lenses of slightly coarser grains or bands of more intense crushing may parallel the lamination. The lamination, which resembles flow structures in some volcanic glasses, is locally accentuated by darker-colored layers and thin trains of dusty magnetite. Many rocks that show mylonitization are relatively inactive chemically, such types as sandstones, quartzites, granites, and quartz-feldspar gneisses being strongly represented, but such rocks as gabbros and peridotites may also be mylonitized. For varieties that display a strong foliation the superfluous name mylonite schist has been used.

Gouges are also fine-grained products of extreme cataclasis along fault zones but have been developed under weak confining pressure. Thus the resulting product, which commonly contains quartz, clay minerals, sericite, chlorite, and other relict rock minerals, is very weakly cohesive.

Vitrified Rocks

Extreme examples of cataclastic metamorphism are rocks transformed into vitreous material, which under the microscope appears as a nonpolarizing glassy substance but which x-rays may reveal to be only cryptocrystalline. Such dark rocks are called ultramylonites and pseudotachylites. The German term Hartschiefer and the English term flinty crush-rock designate similar rocks. These rocks occur as lenticles in mylonites and locally along overthrust belts. In some cases they form small dikes, having been injected in a manner similar to igneous material. Gneisses with veins of ultramylonitic rock have been referred to as trapshotten gneisses. Parent rocks of ultramylonites are the same as those of mylonites.

PYROMETAMORPHIC ROCKS

Pyrometamorphic rocks are those whose textural and mineralogical transformations have been effected chiefly by extreme heat. Such rocks occur along the margins of some dikes and sills, along the floors of lava flows, where volcanic bombs fell into sand, along the floors and roofs of burning coal seams, and as xenoliths in intrusive and extrusive rocks.

Porcellanites (also used for silicified tuffs and some cherts) are hard, aphanitic rocks with the fracture and texture of unglazed porcelain, formed by baking of clays and shales marginal to coal seams ignited either spontaneously or by man. The rocks are very fine grained to cryptocrystalline aggregates of quartz, feldspars, and micaceous minerals.

Fritted or vitrified sandstones (hornstones) (Fig. 50a) consist of

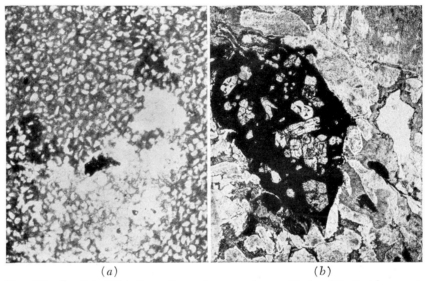

(*a*)   (*b*)

Fig. 50*a, b.* (*a*) Fritted sandstone from contact with basaltic bomb; quartz remnants in lechatlierite, some magnetite. Sunset Crater, Arizona. Nicols not crossed, ×21. (*b*) Xenolith of hornblende granite in basalt; quartz and turbid feldspar partly melted, large hornblende converted to diopside-glass mixture. Mitlechtern, Odenwald, Germany. Nicols not crossed, ×21.

quartz grains, rounded by melting, in a network matrix of silica glass (lechatlierite) or of glass and tridymite. In some examples the tridymite is preserved; in others it has inverted to quartz upon cooling. Clay minerals are converted to feldspars, cordierite, sillimanite, or rarely mullite. In some examples micrographic intergrowths of quartz and potash feldspar are developed. At lower temperatures sandstones show simple recrystallization to very even grained quartz aggregates (resembling "true" quartzites). If the sandstone contained accessory calcite, chlorite, or clay minerals, pyroxenes may be developed.

Where aluminous or siliceous rocks have been included in basalts, gabbros, and ultramafic rocks both recrystallization and partial melting may have occurred. Such rocks are buchites (also basalt jaspis and basalt jasper) and consist of fine-grained aggregates of various combinations of cordierite, mullite, sillimanite, tridymite, corundum, spinel, anorthite to labradorite, augite, enstatite-hypersthene, and magnetite, set in an abundant matrix of light-colored to brownish glass. Rounded residual quartz grains may be preserved. The glass may also contain such crystallites as trichites or globulites, gas pores, and various microlites. The cordierite appears in a variety of forms: hexagonal crystals and spiral, parallel, and irregular clusters (indialite).

Some buchites also show evidence of metasomatism, particularly those enclosed in intermediate igneous rocks. Minerals such as sanidine and plagioclase are introduced. The sanidinites of the Laacher Sea area in Germany (Fig. 50c), which occur as blocks in trachytes and phonolites, contain various combinations of glass, sanidine, cordierite, sillimanite, hypersthene, scapolite, corundum,

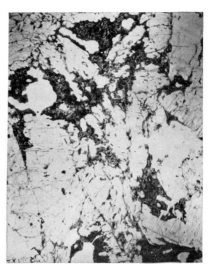

FIG. 50c. Sanidinite; sanidine crystals with interstitial glassy to cryptocrystalline aggregate. Laacher Sea, Germany. Nicols not crossed, ×10.

spinel, and relict staurolite and garnet. They were formed by the combination of thermal metamorphism and soda metasomatism of pelitic sediments. Other sanidinites are hybrids between phonolites (or trachytes) and metamorphosed pelitic sediments and resemble igneous rocks, containing such other species as oligoclase, biotite, sodic amphibole, sodalite, nosean and haüyne. Many of the rocks have a miarolitic, subhedral-granular texture. In sanidine-rich varieties the feldspar forms blocky crystals with other constituents confined to the subordinate interstitial matrix.

Xenoliths of metamorphic rocks, such as schists in basalt, may show alteration of quartz marginally and along cracks to tridymite, some glass with augite and hypersthene microlites, and feldspar spherulites. In others the glass has been partly recrystallized to diopside and intermediate plagioclase.

Xenoliths of plutonic igneous rocks such as granite or granodiorite in intermediate or mafic volcanics and hypabyssal intrusives show selection fusion of their minerals. Biotite is converted to a brown glass with minute crystals of pleonaste, magnetite, sillimanite, and some hypersthene or diopside (Fig. 50b). Hornblende may also be converted to glass with magnetite and diopside. In some cases the potash feldspars remain intact except for opening along cleavages and formation of secondary glass inclusions. At higher temperatures the feldspars are also converted to glass. Quartz, plagioclase, and augite may persist as embayed and fractured remnants.

SPOTTED SLATES AND HORNFELSES

Pelitic Hornfelses

Definition. Pelitic (aluminous) hornfelses are dark, fine-grained, usually massive rocks, consisting mainly of quartz, micas, feldspar, graphite, and commonly cordierite and andalusite.

Mineralogy. Many hornfelses of pelitic derivation contain either andalusite (Fig. 51c) or cordierite or both. The matrix commonly consists of quartz, feldspar, micas, and graphite. Magnetite, pyrite, tourmaline, ilmenite, apatite, and sphene or rutile are common accessories. Both potash feldspar (either orthoclase or microcline) and plagioclase are usually present; the plagioclase normally is albite or sodic oligoclase, rarely more calcic. Biotite occurs in nearly all hornfelses, and primary muscovite, which occurs with or without potash feldspar, indicates somewhat lower-grade metamorphism (Fig. 51b). Garnet, commonly Mn-rich, may substitute for cordierite, particularly in rocks that contain relatively abundant iron. Sillimanite may appear in place of andalusite. Hypersthene occurs in many varieties (Fig. 51a), usually in association with cordierite.

The presence of some Ca in the original sediments may be recorded by accessory diopside or augite, grossularite or vesuvianite, clinozoisite-epidote, and rarely even wollastonite. In Si-deficient varieties accessory spinel, usually pleonaste, and corundum appear. Both spinel and corundum may be found in rocks that contain quartz, indicating that chemical equilibrium was attained only locally.

Common secondary minerals are sericite after andalusite; chlorite and sericite (pinite) after cordierite; sericite and kaolinite after feldspars; chlorite and magnetite after biotite; and hornblende after hypersthene or augite. Cornubianite has been used as a varietal name for micaceous hornfels.

Textures and Microstructures. Cordierite commonly forms highly poikilitic porphyroblasts, usually with ragged, denticulate borders. In some, inclusions are so abundant that the cordierite forms only an irregular sponge. Sector twinning is common, and a bluish tint may be

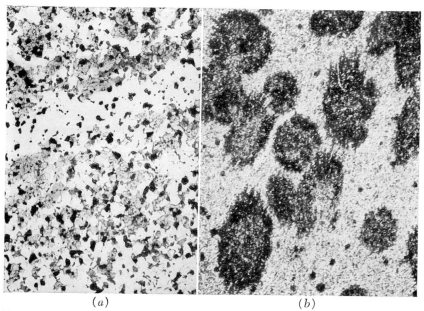

(a)   (b)

Fig. 51a, b. (a) Hornfels; quartz, hypersthene, magnetite. Base of Stillwater Complex, Stillwater Creek, Beartooth Mountains, Montana. Nicols not crossed, ×11. (b) Spotted hornfels; carbonaceous clots in very fine grained sericite-quartz aggregate. Andlau, Vosges Mountains, France. Nicols crossed, ×22.

noticeable. Andalusite also forms anhedral network porphyroblasts stuffed with quartz, biotite, and graphite or appears as euhedral prismatic crystals with rhombic cross sections and with minute graphite flakes symmetrically concentrated along edges, centers, and axial directions (chiastolite) (Fig. 51c). Hypersthene likewise is poikiliticporphyroblastic.

Garnet, biotite, muscovite, and rarely the feldspars may also appear as porphyroblasts, but usually micas, feldspars, quartz, and accessories form as smaller anhedral matrix grains with little or no preferred orientation. In some cases micas form ovoid clusters. Garnet also appears in groups of small rounded crystals. In lower-grade types clear larger quartz grains of clastic derivation may remain. Sillimanite characteristically forms as polycrystalline bundles or sheaves, commonly replacing biotite.

Occurrence and Origin. Hornfelses are formed by contact metamorphism of clays, shales, and graywackes in the innermost zone of batholithic contact aureoles, particularly those of granites, grano-

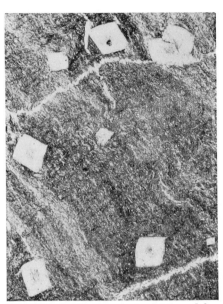

Fig. 51c. Spotted contact schist; andalusite (chiastolite) porphyroblasts in corrugated quartz-mica matrix. Gefrees, Fichtelgebirge, Bavaria, Germany. Nicols not crossed, ×11.

diorites, and tonalites. They may also develop by similar metamorphism of regional metamorphic rocks such as slates, phyllites, and low-grade schists. Two facies are represented—the amphibolite facies (cordierite-andalusite subfacies) and the higher-temperature pyroxene hornfels facies. Sillimanite appears to develop only in the highest intensity environment, close to the batholith. In some cases tourmaline and some feldspar, as metacrysts, represent material introduced. Well-known United States hornfelses occur in the Sierra Nevada batholithic aureole and in the White Mountains of New Hampshire. Classic localities in Europe are near Steige, lower Alsace, and near Oslo, Norway.

Cornéites are biotitic hornfelses produced by heat developed by crushing in sandy beds but localized in shaley beds along crests of anticlines and troughs of synclines through sharp flexion.

Spotted Slates

Spotted slates are chemically equivalent to hornfelses but appear in the outer parts of contact aureoles developed in slates and phyllites. At the lower temperatures the schistosity is retained, and minerals such as hypersthene, sillimanite, and garnet are not developed, and cordierite and andalusite are formed only exceptionally, in highly aluminous types. The normal minerals are muscovite and biotite. Quartz and sodic plagioclase are common.

The rocks have a spotted, or maculose, texture. In the lowest-grade rocks the spots are clots of minute graphite flakes or clusters of tiny magnetite grains (Fleckschiefer). In slightly higher-grade types micas, especially biotite, may appear in aggregates of coarser flakes (Knotenschiefer). In some types andalusite or cordierite forms small but distinct porphyroblasts (Fig. 51c) (Fruchtschiefer, Garbenschiefer, leptynolite).

Matrix micas are usually subparallelly oriented and may "flow around" porphyroblasts. Mica porphyroblasts may be distinctly poikilitic. Quartz veinlets may be locally abundant.

Other Hornfelses

Hornfelses of markedly different composition result from the contact metamorphism of rocks other than shales. Sandstones are converted to quartzites. Feldspathic sandstones, arkoses, and felsic volcanic rocks are recrystallized to granoblastic quartz-feldspar-biotite rocks, resembling some granulites mineralogically, but usually finergrained and nonfoliated. These are called arenaceous hornfelses. Limestones and dolomitic limestones are transformed into marbles and Ca-Mg-silicate rocks. Contact metamorphism of basalts and andesites produced mafic hornfelses—dense, dark-colored granoblastic aggregates of calcic plagioclase, hypersthene, diopside, accessory magnetite, sphene, and apatite, and in some varieties olivine or biotite or hornblende. Such rocks resemble various pyroxene granulites in mineral composition.

MARBLES AND RELATED ROCKS

Marbles

Definition. Marbles consist predominantly of calcite, of calcite plus dolomite, or of dolomite. Here are included only the metamorphic equivalents of the purer $CaCO_3$ and $CaMg(CO_3)_2$ sedimentary rocks. If various Ca, Mg, or Ca + Mg silicates are essential constituents, they become important textural and mineralogical factors, and such rocks are described under the calc-silicate rocks.

Mineralogy. Most marbles are calcitic; others consist chiefly of dolomite; still others contain calcite with variable, usually minor, amounts of dolomite. The nature of the accessory minerals depends to a considerable extent on whether the original rock was a limestone or a dolomite and on the nature of the impurities—siliceous, argillaceous, or both. In a general way, the following correlations may be made:

TABLE 9. RELATION OF ORIGINAL ROCK COMPOSITION TO TYPES OF SILICATES FORMED IN MARBLES

Original sedimentary rock	Type of silicate	Example
Arenaceous or cherty limestone.....	Ca silicate	Wollastonite
Argillaceous limestone.............	Ca-Al silicate	Clinozoisite
Arenaceous or cherty dolomite......	Ca-Mg silicate or Mg silicate + CaCO$_3$	Tremolite Forsterite + calcite
Argillaceous dolomite.............	Ca-Mg-Al silicate	Vesuvianite

Thus the list of accessory constituents is long and the possible combinations are highly variable, owing (1) to original basic chemical

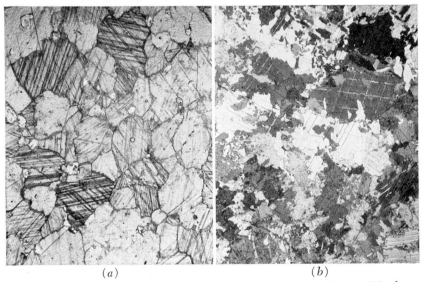

(a)   (b)

FIG. 52a, b. (a) Marble; calcite in granoblastic texture. Tate, Georgia. Nicols not crossed, ×10. (b) Marble; calcite in sutured texture. Felch, Michigan. Nicols crossed, ×10.

differences, (2) to variations in proportions of carbonates, quartz, and clay minerals, (3) to the nature of the clay minerals (illite contributes K), (4) to the presence or absence of Fe, Ti, PO$_4$, H$_2$O, F, etc., and (5) to the possible breakdown of dolomite to calcite and available Mg. Among the more widely distributed silicate accessories are forsterite, diopside (Fig. 52c), tremolite (less usually actinolite), phlogopite, chlorites, serpentine, talc, zoisite, clinozoisite (including thulite), epidote, plagioclase (either albite or calcic types), microcline (less commonly orthoclase), grossularite, wollastonite, sphene, and quartz. Other common accessories include apatite, graphite (Fig. 52c), magnetite, pyrite, pyrrhotite, pyrolusite, hematite. Among the less common accessories are hornblende, muscovite, biotite, zircon, tourmaline (usually dravite), axinite, vesuvianite, scapolite, andradite, chondrodite, ilmenite, chromite, rutile, and pleonaste. Common secondary minerals are serpentine (after forsterite), talc (after tremolite and other silicates), chalcedony, limonite, and leucoxene.

Under certain conditions relatively pure dolomites are decomposed and recrystallized to calcite and periclase, with escape of some CO_2. In the presence of H_2O, periclase is transformed to brucite. These periclase (or more usually periclase + brucite, or brucite alone) marbles are known as pencatites (Fig. 53h) (calcite is nearly equal to periclase ± brucite) or predazzites (calcite > periclase ± brucite). Rare are rhodochrosite marbles and marbles with abundant piedmontite locally associated with other manganiferous metamorphic rocks.

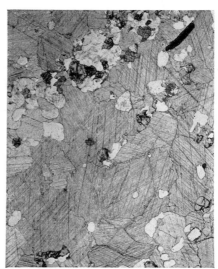

Fig. 52c. Marble; calcite, quartz (clear), diopside (high relief), graphite plate (black), *upper right*. Ruby Mountains, Montana. Nicols not crossed, ×10.

Textures and Microstructures.

Textures vary considerably. In some marbles carbonate grains are arranged in an equigranular granoblastic mosaic (Fig. 52a). More commonly the grains have irregular denticulate margins and tend to form an interlocking to complexly sutured aggregate (Fig. 52b). In some types the carbonate grains are elongate, with parallel axes. Heterogranular types contain coarse irregular anhedra of calcite scattered through a much finer grained calcite mosaic. Twinning lamellae are conspicuous, as is rhombohedral cleavage in some thin sections. Granulated zones and streaks, bent twinning planes, and biaxial character indicate cataclasis. Few textural criteria can be used unequivocably to distinguish calcite from dolomite. Some dolomite marbles tend to be less interlocking, but not invariably so. In calcite the twin lamellae parallel the sides of the cleavage rhomb or bisect only the acute angle of the cleavages. In dolomite they parallel the sides, bisect the obtuse angle usually, the acute angle rarely. A staining test, particularly with $Cu(NO_3)_2$, can usefully be employed on the sawed hand specimen or even the uncovered thin

(a)					(b)

FIG. 53a, b. (a) Ophicalcite; calcite, lobate grains of forsterite partly altered to serpentine, quartz (clear), graphite *upper right*. Moriah, New York. Nicols not crossed, ×10. (b) Pencatite; calcite, brucite rosettes after periclase. Ontario, Canada. Nicols crossed, ×21.

section (Kraus, Hunt, and Ramsdell, *Mineralogy*, 4th ed., pp. 226–227, McGraw Hill Book Company, Inc., New York, 1951).

Banded varieties also occur, either with alternating coarse- and fine-grained layers or with some layers richer in various accessory minerals. Among the more uncommon varieties containing both carbonates in abundance, there are those containing alternations of irregular calcite grains with angular dolomite grains. Others contain dolomite concentrated in lenses and stringers. Some dolomitic marbles are cut by calcite veinlets.

The grain size varies greatly: grains as small as 0.0075 mm have been measured, and anhedra of calcite reach a foot on edge exceptionally. Fine-grained types range in average grain size from 0.02 to 0.5 mm; medium-grained, 0.5 to 1 mm; and coarse-grained, 1 to 5 mm.

Types in which silicates and other accessories are relatively abundant may show more complex textural patterns. Porphyroblasts of chlorite, tremolite, forsterite (usually altered to serpentine), phlogopite, grossularite, clinozoisite, vesuvianite, scapolite, wollastonite, chondrodite, and dravite may be conspicuous. Some vesuvianite groups are set in shells of feldspar. The silicates or other accessories may be concentrated in thin bands, streaks, or granular to radial aggregates.

Many contain inclusions of other minerals. Periclase usually appears as corroded relicts showing cubic cleavage, set in a rounded, whorl-like aggregate of curved brucite plates. Where both serpentine pseudomorphs after forsterite and brucite pseudomorphs after periclase appear in the same rock, some difficulty may arise in separating them. Dravite and chondrodite also occur together and may be confused. The platy and prismatic silicates, as well as the crystal directions of the calcite, are oriented to varying degrees in regional marbles, but are usually irregularly arranged in contact types.

FIG. 53c. Clinozoisite-diopside-scapolite rock; clinozoisite in radiating clusters of twinned and zoned blades. Dillon, Montana. Nicols crossed, ×10.

Occurrence and Origin. Marbles are formed either by contact metamorphism or regional metamorphism of limestones or dolomites. Contact types may also have had some elements metasomatically added, particular H_2O (tremolite, brucite, serpentine), F (apatite, phlogopite, vesuvianite), B (tourmaline, axinite), and S (pyrite, pyrrhotite). Periclase marbles are not found in regional metamorphic assemblages. Examples are known from the Organ Mountains, New Mexico. The following series indicates generally increasing temperature of formation: (1) tremolite, (2) forsterite, (3) diopside, (4) periclase, and (5) wollastonite. Marbles containing these minerals belong in the pyroxene hornfels facies.

In the United States marbles are abundant in southwestern Montana (pre-Cambrian Cherry Creek series) and in northern New York (pre-Cambrian Grenville series). They have been quarried at West Rutland, Vermont (Ordovician), and at Tate, Georgia (Cambrian). A well-known ophicalcite (pre-Cambrian) occurs in Essex County, New York.

Calc-silicate Hornfelses

Definition. Calc-silicate hornfelses are rocks consisting entirely, or chiefly, of Ca-bearing silicates, with little or no calcite; distinguished

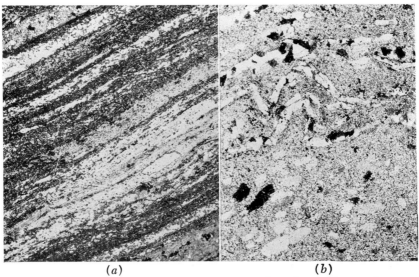

(a)   (b)

FIG. 54a, b. (a) Calc-flinta; dark bands rich in diopside, epidote, and axinite, light bands of quartz and wollastonite. St. Dennis, Cornwall, England. Nicols not crossed, ×10. (b) Calc-silicate hornfels; crenulated bands of diopside in quartz, garnet, vesuvianite, phlogopite. Friedrichsbrunn, Harz Mountains, Germany. Nicols crossed, ×10.

usually by a granoblastic texture, commonly fine-grained. They have also been called calc-flintas.

Mineralogy. The mineralogical composition is commonly variable over short distances, in some cases even within the scale of a thin section, reflecting slight differences in initial composition of the sedimentary layers (Fig. 54a). However, monomineralic and bimineralic rocks also occur. Pyroxenes are common: hypersthene, diopside, or hedenbergite. The garnets belong to the brown or colorless andradite-grossularite series. Calcic plagioclase (andesine to anorthite), vesuvianite (Fig. 54*b*), epidote-group minerals, wollastonite, and scapolite are other common and widespread constituents. Several members of the epidote group may appear together. Accessories are calcite, quartz, sphene, pyrite, graphite, magnetite, microcline, phlogopite, apatite, tremolite, and hornblende.

Textures and Microstructures. The texture is commonly granoblastic, fine to medium-grained. Small-scale mineralogical banding is widespread. Garnet-, pyroxene- or epidote-rich bands may alternate. In some varieties concentric arrangement of mineral species is locally conspicuous. Garnets may show zoning and twinning. Porphyroblastic texture is not common, but minerals such as vesuvianite, garnet, and sphene may be subhedral to euhedral.

Origin and Occurrence. Calc-silicate hornfelses are formed by contact metamorphism of argillaceous limestones and dolomites in which the noncalcareous part was of such an amount that it reacted with all of the carbonate, so that none of the calcite remains. Excellent examples are known from the Sierra Nevadas. Rocks of this group can be referred either to the amphibolite or pyroxene-hornfels facies, most of them to the latter. In the formation of some, metasomatism has been a contributing factor, with introduction of such elements as Fe, F, B, and S.

Calc Schists

Definition. Calc schists are foliated rocks containing calcite as an important to dominant constituent along with silicates and Al silicates of Mg, Ca, Ca-Mg, or of K and Na.

Mineralogy. Calc schists may be subdivided conveniently on the basis of their mineralogical assemblages, which reflect both their detailed original composition and the grade of metamorphism to which they have been subjected:

1. Lowest grade
   Calcite-sericite (cipolin or cipolino)
   Calcite-sericite-chlorite ± albite
   Calcite-antigorite
   Calcite-talc
   Quartz may be present; magnetite and sphene are common accessories; dolomite may proxy in part for calcite
2. Intermediate grade
   Calcite-epidote (or zoisite)-biotite
   Calcite-epidote-tremolite (or actinolite)
   Calcite-tremolite ± dolomite

Muscovite, biotite, albite, sphene, and quartz may be minor or accessory constituents; a lime garnet also may appear in small amounts

3. High grade

Calcite-hornblende (± biotite)

Calcite-diopside ± biotite

Calcite-diopside-grossularite

Calcite-diopside-vesuvianite

Calcite-diopside-epidote (clinozoisite or zoisite)-plagioclase

Calcite-diopside-scapolite

Quartz accompanies most of the above assemblages; sphene, apatite, magnetite, and microcline are widespread accessories; the plagioclase commonly is andesine, but in some types it may be very calcic, bytownite or even anorthite

Textures and Microstructures. The foliation is usually distinct, resulting principally from parallel elongated lenses of calcite (or calcite and dolomite) and parallel arrangement of micas, tremolite-actinolite (Fig. 54c), and hornblende. Individual carbonate grains may also be lensoid. Not uncommon banded textures consist of alternating fine- and coarse-grained carbonate layers, or layer concentrations of micas, epidote-group minerals, diopside, and amphiboles.

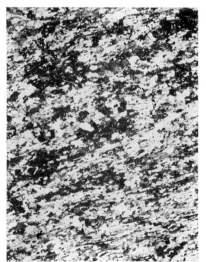

Fig. 54c. Calc schist; calcite, quartz, chlorite, actinolite. Shelby, North Carolina. Nicols crossed, ×10.

The carbonate minerals commonly show marked twinning, much of it apparently formed by twin gliding during plastic deformation. Twin lamellae may be bent. Granulation and various degrees of recrystallization may also be conspicuous, some dolomite appearing as rhombic euhedra. In higher-grade types calcite usually is coarse-grained and may show a small 2V. Orientation of crystallographic directions is the rule.

Micas and chlorite are thinly tabular; biotite flakes and rounded to ovoid grains of epidote-group minerals are widely associated in bands.

Epidote and quartz may be intergrown in a subgraphic to vermicular aggregate. Other constituents typically are anhedral to subhedral. Diopside grains may form a mosaic aggregate. Sphene may be euhedral, rarely in porphyroblasts. In general porphyroblastic texture is rare. Garnet and epidote-group minerals may show some zoning.

Occurrence and Origin. Most representatives are formed by regional metamorphism of impure limestones or dolomitic limestones or of calcareous and dolomitic shales. The limestones contained argillaceous or chloritic material, in some cases quartz or chert as well. Varieties with abundant talc or serpentine result from the low-grade regional metamorphism of ultramafic igneous rocks and grade into talc and serpentine schists. Some calc schists with abundant albite, chlorite, and epidote have been formed by similar metamorphism of basalts.

The micaceous calc schists are regarded as having been formed in the environment of the greenschist facies. Types with epidote-group minerals and tremolite-actinolite are generally referred to the albite-epidote amphibolite facies, and some diopside-bearing varieties may also belong there. Most diopsidic types formed within the range of the amphibolite facies, although some with scapolite and calcic plagioclase have been referred to the granulite facies.

Low-grade calc schists (cipolin) are common in some parts of Switzerland; other calc schists have been described from western Scotland.

Calc-silicate Gneisses, Tactites, and Related Rocks

Definition. Calc-silicate rocks are composed predominantly of one or more of the various Ca, Ca-Mg, Ca-Al, or Mg silicates, usually with some calcite. Included here are rocks called calc-silicate or lime-silicate gneiss and schist, skarn, and tactite. Tactites and skarns are formed under pyrometasomatic conditions; calc-silicate gneisses and schists are of regional metamorphic derivation. For fine-grained calc-silicate rocks the term calc-flintas has been employed.

Mineralogy. Some of these rocks, particularly those of contact origin, tend to be monomineralic, whereas others are mineralogically complex. Among the more common silicates that make up the bulk of some of these rocks are forsterite, serpentine, diopside, hedenbergite, tremolite, actinolite, phlogopite, grossularite, andradite, zoisite, epidote, clinozoisite (Fig. 53c), wollastonite, vesuvianite, plagioclase, sphene, and quartz. Calcite may form much of the rock or may be absent entirely. Plagioclase ranges from andesine to anorthite usually, but more sodic types may also appear. Less common are microcline (even less usually orthoclase), hornblende or edenite, biotite, prehnite, talc, rhodonite, ilvaite, chondrodite, scapolite, dravite, ludwigite, axinite, chlorite, talc, graphite, rhodochrosite, magnetite, hematite, and apatite. In tactites various ore minerals such as scheelite, sphalerite, galena, bornite, pyrite, pyrrhotite, molybdenite, chalcopyrite, and magnetite may also be abundant.

Among the more common monomineralic rocks are those consisting essentially of diopside, of hedenbergite, of tremolite or actinolite, of grossularite (garnetite), of zoisite or clinozoisite, and of wollastonite. Not uncommon are rocks that consist chiefly of such two- or three-mineral combinations as:

Grossularite-diopside
Grossularite-vesuvianite
Grossularite-clinozoisite (or epidote)
Grossularite-anorthite
Diopside-phlogopite
Diopside-tremolite
Serpentine (from forsterite)-calcite—ophicalcite
Grossularite-diopside-wollastonite
Grossularite-diopside-anorthite
Grossularite-diopside-spinel
Grossularite-zoisite (or clinozoisite)-tremolite
Diopside-vesuvianite-wollastonite
Diopside-phlogopite-anorthite
Diopside-phlogopite-tremolite

These combinations occur with or without calcite.

Such minerals as garnet and diopside may show systematic compositional variations which depend on their position in the contact aureole or on their relative age. Diopside-hedenbergite varies in its Mg-Fe^2 ratio, garnet in its grossularite-andradite contents; diopside increasing in Fe^2 with a decrease in metamorphic intensity; garnet increasing in Al (and decreasing in Fe^3) with decreasing metamorphic intensity but increasing in Fe^3 with a decrease in age. In some zoned garnets the outer zones show an increase in Fe^3 (andradite molecule), in others the zoning is nonsystematic, except that within a given crystal the darker zones usually contain more Fe^3.

Common are such varieties as diopside gneiss, diopside schist, tremolite schist, and clinozoisite schist. With increasing amounts of calcite such rocks grade into marbles. Erlan or Erlanfels is a foliated pyroxene-feldspar rock with accessory vesuvianite, sphene, zoisite, and fluorite.

Prehnite-rich rocks, containing in addition diopside, epidote, quartz, and chlorite, are formed by lime metasomatism associated with serpentized ultramafics.

Textures and Microstructures. Many of the monomineralic or bimineralic tactites tend to be coarse-grained and anhedral-granular. If bladed minerals are present, little orientation is evident, although rosettes and stellate groups of such minerals as tremolite, actinolite, clinozoisite (Fig. 53c), diopside, and vesuvianite also occur. Veins, stringers, and irregular segregations, both mono- and polymineralic, are common, and crude layering occurs in some tactites. If sulfides occur abundantly, they may show veining or replacement relations toward the earlier silicates. In mineralogically more complex types, which normally are finer-grained (calc-flintas), banding also occurs, and various minerals, such as vesuvianite, dravite, grossularite, clinozoisite, forsterite, and chondrodite may form porphyroblasts, some of which are poikiloblastic. Grossularite and andradite usually are weakly anisotropic in dodecahedral or trapezohedral euhedra showing zonal structure and sector twinning. To a considerable extent, whether minerals such as grossularite, diopside, forsterite, vesuvianite, and clinozoisite develop euhedral outlines depends upon their abundance. If they occur as isolated crystals in calcite, they may well appear as euhedra, whereas in layers in which they are abundant they form subhedra to anhedra. Minerals such as quartz, calcite, microcline, and plagioclase are normally anhedral. Zoning also may be conspicuous in zoisite, clinozoisite, thulite, dravite, some plagioclases, and vesuvianite. Graphite forms large isolated plates or veinlets of minutely felted aggregates. Thin sections rich in graphite usually display clouds of graphitic dust in balsam along the slide margins.

In ophicalcites (Fig. 53a), rounded and lobate calcite grains are set in a matrix of serpentine pseudomorphous after forsterite. Veinlets of cross-fiber chrysotile may also be common. Other examples contain conspicuous and numerous, thin concentric shells of alternating calcite and serpentine. In addition to the replacement serpentine-forsterite, others are vesuvianite-grossularite, tremolite-diopside, talc-tremolite, sericite-plagioclase, scapolite-plagioclase, and clinozoisite (or zoisite)-grossularite.

In regional metamorphic rocks, wollastonite normally is absent. Calc-silicate schists and gneisses commonly are fine- to medium-grained and banded. Platy and prismatic minerals display a moderate to high degree of orientation. Banding is typically on a small scale, and the mineralogy of adjacent bands may be markedly different:

Rock	*Bands*
Diopside gneiss.........	Diopside-quartz-phlogopite, calcite
Diopside gneiss.........	Diopside, quartz-diopside
Diopside gneiss.........	Diopside, scapolite with diopside blebs
Scapolite marble.......	Scapolite-zoisite, quartz-phlogopite, diopside-tremolite
Diopside-zoisite gneiss..	Diopside-pyrrhotite, zoisite-microcline-quartz
Garnet-zoisite gneiss....	Zoisite, tremolite-zoisite, garnet

A strong tendency toward mineralogical segregation in these rocks also leads to the development of nodules, usually monomineralic or bimineralic, of, for example, clinozoisite, clinozoisite plus garnet, phlogopite, diopside, scapolite, and scapolite plus diopside.

Occurrence and Origin. Calc-silicate rocks result from contact and regional metamorphism of limestones and dolomites containing large amounts of clay, sand, or chert. During metamorphism dolomite is decomposed to calcite, liberating Mg and CO_2. The formation of tactites and skarns is usually assisted by metasomatism, and many of these rocks are largely of pyrometasomatic origin. They are formed usually in contact aureoles around felsic intrusive rocks, particularly granodiorites and granites, and may be genetically associated with pyrometasomatic ore deposits of copper, zinc, tungsten, and iron. Many examples occur in Western states (Bishop, California; Deer Lodge, Montana; Humboldt Range, Nevada). The regional lime-silicate gneisses and schists can usually be placed in the pyroxene-hornfels facies. Examples are reported from the North Conway Quadrangle, White Mountains, New Hampshire, and from the Fitch formation (Silurian) in the Littleton-Moosilauke and Mt. Washington areas, New Hampshire. Other well-known calc-silicate contact metamorphic occurrences are at Crestmore, California; Magnet Cove, Arkansas; and Willsboro, New York (commercial wollastonite).

High-temperature Calc-silicate Rocks

At several localities (Scawt Hill, Larne, Ireland; Little Belt Mountains, Montana; Crestmore, California; Tres Hermanos Mountains and Iron Mountain, New Mexico; Velardeña, Durango, Mexico; and Nanjangud, Mysore, India) siliceous limestones or dolomites have been altered by high-temperature contact metamorphism, particularly around mafic intrusives, to aggregates of calcite and various rare Ca or Ca-Mg silicates. These include larnite, rankinite, scawtite, spurrite, tilleyite, merwinite, and cuspidine, as well as the more common melilite and monticellite. Magnetite, pleonaste, and perovskite are common accessories. Some of these rocks display evidence of retrograde metamorphism, with the development of rare secondary silicates such as afwillite, tobermorite, foshagite, hillebrandite, riversideite, and cebollite.

Most of the aggregates show a fine- to medium-grained granoblastic texture, with some of the constituents subhedral to euhedral. Porphyroblastic texture may also be developed. Under crossed nicols multiple lamellar twinning is conspicuous in many of these rare silicates.

Magnesite Rocks

Magnesite rocks are formed by the metasomatic alteration of limestones, calcitic marbles, dolomites, or dolomitic marbles and form lenses, layers, or irregular bodies. The associated rocks may be unmetamorphosed sediments or they may be metamorphic rocks of different grades—marbles, mica schists, graphite schists, and quartzites, as is typical of the deposits in the Austrian Alps (Veitsch, Styria). Other well-known magnesite deposits are in southern Manchuria, in British Columbia, near Chewelah, Washington, and near Gabbs, Nevada.

The rocks consist principally of magnesite, which in some occurrences is largely free of Fe^2 and in others contain isomorphous Fe^2 in appreciable amounts. Dolomite usually is present, in resorbed relicts in the cores of magnesite grains, as marginal replacements of magnesite grains, in veinlets, as corroded relict blocks, or in a zone marginal to the entire magnesite body. Thin plates of calcite or relict calcite aggregates may also occur. Other minerals are talc, in grains and pseudomorphs after magnesite; scales of graphite; plates of leuchtenbergite; and scattered quartz, serpentine, brucite, and pyrite. Associated in some places are talc masses with porphyroblasts of magnesite and chlorite schists with phlogopite porphyroblasts.

Rocks called sagvandites (Tromsö, Norway) consist of medium- to fine-grained granoblastic aggregates of iron-bearing magnesite (breunnerite) and enstatite (bronzite) with accessory phlogopite and chromite.

The texture is usually granoblastic, with little or no orientation of the magnesite anhedra. In some types the grain size varies markedly over short distances, with some grains attaining a diameter of an inch or more. Other types (pinolite) consist of lenses of light-colored magnesite grains in a netlike matrix of dark finer-grained magnesite. Along the margins of some magnesite masses cataclastic textures become prominent.

Rocks named listwänites, which are widespread in the Ural Mountains, consist of various carbonates—chiefly magnesite or ferroan magnesite but also dolomite, ankerite, and calcite, together with variable amounts of quartz, talc, and accessory chlorite, antigorite, magnetite, and chromite. Some of the talc appears to be pseudomorphous after enstatite. Some of these rocks are considered to represent metamorphosed limestones or dolomites, whereas others may be hydrothermally altered serpentinites.

QUARTZITES AND RELATED ROCKS

Definition. Quartzites are metamorphic rocks consisting predominantly of quartz, although some rocks labeled quartzites contain as much as 40 per cent other minerals.

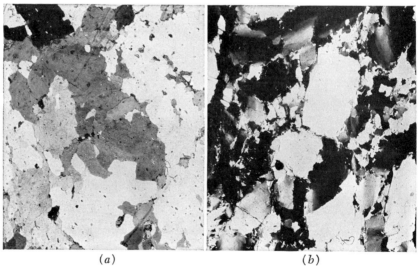

(a)   (b)

FIG. 55. (a) Quartzite. Southern Ruby Mountains, Montana. Nicols crossed, ×10. (b) Quartzite. Henry's Lake, northeastern Idaho. Nicols crossed, ×10.

Mineralogy. In most quartzites quartz is by far the most abundant constituent, constituting 60 to 95 per cent of the rock (Figs. 55a, b). Minor minerals are numerous and varied, and several major mineralogical varieties of quartzite have been distinguished on the basis of the most important accompanying minerals:

1. Micaceous quartzite: muscovite, biotite, or both. Some micaceous quartzites are bright green owing to the presence of a chromian muscovite. Itacolumite is a micaceous quartzite.

2. Feldspathic quartzite: microcline (or orthoclase), sodic plagioclase, or both.

3. Aluminous quartzite: andalusite, kyanite or sillimanite, corundum, and sericite; in some cases with diaspore, lazulite, spinel, alunite, pyrophyllite, rutile, jarosite, zircon, apatite, topaz, kaolinite, barite, leucoxene, limonite, and opal. Many varieties, such as andalusite quartzite, andalusite-sericite quartzite, corundum quartzite, alunite quartzite, and diaspore-sericite quartzite, have been distinguished.

4. Garnetiferous quartzite: almandite alone, or with various other minerals including cummingtonite or hornblende.

5. Chloritic quartzite: pennine, clinochlore, or ripidolite. Some chlorite is secondary after biotite.

6. Actinolitic quartzite: actinolite, clinozoisite, accessory epidote, ilmenite, zircon, and biotite.

Widespread but usually minor accessories, other than those listed above, include magnetite, ilmenite, rutile, sphene, zircon, tourmaline, cordierite, epidote, diopside, pyrite, apatite, and calcite. Secondary constituents and their parent species include sericite (feldspar, cordierite, and Al_2SiO_5 minerals), chlorite (biotite), leucoxene (ilmenite), and limonite (magnetite).

The schistose grits of Scotland are largely metagraywackes that have undergone varying degrees of metamorphism. Some are merely cataclastically deformed; in others quartz and potash feldspar have been recrystallized, some albite porphyroblasts may have been developed, and the clayey matrix has been transformed to a fine-grained sericite-chlorite-magnetite aggregate.

Itacolumite is a low-grade micaceous quartzite that is somewhat flexible in thin slabs. Muscovite is in well-oriented flakes that may be arranged in thin layers. Quartz grains are elongated somewhat and interlock moderately. Ilmenite and magnetite are accessories. Localities include the Sauratown Mountains, Stokes County, North Carolina; Jind State, Punjab, India; Itacolumi Mountain, Minas Geraes, Brazil; and the Ural Mountains, U.S.S.R.

Textures and Microstructures. Most quartzites have an equigranular, granoblastic texture, with the equant grains only slightly interlocking. In some types coarser, anhedral quartz grains or clusters are scattered through a finer-grained matrix. The quartz may contain various inclusions—fluid, dust, rutile needles, and feldspar blebs. In conglomeratic quartzites (psammitic or conglomerate gneiss) former quartz pebbles are rotated so that their long axes lie within the foliation planes, or the pebbles are deformed, elongated to augen, thin lenses, or even pencils. An excellent example of a stretched-pebble conglomeratic quartzite occurs in the Clough formation (Silurian) in the Littleton-Moosilauke area, New Hampshire. The grain size of quartzites varies from fine to coarse; fine-grained types appear sacharroidal megascopically, whereas coarser types appear glassy.

Petrofabric studies reveal that the optic axes of the quartz grains usually are well oriented in one of several patterns. Rarely, however, are the individual grains markedly elongate, yet in some quartzose schists a distinct elongation and parallelism are evident, which, coupled with thin parallel films of sericite, imparts a marked schistosity to the rock.

Porphyroblasts, in many cases poikilitic, are formed by such minerals as garnet, andalusite, cordierite, microcline, and albite. Some garnet is skeletal. In micaceous quartzites the micas may be unoriented, they may be disseminated but parallelly oriented, or they may be concentrated in thin bands and oriented parallel. Other minerals that in some varieties assume parallel orientation include chlorite, feldspars, and amphiboles. Chlorite forms individual flakes usually, but also appears in platy, radial aggregates.

In some quartzites cataclastic structures including Böhm striations, conspicuous undulatory extinction, biaxial character, and marginal granulation are widespread features. Others contain crosscutting veinlets of secondary quartz or of chlorite and quartz.

Secondary quartzites show relict granitic and porphyritic textures.

Occurrence and Origin. Quartzites are formed by contact or regional metamorphism of sandstones, feldspathic sandstones, micaceous sandstones, argillaceous sandstones, calcareous sandstones, and some cherts. Small quartzite lenses may also be formed by regional metamorphism of quartz veins. In some feldspathic quartzites, the feldspar is believed to have been introduced metasomatically. Secondary quartzites are allegedly formed by large-scale metasomatic replacement of mainly felsic to intermediate rocks, particularly volcanic and hypabyssal types. Jasperoid is a metasomatic quartzite formed by the replacement of limestones by hydrothermal solutions genetically associated with various types of ore deposits (example: Aspen, Colorado). Examples of important, well-known quartzites are the Ortega (pre-Cambrian) quartzite of northern New Mexico, the Sioux (pre-Cambrian) quartzite of northwestern Iowa and adjacent South Dakota, the Antietam (Lower Cambrian) quartzite of Maryland, and the Baraboo (pre-Cambrian) quartzite of Wisconsin. Fuchsite quartzites (pale to deep emerald green) are known in the Medicine Bow Mountains of Wyoming (Medicine Peak quartzite, pre-Cambrian). Many and various secondary quartzites have been described from the U.S.S.R.

ARGILLITES, SLATES, AND PHYLLITES

Argillites

Although some petrographers prefer to regard them as sedimentary rocks, most argillites show some recrystallization and may well be considered as very low grade metamorphic rocks. Argillites are massive fine-grained rocks, usually thinly, even seasonally banded (varved), containing quartz, feldspar, chlorite, and some clay minerals, probably chiefly illitic. Most of the particles are of silt size with scattered coarser pieces of quartz or even small rock fragments. Good examples occur in the late pre-Cambrian Belt rocks of northwestern Montana and in the Upper Huronian of Ontario, Canada.

Slates

Definition. Slates are fine-grained to aphanitic metamorphic rocks with a highly developed foliation, called slaty cleavage, by means of which the rock is enabled to split along closely spaced, parallel, and relatively smooth planar surfaces. Except for a few rare metacrysts or porphyroblasts the minerals of slates are not identifiable megascopically, and even under the microscope with highest magnification, an unresolvable fraction usually remains. X-rays may be needed to identify these matrix materials positively.

Mineralogy. The main constituents of the coarser, optically identifiable fraction are quartz, chlorite, sericite, biotite, magnetite, hematite, rutile, pyrite, calcite, dolomite, and organic material. Less common are epidote, albite, apatite, zircon, tourmaline, rhodochrosite, barite, gypsum, and ilmenite. The cryptocrystalline matrix or paste has been demonstrated, by means of x-rays, to consist chiefly of illite and chloritic-type clay minerals, although kaolinite also occurs in some slates.

Textures and Microstructures. The texture is fine-grained to cryptocrystalline, with a high degree of parallel orientation of both the coarser and finer minerals, not uncommonly in minute lenses and stringers. Banding of sedimentary inheritance may be at various angles to the foliation. In addition to the primary foliation or slaty cleavage, which is the result of mineral orientation, a secondary or false cleavage may be present across the major structure. This secondary structure results from the parallelism of the axial planes of numerous minute folds or plications. In some places the corrugations pass into tiny shear fractures. Small lenses of semiradial calcite, chlorite, quartz (Fig. 56*a*), or muscovite appear in some varieties. Porphyroblasts are not common, consisting of magnetite, pyrite, or chlorite in euhedral flakes transverse to the foliation. Pressure-shadow growths of quartz or of quartz and chlorite may be developed on two sides of the magnetite or pyrite crystals, elongated with the foliation direction. Chlorite also forms rhombs pseudomorphous after carbonate. Quartz appears both in rounded grains and as irregular patches of cement. Rutile is an abundant matrix mineral, forming minute needles (clay slate needles) of random arrangement within foliation planes. Many purple or reddish slates have green spots of circular, ellipsoidal, or irregular outline, which range from a fraction of an inch to several inches in diameter. The difference in color is due to the absence of hematite in the green areas, which usually contain more calcite.

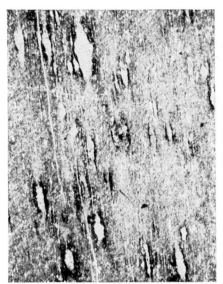

FIG. 56*a*. Slate; coarser quartz lenses in quartz-sericite-chlorite-magnetite matrix. Granville, New York. Nicols not crossed, ×22.

Occurrence and Origin. Slates are formed by low-grade regional metamorphism of clays and shales, very rarely of tuffaceous rocks. The fine-grained texture is largely inherited; recrystallization is minor. Slates are included in the chlorite zone of regional metamorphism, formed under the environment of the muscovite-chlorite subfacies of the greenschist facies. In the United States slates occur in Pennsylvania (Martinsburg formation, Ordovician age), in New York (Mettawee formation, Cambrian age), in various other parts of the Appalachian belt, and also in the Upper Peninsula of Michigan (pre-Cambrian).

Phyllites

Definition. Phyllites are fine-grained, micaceous rocks with a highly developed foliation, intermediate in perfection between slaty cleavage and schistosity. Usually a satiny luster is characteristic. Also in grain size and mineralogy, phyllites lie between slates and mica schists, and no sharp boundaries separate them. Indeed, sericite schists or microcrystalline schists are phyllites.

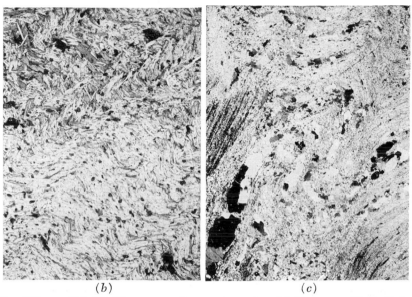

(b)　　　　　　　　　(c)

Fig. 56b, c. (b) Phyllite; muscovite, quartz, minor biotite, magnetite; plicated foliation. Albemarle County, Virginia. Nicols not crossed, ×22. (c) Phyllite; muscovite, crumpled quartz bands, magnetite. Eastern Beartooth Mountains, Montana. Nicols crossed, ×10.

Mineralogy. Phyllites contain chiefly fine-grained muscovite (sericite) (Fig. 56b), chlorite, quartz, and the accessories magnetite, hematite, ilmenite, rutile, tourmaline, zircon, graphite, and pyrite. Some types are calcareous, with calcite and epidote relatively abundant. Less common are albite, chloritoid, and biotite. Limonite is a common secondary constituent. Phyllites fall into three convenient mineralogical types: sericite phyllites, chlorite phyllites, and sericite-chlorite phyllites. Exceptionally rocks that are phyllites megascopically contain relatively abundant fine-grained biotite in bands or even scattered garnet porphyroblasts. The mica of phyllites is a true muscovite; illite does not normally persist.

Textures and Microstructures. The texture is fine-grained, but with all constituents microscopically identifiable. A very high degree of orientation is characteristic, with elongation of quartz as grains or narrow aggregated lenses and stringers, and sericite and chlorite in parallel flakes and pods. Iron oxide minerals and graphite appear in rounded, relatively coarse clusters, as lenticular dusty clouds or as fine general disseminations. Some chlorite forms oriented ovoid clusters with individual flakes in a semiradial arrangement. Quartz also appears in irregular cementing patches that include chlorite shreds. Epidote forms grains and irregular granular masses. Calcite forms both large anhedra and cementing, finer-grained aggregates. Relatively rare feldspar contains chlorite, epidote, and quartz inclusions. In layered types, thin quartzose bands alternate with sericitic or chloritic bands. Some phyllites contain porphyroblasts of pyrite, magnetite, and exceptionally, garnet. Pressure shadows of chlorite and quartz may flank the magnetite and pyrite porphyroblasts. As in slates, secondary cross foliation (false cleavage) is also common. Irregular crenulations (Fig. 56c) and puckerings may be marked by segregations of coarse quartz or chlorite, and veinlets of these minerals may also transect the rocks.

Occurrence and Origin. Phyllites are formed by low-grade regional metamorphism of shales and clays. Phyllites are included in the chlorite zone of regional metamorphism and are formed under the metamorphic environment of the muscovite-chlorite subfacies of the greenschist facies. Phyllites are of slightly higher metamorphic grade than slates, slightly lower than micaceous schists. In the United States representative phyllites occur in the Allamoore (pre-Cambrian) formation of the Sierra Diablo foothills of northwest Texas, in the type section of the pre-Cambrian Cherry Creek series, south of Ennis, Montana, and in Dutchess County in southeastern New York.

MICACEOUS SCHISTS

Chlorite Schists and Related Rocks

Definition. Chlorite schists are rocks with a marked schistose texture containing a chlorite as the principal micaceous mineral, usually with one or more other micaceous minerals and quartz ± albite as the other main components. Some of the rocks called greenschists (or greenstones) are chlorite schists (Fig. 57a).

Mineralogy. Various mineralogical combinations occur:

Chlorite, quartz ± albite
Chlorite, albite
Chlorite, muscovite ± garnet
Chlorite, biotite, quartz ± albite, epidote
Chlorite, garnet

The more common chlorite species are clinochlore, pennine, or prochlorite. If garnet is present, it is spessartitic in composition. Quartz usually is abundant but in some varieties becomes subordinate to albite

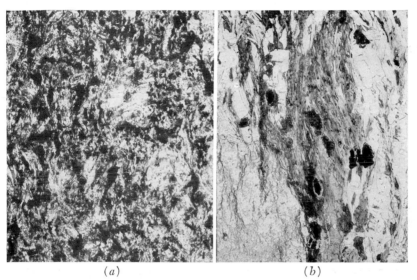

(a)   (b)

Fig. 57a, b. (a) Chlorite schist (greenschist); chlorite, epidote, albite, muscovite, quartz, sphene. Bluemont, Virginia. Nicols crossed, ×22. (b) Chlorite-muscovite schist; chlorite, muscovite, quartz, magnetite. Eight Mile Park, Fremont County, Colorado. Nicols not crossed, ×10.

and may even be reduced to accessory status or be absent entirely. Muscovite (Fig. 57b) or biotite may be present in varying amounts. Magnetite, epidote, or chloritoid may also be abundant. Accessories include rutile, tourmaline, hematite, ilmenite, apatite, pyrite, and sphene; less common are talc, serpentine, corundum, kyanite, graphite, hornblende, tremolite, actinolite, or carbonate (calcite, dolomite, or magnesite). Propylite is a metasomatic chlorite rock consisting of mixtures of chlorite, pyrite, epidote, quartz, alkali feldspar, some zeolites, sericite, and carbonate. It is formed by the low-temperature hydrothermal alteration of andesites and basalts (rarely rhyolites). Adinole is an albite-quartz-chlorite rock with accessory epidote, actinolite, sphene, pyrite, magnetite, and calcite, formed by the low-grade contact metasomatism of shales, argillites, and slates by diabases. Spilosite is similar without quartz; desmosite is a banded spilosite.

Textures and Microstructures. The texture is usually fine- to medium-grained, well foliated, with a high degree of orientation of the micaceous constituents. In some of the finer-grained types, which approach phyllites, the chlorite shows a tendency to collect in aggregates and patches. Chlorite also may be porphyroblastic in a mica-quartz matrix. Albite forms minute anhedra to rounded porphyroblasts, with twinning absent or inconspicuous. It includes chlorite and magnetite. Garnet usually appears as porphyroblasts, as may pyrite, tremolite, magnetite, and chloritoid. Decussate textures appear in some chlorite schists, particularly coarse-grained types.

Occurrence and Origin. Chlorite schists are formed by the low-grade regional metamorphism of pelitic sediments, some ultramafic igneous rocks, basalts, and diabases, under the environment of the biotite-chlorite subfacies of the greenschist facies. Some chlorite schists are developed through retrograde metamorphism of biotite schists or amphibolites. A well-known chlorite schist occurs at Chester, Vermont. Others are in northern Michigan, in the pre-Cambrian rocks of Wyoming, Colorado, Montana, Utah, and New Mexico, and in the low-grade zone of the Ammonoosuc Volcanics (Ordovician) of the Littleton-Moosilauke area, New Hampshire.

Chloritoid Schists

Definition. Chloritoid schists are schistose rocks containing chloritoid (or ottrelite, a manganiferous variety) as the principal micaceous constituent, usually combined with a chlorite or muscovite.

Mineralogy. Two common types are chloritoid-muscovite schist and chloritoid-chlorite schist. Ottrelite schists are also included here. Chloritoid commonly contains numerous inclusions or is zoned, either concentrically or in hourglass structure. Twinning is common, and in the same rock specimen 2V may be highly variable, or both monoclinic and triclinic chloritoid may occur together. Chloritoid rocks may be very rich in fine-grained muscovite (Fig. 57c), with or without chlorite; a few types contain chloritoid as the only essential micaceous mineral. Quartz varies from a minor to a major constituent. Accessories are rutile, sphene, ilmenite, magnetite, tourmaline, zircon, hematite, epidote, albite, pyrophyllite, garnet, and staurolite. Under higher grades of metamorphism chloritoid may be converted to staurolite.

Textures and Microstructures. The matrix is markedly schistose and not uncommonly fine-grained. Chloritoid and ottrelite typically form euhedral to ragged porphyroblasts, either generally parallel with the foliation or unoriented with respect to the structure. In some types, however, porphyroblasts are absent, and chloritoid is finely intergrown with sericite. Pressure shadows may appear, consisting mainly of coarse quartz or of quartz with some muscovite. Some crystals are markedly poikiloblastic. Some porphyro-

blasts show evidence of rotation during growth with sinuous lines of inclusions or planes of inclusions not parallel with the foliation. Aggregates of radiating chlorite plates or of sheaflike groups are also common, and in such, the flakes usually have irregular to ragged terminations. Alteration rims if quartz-kaolinite surround chloritoid in some examples.

Occurrence and Origin. Formed by low- to medium-grade regional metamorphism of pelitic sediments rich in Al and Fe but relatively low in K, Ca, and Mg. These rocks are placed by some theorists in the chloritoid-almandite subfacies of the

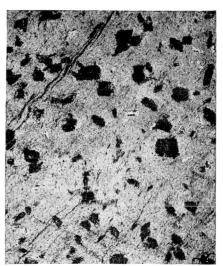

Fig. 57c. Chloritoid schist; porphyroblasts of chloritoid in quartz-sericite matrix. Red Rock Quadrangle, New Mexico. Nicols not crossed, ×10.

albite-epidote-amphibolite facies, but chloritoid may also be developed in rocks of suitable composition under the environment of the biotite-chlorite subfacies of the greenschist facies. Apparently chloritoid is stable through a rather wide temperature range. In some localities, notably Belgium, the formation of chloritoid can be correlated with proximity to repeated overthrusts, along which a local higher-intensity environment prevailed. In the United States chloritoid schists are exemplified by occurrences in Lancaster County, Pennsylvania; in Dutchess County, New York; and in the Deep River region of North Carolina. Well-known examples also occur in the St. Gotthard district of Switzerland.

Stilpnomelane Schists

Definition. Stilpnomelane schists are schistose rocks containing stilpnomelane as an essential constituent, usually in association with various combinations of quartz, albite, chlorite, actinolite, and epidote.

Mineralogy. The stilpnomelane is usually the brown ferric type, but some schists also contain the green ferroan type, which may be rimmed by the brown. Rarely the brown and green types occur interleaved. The various mineral assemblages with which stilpnomelane occurs are:

Quartz-albite
Quartz-muscovite
Quartz-chlorite
Quartz-garnet
Quartz-muscovite-chlorite-garnet
Quartz-albite-epidote-chlorite $\pm$ garnet
Quartz-albite-epidote-actinolite
Albite-epidote-chlorite
Albite-epidote-actinolite $\pm$ chlorite
Albite-actinolite
Albite-chlorite-muscovite
Chlorite-epidote $\pm$ magnetite
Garnet-calcite $\pm$ chlorite
Garnet-pyrite-sphene
Magnetite-garnet-actinolite-apatite

The most common associated minerals are quartz, albite, epidote, actinolite, and chlorite, which occur in essential to accessory amounts or may be entirely absent. Muscovite and spessartitic garnet may be essential, whereas calcite, magnetite, sphene, and apatite only rarely exceed accessory status. Other accessories are biotite, rutile, and tourmaline.

Textures and Microstructures. Stilpnomelane occurs in fine to coarse plates in subparallel to crisscross groups and bands, or in semiradial sheaflike groups of curving plates. It appears to be most coarsely developed in schists containing albite, epidote, chlorite, and actinolite. It also forms transgressive veinlets, and in many rocks replaces chlorite. Common are interlayerings with pale green prochlorite; chlorite-muscovite interleavings also occur. Sphene and epidote are inclusions; and some stilpnomelane plates are markedly poïkiloblastic. Quartz and albite form anhedral granules, although the feldspar also appears as porphyroblasts with cores crowded with inclusions of garnet, epidote, and magnetite; it is rarely twinned. Quartz, which may display pronounced undulatory extinction, also appears as blebs in feldspar. Euhedral minerals include actinolite and garnet. Actinolite also forms porphyroblasts that may be intergrown with stilpnomelane plates. Sphene, calcite, pyrite, and epidote are usually anhedral, but sphene and epidote may also be euhedral. Many stilpnomelane schists show mineralogical banding.

Occurrence and Origin. Stilpnomelane is formed by low-grade regional metamorphism (greenschist facies) of various quartz-feldspar sediments containing a high ratio of Fe to Mg. Well-studied occurrences are found in Lake Wakatipu region, Western Otago, New Zealand. Because it is easily confused with biotite, stilpnomelane is doubtless more widespread than has been reported.

Muscovite Schists

Definition. Muscovite schists are schistose rocks containing muscovite as the principal micaceous mineral, in many cases accompanied by other micaceous minerals. Quartz normally is very abundant, without, or less commonly with, much feldspar.

Mineralogy. Muscovite schists are conveniently grouped on the basis of the main accompanying minerals.

Muscovite ± garnet
Muscovite-chlorite
Muscovite-chloritoid ± garnet
Muscovite-biotite-chloritoid
Muscovite-biotite ± garnet
Muscovite-tourmaline (Fig. 58*b*) ± biotite ± garnet

In this group also may be included the rare paragonite schists, but paragonite cannot be distinguished from muscovite in thin section. Also included are mica schists that contain a green chromian muscovite (fuchsite).

The proportions of the various constituents vary considerably. The micaceous minerals may exceed quartz, but not uncommonly the reverse is true. Quartz normally dominates over feldspar, but in some types orthoclase (or microcline) and/or oligoclase-andesine occur abundantly. However, muscovite-rich schists in general are poor in potash feldspar, and feldspar may be absent or merely accessory (Fig. 58*a*). Other minerals that may be present in essential amounts are almanditic garnet and epidote.

The accessories are numerous; common are magnetite, ilmenite, hematite, zircon, apatite, sphene, and rutile; less common are kyanite, sillimanite, andalusite, staurolite, graphite, zoisite, cordierite, pyrite, pyrrhotite, and spinel. Alteration minerals are sericite, kaolinite, limonite, leucoxene, and chlorite ± magnetite and sphene. Chlorite replaces biotite and garnet. Accessories reported from fuchsite schists are oligoclase, chlorite, tremolite, clinozoisite, sphene, tourmaline, chromite, magnetite, pyrite, and pyrrhotite.

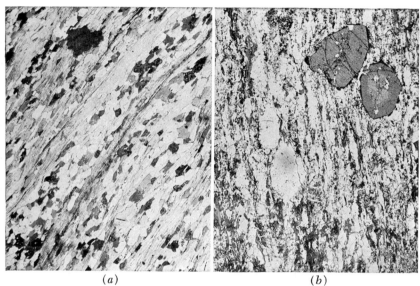

(a)   (b)

FIG. 58. (a) Muscovite schist; muscovite bands, quartz bands. Drill core, Porcupine Dome, Rosebud County, Montana. Nicols crossed, ×10. (b) Muscovite-tourmaline schist; muscovite, biotite, quartz, zoned tourmaline metacrysts, magnetite, minor feldspar. Black Hills, South Dakota. Nicols not crossed, ×10.

Textures and Microstructures. The micaceous minerals usually show a definite parallelism, occurring as elongate, flaky aggregates, plaited layers or single plates, and shreds, commonly with irregular margins. Parallel to irregular intergrowths occur between muscovite-chlorite, chlorite-biotite, and biotite-chlorite. The flakes may be curved, folded, crumpled, or intensely wrinkled. Some types also contain large unoriented porphyroblasts of muscovite, which may be poikiloblastic toward quartz. Other porphyroblastic minerals include garnet, tourmaline (Fig. 58b), chloritoid, and accessory kyanite, andalusite, and staurolite. Tourmaline may also form conspicuous radial clusters, and large metacrysts of potash feldspar appear in some varieties. The quartz is anhedral, not uncommonly in slightly elongate grains or in monomineralic lenses, stringers, and layers. Undulatory extinction may be marked. Garnets also may be skeletal as well as porphyroblastic, and inclusions of quartz and the micaceous minerals are common. Biotite commonly includes zircon, surrounded by pleochroic halos. Rutile forms anhedral grains or euhedral twinned crystals.

Some varieties are layered with bands of varying grain size or mica content (Fig. 58a).

Occurrence and Origin. Muscovite schists are common and widespread rocks of many metamorphic regions, including New England, the central and southern Appalachian belt, and the pre-Cambrian areas of the Western states. They are formed by the low- to medium-grade regional metamorphism of pelitic sediments. Muscovite, muscovite-chlorite, and muscovite-biotite types are somewhat lower grade (biotite-chlorite subfacies of greenschist facies) than types containing almandite and chloritoid (albite-epidote amphibolite facies). Some fuchsite schists have been ascribed to chromian metasomatism. Fuchsite schist occurs near Rutland, Vermont.

Biotite Schists

Definition. Biotite schists are schistose rocks containing biotite as one of the major essential minerals and as the principal micaceous mineral.

Mineralogy. Biotite schists show considerable variation in mineralogy, the principal types being distinguished chiefly on the presence of other micaceous minerals, amphiboles, or various Al silicates. In addition there is considerable variation in the quartz-feldspar ratio, from types quartz-rich and mainly feldspar-free through some that contain both in abundance to others nearly quartz-free. Some of the main types are:

Biotite (quartz)	Biotite-andalusite
Biotite-muscovite	Biotite-hornblende
Biotite-chlorite ± chloritoid	Biotite-epidote
Biotite-garnet	Biotite-plagioclase

The biotite is usually light or red brown in color, but green brown, deeper olive brown, dark brown, and dark red brown shades also appear. The common feldspar is plagioclase, albite to andesine, although in some rocks more calcic varieties may occur. Garnet varies from a spessartite-almandite to an almandite-rich type (Fig. 59*a*). Other minerals present in small to moderate amounts are tourmaline, microcline, sillimanite, staurolite, diopside, and rarely corundum (Fig. 59*b*). Accessories are also numerous and varied: pyrite, hematite, magnetite, ilmenite, graphite, apatite, zircon, sphene, rutile, calcite, cordierite, kyanite, actinolite, and anthophyllite. Secondary minerals are chlorite chiefly from biotite, staurolite, garnet, and hornblende; sericite after feldspars, staurolite, andalusite, kyanite, and

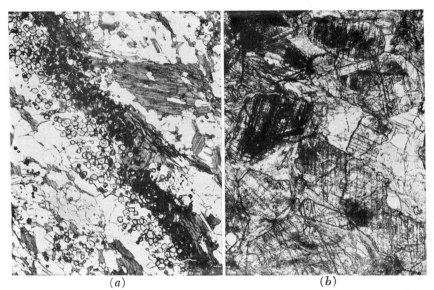

(*a*)   (*b*)

FIG. 59. (*a*) Biotite-garnet schist; biotite, garnet, quartz, magnetite, minor feldspar. Latah County, Idaho. Nicols not crossed, ×10. (*b*) Corundum-biotite schist; zoned porphyroblasts of corundum in biotite. Dillon, Montana. Nicols not crossed, ×10.

sillimanite; leucoxene after rutile and ilmenite; and limonite after various iron-bearing minerals.

Gradations from biotite schists into calc schists, chlorite schists, amphibolitic schists, or sillimanite schists are not uncommon.

Textures and Microstructures. The rocks commonly display a marked schistosity, brought about mainly by the parallel alignment of abundant biotite, muscovite, and primary chlorite but also in some cases of such constituents as tourmaline, hornblende, and ilmenite, and even of lenticular quartz grains. Or the quartz or quartz and plagioclase may form a granular mosaic. Porphyroblasts are common: biotite, chloritoid, chlorite, garnet, tourmaline, andalusite, staurolite, and albite. In many cases porphyroblasts are poikilitic, especially in interior parts. Biotite porphyroblasts may include such species as quartz, plagioclase, zircon, hematite, and ilmenite. Andalusite contains quartz, sillimanite, tourmaline, and other species. Garnet and staurolite also may show marked poikiloblastic structure. In some garnets the inclusions are spirally arranged indicating rotational growth (snowball garnets). In others quartz inclusions form thin plates with parallel arrangement different in different garnet sectors. Staurolite crystals may be large, euhedral, and twinned in the characteristic crosses. In some varieties biotite porphyroblasts have been fractured and healed by new finer-grained biotite flakes across the foliation. Various parallel intergrowths appear—biotite-ilmenite, andalusite-sillimanite, and muscovite-chlorite.

Mineralogical banding is conspicuous in many types, and lineation may also be present, although it is difficult to note in thin section.

Occurrence and Origin. The presence of much (primary) chlorite indicates regional metamorphism of low grade; with increasing intensity biotite becomes more abundant. The development of abundant garnet (particularly almandite) indicates a further increase in grade, and kyanite and sillimanite appear commonly only in the highest-grade types. The last is referred to the top of the amphibolite facies, approaching the granulite facies; whereas the other varieties were formed in the environment of the kyanite-staurolite subfacies of the amphibolite facies. Chloritic types approach the greenschist facies.

The presence of large subhedral andalusite porphyroblasts has been ascribed to contact metamorphism that preceded or followed regional metamorphism. In many cases, however, field evidence for polymetamorphism is absent. Andalusite (and cordierite) may also apparently develop in an environment of deficient stress or even with continued moderate temperatures after cessation of stress. The rocks were formed from pelitic sediments—clays, shales, and argillites of varying composition, with some containing calcite or dolomite (epidote, hornblende, diopside, sphene, calcite). Usually the ratio of Al to K is too high for potash feldspar to form, and some such feldspar metacrysts may be introduced, together with some quartz. In some varieties tourmaline metacrysts have been formed metasomatically.

Some of these schists have also been formed from rocks such as quartz latite tuffs, contaminated by argillaceous material or latitic and dacitic tuffs that contained arenaceous fractions. In some districts dark biotite-plagioclase schists, usually with some hornblende, epidote, and quartz represent metamorphosed kersantites and minettes. Examples are widespread, occurring in pre-Cambrian formations of Idaho, Montana, Colorado (Idaho Springs formation), Texas, New Mexico, and the Black Hills and also in the Appalachian belt, pre-Cambrian and younger (Albee formation, Ordovician? and Fitch formation, Silurian, New Hampshire). Good examples of andalusite-bearing types are in the Littleton (Devonian) formation of the Sunapee Quadrangle, New Hampshire; near Berrenda, Madera County, California; and in the Rinconada member of the Ortega formation (pre-Cambrian) of north-central New Mexico.

Graphite Schists

Definition. Graphite schists are schistose rocks containing graphite as an important constituent, usually in the order of 5 to 10 per cent.

Mineralogy. Although graphite usually is less than 10 per cent of

Fig. 60a. Graphite schist; graphite, quartz, kaolinized feldspar. Tendoy Mountains, Montana. Nicols not crossed, ×10.

the rock, its blackness and physical properties make it the most conspicuous mineral both microscopically and megascopically (Fig. 60a). Many rocks included as graphite schists actually contain only 2 to 5 per cent of graphite. The other constituents are variable, although most graphitic schists are dominantly micaceous. Other essential minerals include muscovite, biotite, quartz, orthoclase, garnet, and sillimanite in various combinations. Accessories are plagioclase, apatite, zoisite, epidote, magnetite, ilmenite, hematite, pyrite, rutile, zircon, and tourmaline, and alteration minerals are leucoxene, calcite, chlorite, sericite, limonite, and kaolinite.

Textures and Microstructures. The texture is usually schistose, but gradations to gneissic types also occur. Graphite forms small spangles and shreds, segregations and lenticles, layers and veinlike masses. Graphite plates may be curved or crumpled, with edges appearing scallopy under high magnification and irregularly oriented grinding striations appearing in reflected light. Thin sections containing much graphite may display graphitic dust in balsam along their margins. In some types graphitic layers may be markedly contorted. Garnet usually appears as porphyroblasts, commonly with inclusions of quartz, feldspar, and graphite. Graphite inclusions in garnet may take the form of thin plates or dusty aggregates, which may be zonally concentrated. Graphite may also be included in feldspar or form rims around feldspar.

Occurrence and Origin. Graphite is formed by the medium- to high-grade regional metamorphism (usually sillimanite-almandite sub-facies of the amphibolite facies) of carbonaceous pelitic sediments such as black shales. Graphite is associated with garnetiferous mica schists and sillimanite schists. Also graphite is a widespread accessory in kyanite and sillimanite schists and marbles. Well-known United States examples include those of Chilton, Coosa and Clay Counties, Alabama, and of McDowell County, North Carolina (Brevard formation, pre-Cambrian). Various other highly carbonaceous metamorphic rocks generally not suitable for thin-section studies include anthracite, graphitoid (impure massive graphite), and rock graphite (massive impure graphite formed by high-temperature contact metamorphism of coal).

Talc Schists and Soapstones

Talc Schists

Definition. Talc schists are foliated rocks containing talc as the principal mineral.

Mineralogy. Some types consist primarily of talc, with only accessory amounts of other minerals, such as magnetite. Others consist of such combinations as:

Talc-antigorite (Fig. 60*b*)	Talc-tremolite (Fig. 60*c*)
Talc-carbonate	Talc-anthophyllite
Talc-chlorite	Talc-cummingtonite

Textures and Microstructures. The rocks usually are markedly schistose, with parallelism of talc flakes and other flaky or prismatic constituents. Talc also forms lenticles in which individual flakes may lie across the foliation direction. Carbonates (dolomite or magnesite) appear in anhedra; magnetite in fine dust or small euhedra. Corroded remnants of pyroxene appear rarely.

Occurrence and Origin. Talc is associated with serpentine (antigorite) schists and may grade into tremolite, anthophyllite, or cummingtonite schists. Talc is formed by low-grade regional meta-

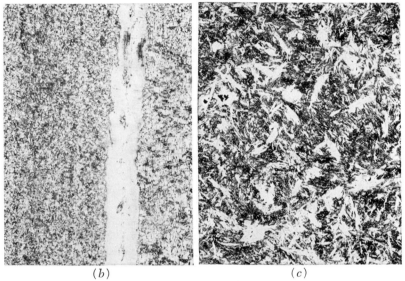

| (*b*) | (*c*) |

Fig. 60*b*, *c*. (*b*) Talc-serpentine schist; talc with band of cross-fiber antigorite. Red Rock Quadrangle, New Mexico. Nicols crossed, ×10. (c) Talc-tremolite rock; talc replacing tremolite. Turrett, Colorado. Nicols not crossed, ×10.

morphism (greenschist facies) of peridotites or serpentinites. The presence of amphiboles indicates somewhat higher metamorphic intensity. Important pre-Cambrian talc schists occur in the northwestern Adirondack Mountains.

SOAPSTONES

Soapstones are talc-rich rocks; there are two main mineralogical types: (1) talc, carbonate, chlorite, and accessories, with carbonate being usually dolomite + magnesite, less usually magnesite or dolomite alone, rarely calcite; (2) talc, tremolite, chlorite, and the accessories magnetite, chromite, pyrrhotite, and pentlandite. Massive talc rocks, which may be cryptocrystalline, bladed (after tremolite) or flaky, also contain such minerals as quartz, chalcedony, graphite, and pyrite. Most soapstones and massive talcose rocks have been formed by low-grade metasomatism of carbonate or ultramafic rocks. Significant soapstone deposits occur in Vermont, Virginia, North Carolina, Georgia, Montana, and California.

Pyrophyllite Schists

Definition. Pyrophyllite schists are markedly schistose to imperfectly foliated rocks consisting principally of pyrophyllite and quartz.

Mineralogy. The two most abundant minerals are pyrophyllite and quartz, the proportions varying considerably. A distinction can be made between pyrophyllite schists (less quartz) and pyrophyllite-quartz schists (more quartz). Other minerals that may be present in essential amounts are chlorite, chloritoid, sericite, kaolinite, pyrite, and feldspar. Accessories include hematite, magnetite, ilmenite, leucoxene, epidote, zoisite, calcite, alunite, diaspore, sphene, rutile, and zircon. Relict minerals are potash feldspar, plagioclase, quartz, zircon, and apatite.

Textures and Microstructures. The texture may be strongly schistose with marked parallelism of pyrophyllite flakes and shreds. This texture may be in part inherited from the platy or flow structures of the original volcanic rocks. In only partly pyrophyllitized types the directional texture may be much less pronounced. Normally the rocks are fine-grained, so that the optical properties of pyrophyllite are measured with difficulty. Ghosts of quartz or feldspar phenocrysts appear in some varieties. Pyrophyllite, sericite, and chlorite are usually in minute flakes or shreddy plates. Rarely pyrophyllite forms minute rosettes. Chloritoid may appear in porphyroblasts. Quartz is mainly interstitial, fine-grained to microcrystalline, with some single anhedra and clusters, embayed by pyrophyllite.

Occurrence and Origin. Pyrophyllite is formed by hydrothermal alteration of felsic to intermediate volcanics, into which pyrophyllite rocks grade. Parent types include rhyolite, quartz latite, dacite, and andesite flows and similar breccias and tuffs. In such rocks pyrophyllite bodies form elongate lenses to irregular masses. Pyrophyllitization, which usually follows extensive silicification and is also accompanied by silicification, is considered to take place at temperatures below 400°C. The Deep River region of North Carolina, the San Dieguito area of San Diego County, California, and the Conception Bay area of Newfoundland contain examples of these rocks.

SILLIMANITE-GROUP SCHISTS AND GNEISSES
AND RELATED ROCKS

The sillimanite group of minerals includes sillimanite, kyanite, and andalusite. Rocks rich in staurolite may also be conveniently placed here, for staurolite is similar in composition and commonly closely associated. There is no need, however, to describe andalusite-bearing schists separately, for most of these are rich in mica, commonly biotite, and contain andalusite mainly as porphyroblasts. Also included here are the associated cordierite gneisses, sapphirine rocks, and various metasomatic rocks rich in aluminum silicates.

Staurolite Schists and Gneisses

Definition. Staurolite schists and gneisses are schistose or gneissic rocks containing staurolite as one of the principal aluminum silicates.

Mineralogy. Staurolite may be the only essential aluminum silicate, but commonly it occurs with kyanite or garnet (Fig. 61a). Other species usually present are biotite, muscovite, quartz, and sodic plagioclase. Accessories include andalusite or sillimanite, chloritoid,

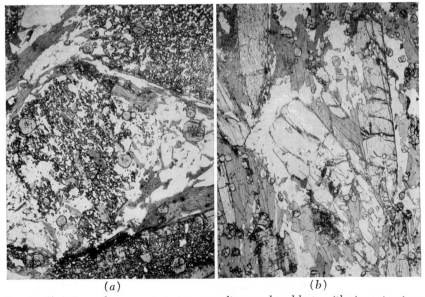

(a)   (b)

FIG. 61. (a) Staurolite-garnet gneiss; staurolite porphyroblasts with sieve structure, garnet, biotite, quartz, feldspar. Henry's Lake, northeastern Idaho. Nicols not crossed, ×10. (b) Kyanite gneiss; kyanite porphyroblasts, biotite, garnet, quartz, feldspar, magnetite. Burnsville, North Carolina. Nicols not crossed, ×10.

magnetite, ilmenite, graphite, zircon, and apatite. Chlorite and sericite are widespread secondary constituents. Staurolite may be completely altered to fine-grained sericite—"shimmer aggregates."

Textures and Microstructures. A well-developed foliation is typical, particularly in more micaceous varieties. Staurolite forms small grains and euhedral porphyroblasts, which may be crowded with oriented lenticular inclusions, particularly of quartz (sieve structure). The porphyroblasts may or may not show orientation parallel with the foliation. Other minerals included are garnet, biotite, and graphite. Staurolite may be twinned, color-zoned, and inclusion-zoned. Some alteration, commonly marginal, to sericite, chloritoid, or chlorite may be conspicuous. Quartz veinlets may transect the poikilitic staurolite crystals. Mineral banding may characterize coarser-grained types.

Occurrence and Origin. Staurolitic schists and gneisses form by medium-grade regional metamorphism of pelitic sediments, particularly those relatively rich in ferrous iron. In some areas staurolite appears before kyanite, and a distinct staurolite isograd may be mapped. Rocks of this type are referred to the lower-intensity part of the amphibolite facies (staurolite-kyanite subfacies). Excellent examples occur in the Littleton (Devonian) formation of New Hampshire; in Patrick and Henry Counties, Virginia; near Little Falls, Minnesota; in Hondo Canyon, south of Taos, New Mexico.

Kyanite Schists and Gneisses

Definition. Kyanite schists and gneisses are kyanite-rich rocks with a well-developed schistosity or gneissic structure.

Mineralogy. Various combinations are common:

Kyanite-muscovite schist
Kyanite-biotite ± garnet (Fig. 61b) ± staurolite schist or gneiss
Kyanite-biotite-sillimanite ± garnet schist or gneiss

Less common are kyanite-ottrelite schists. Some varieties are quartzose, others feldspathic; others contain both quartz and feldspar as essential constituents. The feldspar is usually oligoclase or andesine, but minor orthoclase or microcline may also appear. Accessories are andalusite, tourmaline, zircon, rutile, topaz, magnetite, ilmenite, graphite, apatite, pyrite, and hematite. Sericite, kaolinite, chlorite, pyrophyllite, hematite, and leucoxene are secondary.

Textures and Microstructures. The well-developed foliation results chiefly from the parallel position of mica flakes and kyanite blades, which usually lie with (100) within the schistosity planes. Banding is not common, although some types contain kyanite-rich and -poor layers. Kyanite appears in prismatic crystals with irregular terminations; it may be poikiloblastic, porphyroblastic, or both, with quartz the commonly included species. Kyanite also forms lenticular aggregates of blades and even fibers. Sillimanite replaces kyanite in parallel growths or corrodes it marginally. Sericite also veins and replaces kyanite. Garnet forms both as a matrix mineral or in porphyroblasts. Not uncommonly the latter are poikilitic, including such species as quartz, staurolite, biotite, muscovite, rutile, and magnetite, which may be centrally segregated and arranged parallel with the foliation.

Occurrence and Origin. Kyanite rocks are formed from pelitic sediments by medium-grade regional metamorphism (amphibolite facies, kyanite-staurolite subfacies); lower grade than sillimanite-rich rocks. Examples are in the Orfordville formation (Ordovician) of New Hampshire; in the Carolina gneiss of the North Carolina Blue Ridge; in the Ennis area, Montana; and in the Petaca district of northern New Mexico.

Sillimanite Schists and Gneisses

Definition. Essential sillimanite is the principal aluminum silicate. Foliation is marked.

Mineralogy. Some of the main varieties are:

Sillimanite-biotite (Fig. 62a) ± garnet schist or gneiss
Sillimanite-kyanite-biotite ± schist or gneiss
Sillimanite-garnet schist
Sillimanite-garnet-quartz-orthoclase granulite (khondalite)
Massive sillimanite rock (Fig. 62c)

Quartz (Fig. 62b) or feldspar or both are common in many varieties. Both sodic plagioclase and potash feldspar, either orthoclase or microcline, are well represented. Zircon, magnetite, graphite, rutile, tourmaline, and apatite are widespread accessories. Staurolite, andalusite, cordierite, muscovite, corundum, and pyrite are less common, although some sillimanite-andalusite and sillimanite-pseudoandalusite (sericite) schists are known. In these sillimanite may form as an outer shell around andalusite. Of peculiar composition are the localized massive sillimanite rocks, containing 90 per cent + sillimanite and only traces of biotite, quartz, tourmaline, and rutile or corundum.

Textures and Microstructures. The texture is schistose to gneissic, fine- to coarse-grained. In some the foliation is exceedingly irregular, and in others much granitic material, as lit-par-lit stringers, has been injected. Sillimanite is regularly distributed as fibers and small bundles of fibers or concentrated in discoidal masses and elongate streaks, usually finely intergrown with quartz. The resistance of these to weathering results in a knobby surface. Rarely also sillimanite forms larger single crystals, subhedral to euhedral, with the characteristic diamond-shaped cross section, and may even appear as porphyroblasts

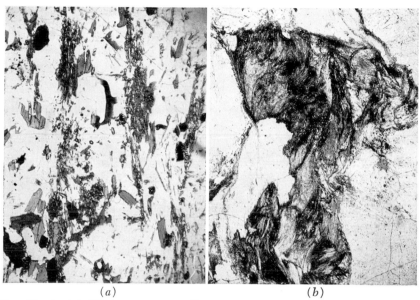

(a) (b)

Fɪɢ. 62a, b. (a) Sillimanite gneiss; sillimanite in "trains" of small needles, biotite, quartz, feldspar, magnetite. Cripple Creek Quadrangle, Colorado. Nicols not crossed, ×22. (b) Sillimanite schist; crenulated fibrous sillimanite, quartz. Ennis, Montana. Nicols crossed, ×10.

having, in some rocks, a diverse orientation. Much sillimanite apparently formed late, replacing biotite or, less usually, garnet in curving trains (Fig. 62a) of fibers or corroding kyanite marginally. Subparallel needles of sillimanite are also crowded into quartz grains. In some varieties sworls and radial clusters of curving sillimanite fibers are conspicuous (Fig. 62c). Almandite garnet appears as spongy matrix anhedra, highly poikiloblastic, or as porphyroblasts which also may include other minerals, especially quartz. Sillimanite shows varying degrees of replacement—by sericite, pyrophyllite, and by shells of quartz, muscovite, and staurolite. In some varieties sillimanite is pseudomorphous after kyanite or even andalusite, in the latter case together with muscovite and staurolite.

Massive sillimanite rocks are characterized by a poor foliation and microscopically by a felted texture with interlocking sheaves and radial aggregates of sillimanite needles, as well as scattered larger sillimanite euhedra.

Occurrence and Origin. Sillimanite is formed through high-grade regional metamorphism of pelitic sediments, commonly close to the roof or margins of granitic batholiths or where biotitic schists have

Fig. 62c. Massive sillimanite rock; radiating blades of coarse sillimanite, corundum, *upper center,* rutile (black). India. Nicols crossed, ×10.

been intensely injected by granitic or pegmatitic material. Rocks of this type belong to the sillimanite-almandite subfacies of the amphibolite facies. Massive sillimanite rocks are commonly marginal to pegmatite dikes or sills and probably are partly metasomatic in origin. The discoidal quartz-sillimanite segregations may represent original clay lenses or may have been formed through metamorphic segregation. Sillimanite schists and gneisses are exemplified by numerous occurrences in the Piedmont of North and South Carolina and Georgia; also in the Blue Ridge near Franklin, North Carolina; in various New England localities; in the pre-Cambrian Idaho Springs formation in Colorado; in Taos and Rio Arriba Counties, New Mexico; and near

Troy, Idaho. Nodular sillimanite rocks have been reported from the Colorado Front Range and from near Dillon, Montana. Massive sillimanite rock also occurs near Dillon.

Cordierite Gneisses

Definition. Cordierite gneisses are gneissic rocks containing essential and usually abundant cordierite.

Mineralogy. The main varieties include:

Cordierite-biotite $\pm$ sillimanite
Cordierite-muscovite
Cordierite-almandite
Cordierite-anthophyllite
Cordierite-andalusite

Some types are quartzose; others carry both quartz and sodic plagioclase; and some quartz-poor varieties contain considerable microcline. Accessories are magnetite, pleonaste, sillimanite, kyanite, staurolite, graphite, pyrite, epidote, allanite, zircon, and sphene. Chlorite, chloritoid, and hornblende are rare.

Textures and Microstructures. Cordierite gneisses are usually medium- to coarse-grained, crudely foliated, rarely schistose. Cordierite is anhedral and may form elongate grains. Lamellar twinning is common in parts of the grains. Margins may be altered to a fine-grained chlorite-sericite aggregate (pinite), which also veins the grains. Some cordierite grains are jammed with minute inclusions of pleonaste or of magnetite. Other cordierite crystals are strongly poikiloblastic, even netlike, including quartz and feldspar. In some varieties cordierite has been developed at the expense of biotite and in turn is partly replaced by a sillimanite-plagioclase aggregate. Garnet grains may be in part replaced by a mixture of biotite, cordierite, and pleonaste. Some types show banding with biotite-cordierite-sillimanite layers alternating with quartz-feldspar layers.

Occurrence and Origin. Cordierite is formed by high-grade regional metamorphism, probably at high temperatures but under relatively lower stress from pelitic sediments rich in magnesium. Some cordierite-anthophyllite gneisses are regarded as having resulted from the metasomatism of quartz-feldspar rocks such as leptites. Some cordierite gneisses with complex mineralogical assemblages may have undergone more than one period of metamorphism, and the assemblage may not be in equilibrium. Anatexis has been postulated as being important in the development of some coarse-grained cordierite gneisses. Cordierite gneisses occur near Guffey, Colorado; in the Laramie Range, Wyoming; and near Guilford, Connecticut.

Sapphirine Rocks

Sapphirine-bearing metamorphic rocks include gneissic to granulitic types, characterized by the presence of sapphirine either as an essential or minor constituent. Other minerals commonly present are biotite (less usually phlogopite), spinel (pleonaste or hercynite), basic plagioclase (labradorite to anorthite), hornblende, and enstatite-hypersthene. Less common are corundum, diaspore, kornerupine, cordierite, and orthoclase. The proportions of the various major and minor constituents vary greatly. Uncommon associates include anthophyllite, titanian magnetite, zircon, sillimanite, and garnet. The rocks are gneissic to granoblastic and may have coarse schlieren, streaks, and lenticles of contrasting mineralogy. Rocks composed mainly of anorthite, spinel, corundum, diaspore, and sapphirine have been called sakenites. Spinel-sapphirine rocks have been called sapphirinites. The blue pleochroic sapphirine is anhedral to euhedral. In some rocks it is closely associated with spinel, even forming rims around spinel grains and replacing them. Sapphirine rocks appear to be formed chiefly under very high temperature conditions. In some cases they are hybrid rocks formed by metamorphism and metasomatism of aluminous xenoliths by mafic magma, or contact migmatites around a granitic intrusive, or mafic xenoliths included in granitic masses. The more extensive sapphirine gneisses of Madagascar are believed to have been formed by the contact metamorphism of magnesian marls and clays. Sapphirine apparently forms by the addition of SiO_2 to spinels or by the decomposition of biotite to cordierite and sapphirine. The recorded metamorphic occurrences are at Fiskernäs, Sukkertoppen, and Avisisarfik, all three in Greenland; Val Codera, Italy; Sakeny, Madagascar; Vizagapatam, India; Marignisandougou, French Guinea; Dangin, Western Australia; and Blinkwater, Transvaal.

Topaz, Dumortierite, and Andalusite Rocks

Rocks containing abundant topaz (topazfels) are of high-temperature metasomatic origin, usually replacing a variety of other metamorphic rocks. The topaz rocks of Kharsawan State, India, contain topaz, muscovite, corundum, rutile, and magnetite. Those at Jhar Gobindpur, Shirbai, India, consist of topaz, muscovite, kyanite, quartz, rutile, and fluorite. A rock composed almost exclusively of cryptocrystalline to microcrystalline topaz occurs near Jefferson, South Carolina, in association with a gold quartz lode.

Dumortierite rocks occur at Oreana, Nevada, and near Quartzite, Arizona. At the former, lenses of andalusite rock in quartz-sericite schist are replaced by dumortierite in three generations: (1) coarse blue euhedra, (2) matted pink or lavender fibers, and (3) pink fibers or single pink crystals. At Quartzite dumortierite rock that also contains andalusite, kyanite, sillimanite, pyrophyllite, quartz, and rutile apparently resulted from the replacement of sericite schist. Hydrothermal andalusite rocks are exemplified by the occurrences at Oreana, Nevada; at White Mountain, Mono County, California (with quartz and diaspore); in Kazakhstan, U.S.S.R.; and at Boliden, Sweden.

QUARTZ-FELDSPAR GNEISSES AND RELATED ROCKS

In this group are included metamorphic rocks in which quartz and feldspar, chiefly potash feldspar, are dominant constituents. Such rocks are formed by metamorphism of felsic igneous rocks, including granites, rhyolites, rhyolitic tuffs, granodiorites, and quartz latites and of psephitic sedimentary rocks such as arkoses and feldspathic sandstones. The main types are the granitic gneisses, alkali granite gneisses, psephitic gneisses, felsic ("acid") granulites, and leptites.

Quartz-Feldspar Gneisses

Definition. Quartz-feldspar gneisses are coarse-grained gneissic rocks containing quartz, feldspar, and biotite (less usually hornblende) as the main essential minerals.

Mineralogy. Quartz and feldspar are usually dominant (commonly 75 per cent), although the ratio of these to the other constituents may vary considerably. Some types contain both sodic plagioclase (commonly oligoclase; range, albite-andesine) (Fig. 63a) and potash feldspar (either orthoclase or microcline) in abundance. In others plagioclase is the dominant feldspar, with garnet as a common accessory. Still others contain little plagioclase. The potash feldspar may be perthitic. Both orthoclase and microcline have been reported from the same rock. A few rare types are feldspar-rich and quartz-poor, approaching syenites or monzonites in composition. Hornblende-bearing types contain abundant potash feldspar less commonly. Biotite and/or muscovite are common. Hornblende may occur alone or with biotite. Other subordinate constituents are almandite and epidote-zoisite.

Accessories are varied: apatite, zircon, sphene, pyrite, hematite, magnetite, ilmenite, calcite, tourmaline, allanite, sillimanite, and kyanite. Rare are anthophyllite, staurolite, cordierite, rutile, and graphite. Common alteration minerals include kaolinite, sericite, and chlorite.

A rock name widely used by European petrologists is kinzigite, which is a quartz-oligoclase gneiss containing prominent garnet and usually biotite (Fig. 63*b*). Some also have essential microcline, and others contain cordierite ± anthophyllite.

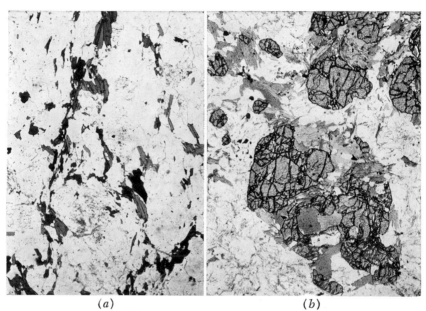

(a)   (b)

Fig. 63. (*a*) Quartz-feldspar gneiss; biotite, quartz, oligoclase, minor microcline. Munroe, Connecticut. Nicols not crossed, ×11. (*b*) Garnet gneiss (kinzigite); quartz, oligoclase, biotite, garnet porphyroblasts. Jackson County, North Carolina, Nicols not crossed, ×11.

Textures and Microstructures. Many of the rocks show a well-defined planar orientation of their minerals, particularly micas and hornblende. In addition, feldspar grains may be similarly arranged, and in some varieties quartz also appears in parallel elongated grains or lenticles. Quartz-feldspar aggregates may show a mosaic texture, or quartz grains may show sutured margins. In some varieties mineralogical banding is pronounced, either between felsic and mafic layers or between coarse quartzose bands and finer-grained quartz-feldspar bands. The mafics may also appear clustered in irregular lenses or streaks, and quartz also forms ellipsoidal aggregates. In some examples the grain size is relatively uniform throughout; in others, including those derived from granite porphyries or conglomeratic sandstones, considerable grain-size variation is characteristic.

Cataclastic structures are not uncommon—broken quartz and feldspar grains, undulatory extinction, mortar structure, bent feldspar cleavages and twin units, as well as fractures and veinlets of quartz, sericite, and epidote. Poikilitic structures may be present in microcline and garnet, both of which usually include quartz, the latter in some cases only centrally. Twinning in plagioclase may be obscure, very fine, or even absent. Plagioclase zoning of various types may be conspicuous in some orthogneisses of this group.

Feldspars may show turbid zones or cores. Overgrowths of epidote on allanite have been reported. Quartz and feldspar (both orthoclase or oligoclase) may be blastoporphyritic, and microcline may also appear as porphyroblasts. In addition to perthitic intergrowths, antiperthitic, micropegmatite, and myrmekitic intergrowths occur. Biotite may contain abundant inclusions, particularly of rutile, zircon, apatite, and magnetite. Muscovite may be developed in large plates, poikilitically including other species, or in vermicular intergrowths with biotite and feldspars. Garnet rarely occurs as porphyroblasts but may be concentrated in granular lenses.

Noteworthy in some granitic gneisses and kinzigites are thin grain-boundary veinlets or films of quartz, commonly between microcline grains or between microcline and garnet.

Occurrence and Origin. Quartz-feldspar gneisses are derived either from felsic igneous rocks—granites, aplites, granodiorites, quartz syenites, and their porphyries (less commonly their extrusive equivalents) or from impure arenaceous sediments such as arkoses, feldspathic or argillaceous sandstones, and conglomeratic sandstones. The metamorphism is regional, deep-seated, and high-grade, the products usually being referred to the granulite facies. Criteria (in addition to field evidence) that may assist in determining the nature of the parent rock are:

From igneous rocks
  1. Blastoporphyritic texture
  2. Plagioclase of the same composition throughout and of uniform zoning
  3. Potash feldspar of the same type and in excess of quartz
  4. Euhedral zircon, of the same variety throughout

From sedimentary rocks
1. Considerable variation in grain size in a mineral species
2. Thin banding, especially of the heavy accessories, representing relict bedding
3. Variation in composition of different grains of plagioclase in the same rock
4. Different kinds of plagioclase zoning in the same rock
5. Presence of sillimanite, kyanite, cordierite, staurolite, and calcite
6. Quartz in considerable excess of feldspar

Biotitic, sillimanitic, and garnetiferous quartz-feldspar paragneisses constitute an important part of the Grenville series (pre-Cambrian) in New York State. Micaceous quartz-feldspar orthogneisses are widespread in the pre-Cambrian of Colorado and southwestern Montana. Other examples of both types occur in the Appalachian belt in Massachusetts, New York, and North Carolina.

Felsic Granulites

Definition. Felsic granulites are granoblastic metamorphic rocks consisting mainly of quartz, feldspars and lesser garnet, sillimanite, and accessories. Biotite is usually rare; hornblende is not common; sphene is absent. In many places felsic and intermediate to mafic granulites alternate in bands. No sharp separation from some quartz-feldspar gneisses is possible. To some investigators the term granulite is restricted to granoblastic metamorphic rocks consisting predominantly of quartz, feldspar with garnet, and other subordinate minerals. However, the term has also been used in a more general way, to include not only such felsic (acid) granulites but even intermediate and mafic granoblastic rocks containing chiefly plagioclase, pyroxene, and garnet. These pyroxene granulites are here grouped with the intermediate and mafic charnockites, and similarly, the felsic (acid) charnockites are placed with the felsic (acid) granulites.

Mineralogy. Quartz, which contains gas or rutile inclusions, may be subordinate to the combined feldspars. Potash feldspar is either orthoclase or microcline. Some orthoclase is converted to microcline, the conversion beginning with undulatory extinction; next appear patches of gridiron twinning in these strained areas; and finally the grain is completely transformed. The orthoclase may be perthitic or nonperthitic. In some cryptoperthites the Or:Ab ratio $= 50:50$. In many felsic granulites the plagioclase is An_{20-30}, and in varieties poor in orthoclase it may be as calcic as An_{40}. That of the andesine range commonly is antiperthitic with stubby or hairlike orthoclase inclusions. Garnet varies considerably in composition, but is chiefly pyrope-almandite. Other minerals that may be common locally are sillimanite or kyanite, cordierite, diopside, hypersthene, hornblende, and graphite. Biotite may proxy for garnet but usually is absent in sillimanite types or in some areas in types characterized by platy quartz. Accessories are ilmenite, magnetite, hematite, pyrite, pyrrhotite, rutile, apatite, mona-

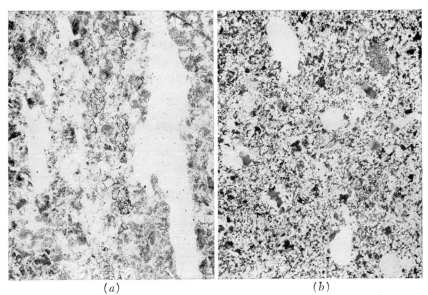

(a)　　　　　　　　　　　　　(b)

Fig. 64. (a) Sillimanite granulite; sillimanite (high relief, diamond-shaped crystals), kaolinized orthoclase, lenticles of quartz. Blacktail Deer Creek, Montana. Nicols not crossed, ×10. (b) Leptite; porphyroblastic quartz, oligoclase-quartz-muscovite matrix. Mauri, Finland. Nicols crossed, ×10.

zite, kornerupine, zircon, corundum, and spinel. Uncommon are muscovite, epidote, chlorite, and scapolite. The main mineralogical types of felsic granulites are:

Garnet granulite ("normal" granulite or leptynite)
Garnet-sillimanite granulite (included here are the khondalites; kodurites are associated rocks consisting of orthoclase, spessartite-andradite, and apatite)
Garnet-kyanite granulite
Sillimanite granulite (Fig. 64a)
Garnet-cordierite granulite (laanilite)
Cordierite-biotite granulite

Biotite granulite
Hornblende granulite
Garnet-pyroxene (diopside, hypersthene) granulite
Graphite granulite
Magnetite-biotite granulite

The hornblende, usually a greenish brown type with strong pleochroism, contains considerable Al in the Si positions and is relatively rich in Fe and Ti. The hypersthene, which is rather variable in composition like the garnet, is usually strongly or moderately pleochroic.

Textures and Microstructures. Many granulites are xenomorphic-granoblastic. In others the quartz is flattened into plates or lenticles parallel with the foliation. In outcrops many are banded or layered with alternating light (felsic granulitic) and dark ("charnockitic") layers. In biotitic types some of the mica forms thin seams. Most are even-grained rocks, but garnet, orthoclase, and oligoclase may form metacrysts. The garnet commonly contains centrally concentrated quartz inclusions. Plagioclase, usually not zoned, may have turbid cores. Garnet rims on hypersthene or biotite are conspicuous in some types; in others pyroxene is marginally replaced by hornblende. Sillimanite commonly appears in subhedral to euhedral grains with the characteristic rhombic cross section. Fibrolitic sillimanite is uncommon. In many granulites local cataclastic effects can be observed.

Occurrence and Origin. Felsic granulites are formed by deep-seated regional metamorphism under very high temperature and pressure (granulite facies) from a variety of parent rocks:

Biotite granulite: rhyolite, granite, trachyte, quartz syenite, syenite, arkosic sandstone
Quartzose garnet granulite: arkosic sandstone, rhyolite, rhyolite tuff, granites
Cordierite-biotite granulite: arenaceous or silty shale
Graphite granulite: silty carbonaceous shale
Garnet-sillimanite (kyanite) granulite: shale
Sillimanite-rich granulite: kaolin

Some well-known localities include Saxony, Ceylon, and Lapland.

Leptites. Leptites, a term not much used in the United States but widely employed in Europe, particularly Scandinavia, are fine-grained quartz-feldspar metamorphic rocks whose fine grain reflects the original grain size of the parent rocks. The principal minerals are quartz, oligoclase-andesine, microcline or orthoclase, biotite and/or hornblende. As such they are generally the mineralogical equivalent to fine-grained felsic granulites as the term is here used, but may be of lower metamorphic grade. Some are plagioclase-rich, others contain less plagioclase than potash feldspar Quartz and feldspar together usually constitute about 75 per cent of the rock. Accessories are zircon, magnetite, apatite, sphene, epidote, and less commonly cordierite, diopside, and grossularite. The quartz-feldspar aggregate is granoblastic ("pavement" texture), with parallel biotite and amphibole. Some types are banded, which may represent a modified fluidal texture. Halleflintas or halleflint gneisses are aphanitic porcelanoid types, commonly banded. Some leptites show blastoporphyritic quartz (Fig. 64*b*) or feldspar or lenses of coarser quartz and feldspar; in others amygdaloidal or tuffaceous textures are relict. Most leptites result from regional metamorphism of felsic to intermediate volcanic rocks: rhyolites, quartz latites, dacites, and their tuffaceous varieties. Others are formed from pelitic sediments or from contaminated tuffs, especially those leptites that contain cordierite, garnet, or pyroxene. Metarhyolites are known from the pre-Cambrian of northern New Mexico and northwestern Texas.

Alkali Gneisses

The rare rocks included in this group are those formed chiefly by the high-grade regional metamorphism of alkali granites. The main varieties include riebeckite gneiss, riebeckite granulite, aegirine granulites, and arfvedsonite gneiss. Riebeckite gneisses contain alkali feldspar, quartz, riebeckite, and aegirine. Some varieties are schistose and largely feldspar-free. Others contain quartz, albite, riebeckite, and garnet. Aegirine granulites containing orthoclase, albite, minor quartz, aegirine, riebeckite, and garnet have also been formed by alkali metasomatism of micaceous schists.

PYROXENE GRANULITES, CHARNOCKITES, ECLOGITES, AND RELATED ROCKS

Pyroxene Granulites and Charnockites

Definition. The terms charnockite and charnockite series have been widely misused. As originally defined by Holland, the charnockite series of India was a group of diverse, hypersthenic Archean rocks with an even-grained, granulitic texture. Charnockite, *sensu stricto*, was employed for a quartz-feldspar-hypersthene–iron ore rock within this series. Holland specifically stated that charnockite " . . . is not a name for any hypersthene granite occurring in other petrographical provinces." This would make it equivalent to what are now generally called acid charnockites. Quensel, who has restudied charnockites from all over the world, uses the term charnockite as a collective designation for all charnockitic rocks, including felsic (acid), intermediate, and mafic (basic) types. Charnockites are granoblastic rocks containing antiperthite, sodic plagioclase, hypersthene, diopside, garnet, and ore minerals.[1] Charnockites are thus varieties of granulites (in the widest sense), characterized by pyroxene(s). Most rocks termed pyroxene granulites are mineralogically similar to charnockites, and felsic (acid) charnockites are granulites (*sensu stricto*).

Mineralogy. The three main varieties of charnockite differ chiefly in the ratio of light- to dark-colored constituents. Felsic (acid) charnockites contain more Si than the intermediate and mafic varieties and also contain more orthoclase and have somewhat more sodic plagioclase.

In mafic charnockites plagioclase is the predominant feldspar, commonly sodic andesine to calcic oligoclase, although in rocks from some localities it is as calcic as An_{55-70}. Much of it is antiperthitic, with lamellae and blebs of orthoclase; orthoclase rarely occurs as discrete individuals. The plagioclase rarely shows twinning, a feature characteristic of most charnockites. Diopside may be more abundant than hypersthene, which is faintly to strongly pleochroic. Some diopside individuals contain platelets of exsolved ilmenite. As much as 20 per cent lilac garnet (pyrope-almandite) may be present (Fig. 65a). Accessories are hornblende (which may be essential in some variants), biotite, apatite, ilmenite, hematite, and magnetite.

In intermediate charnockites orthoclase occurs both in individual grains and as inclusions in antiperthitic oligoclase. Gradations occur between oligoclase antiperthite and orthoclase perthite. Diopside usually exceeds hypersthene, which is more iron-rich than that in mafic charnockites. Garnet is also usually abundant. In some varieties deep greenish brown hornblende, low in OH, is more abundant than pyroxenes. Apatite, zircon, biotite, ores, and rare epidote and sphene are accessories. Secondary minerals are quartz, calcite, and serpentine (after hypersthene).

Textures and Microstructures. The texture is fine- to medium-grained, granoblastic, usually even-grained, although large individuals

---

[1] The following are all useless local or varietal names for charnockites: akafoamite, arendalite, bugite, enderbite, epibugite, ivoirite, katabugite, and sabarovite.

of diopside appear in some varieties. All the constituents normally are anhedral, with some diopside being poikiloblastic and some garnet skeletal. Thin banding or streaking characterizes some charnockites, with layers of mafics (hypersthene plus garnet; diopside; hornblende) alternating with feldspathic layers. Some mafic foliated charnockites have been called pyroxene gneisses. The hypersthene forms granular rims or crystallographically continuous overgrowths on diopside; rarely cores of hypersthene are overgrown by single-crystal rims of

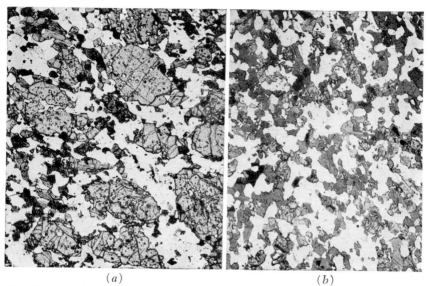

(*a*)   (*b*)

Fig. 65. (*a*) Charnockite; hypersthene, garnet porphyroblasts, quartz, plagioclase, magnetite. Sheridan district, Montana. Nicols not crossed, ×10. (*b*) Augite gneiss; augite, hornblende, andesine, magnetite. Hell Roaring Plateau, Beartooth Mountains, Montana. Nicols not crossed, ×10.

diopside. The presence of abundant antiperthite and the common absence of twinning in plagioclase are characteristic textural features.

Occurrence and Origin. Charnockites are widespread in the pre-Cambrian of India, and there are also well-known occurrences in southwestern Sweden; near Arendal, Norway ("arendalites"); near Dangin, Australia; and in Uganda. Charnockites are associated with garnet gneiss (khondalite), hypersthene gneiss, and various types of quartz-feldspar gneiss. Charnockites were originally believed to be plutonic igneous rocks, but there is ample evidence for their metamorphic origin under conditions of great confining pressure, high temperature, and absence of water. The chemical variability of charnockites reflects variations in original composition. Some intermediate charnockites have been regarded as syntectic hybrid rocks. Charnockites were formed under environmental conditions belonging to the granulite facies. Suggested rocks from which the various charnockites could have been derived include monzonites, quartz diorites, diorites, dacites, and andesites for the intermediate types; and basalts and norites for the mafic types. However, some charnockites may be second-generation metamorphic rocks, formed from felsic to mafic gneisses.

Eclogites

Definition. Eclogites are medium- to coarse-grained, poorly foliated to nonfoliated rocks consisting chiefly of garnet and the sodic pyroxene omphacite, a member of the diopside-jadeite series.

Mineralogy. Garnet and pyroxene together usually make up the bulk of the rock, although in some varieties kyanite, zoisite, and an amphibole become essential constituents. Pyroxene is usually in excess of garnet. The garnet is mainly pink almandite–pyrope. The pale green omphacite is likewise variable in composition, some types containing considerable Fe^3. It may show some optical variation in a single rock specimen. The amphibole, which is normally uralitic, is either hornblende or glaucophane, less commonly actinolite. Epidote or clinozoisite may be present instead of zoisite. Enstatite or diopside may be present in addition to omphacite. Other accessories are rutile (very common), quartz, calcic plagioclase, ilmenite, magnetite, apatite, pyrrhotite, pyrite, muscovite, spinel, and sphene. Less widespread are chlorite, albite, lawsonite, pumpelleyite, olivine, and allanite. Types with abundant amphibole have been referred to as either hornblende or glaucophane eclogites.

Textures and Microstructures. Both garnet and omphacite are xenoblastic, with some or much of the garnet in ovoid to irregular porphyroblasts. Most of the rocks are medium- to coarse-grained, heterogranular, very rarely fine-grained. There may be a crude foliation owing to a rough alignment of stubby pyroxene grains. Garnet shows various types of alteration: (1) kelyphitic borders of fibrous hornblende plus calcic plagioclase, (2) general alteration to hornblende plus magnetite, and (3) general replacement by chlorite. Omphacite is replaced by hornblende, glaucophane, actinolite, or an intimate intergrowth of diopside and plagioclase. Rutile is widely replaced by sphene. Some varieties show nearly complete uralitization of the pyroxene.

Occurrence and Origin. Eclogites occur in the following associations:

1. Schlieren and lenses in garnetiferous anorthosites, garnetiferous charnockites, pyroxene granulites, and pyroxene gneisses
2. Schlieren and nodules in pyroxenite and dunite and in kimberlite of volcanic necks and pipes
3. Lenticular masses in granite gneiss and migmatite and associated with amphibolite in paragneisses
4. Irregular masses associated with glaucophane rocks intruded by peridotites

Eclogites, which have a very limited compositional range, approximating that of gabbros or basalts, are the type rocks (and only representatives) of Eskola's eclogite facies, conventionally denoting high temperature, extreme pressure, and absence of water. Doubtless many eclogites were formed by recrystallization (or crystallization?) at great depths and were subsequently transported en masse to nearer-surface environments. Some petrographers prefer to regard them as deep-seated igneous rocks. Many eclogites show conspicuous retrogressive mineralogical changes between garnet and pyroxene accompanying the introduction of water. In the United States eclogites have been described from the glaucophane schist belt of the California Coast Ranges. European examples occur in the Tyrol, Norway, France, and in the Fichtelgebirge of Bavaria.

Jade

Jade consists principally of the pyroxene jadeite, in some cases with very subordinate to trace amounts of such minerals as albite, muscovite, actinolite, wollastonite, nepheline, magnetite, sphene, analcite, picotite, quartz, prehnite, natrolite, thomsonite, hydrogrossular, and pectolite. The rock not uncommonly shows irregular color mottling or gently contorted banding in shades of green. Jadeite is normally granular to subhedral, stubby-prismatic, less usually finely felted. Some pyroxene grains tend to be porphyroblastic, and both equigranular and heterogranular textures occur. In some cases fine-grained streaks may be due to crushing. The orientation usually is random. The jadeite is uniformly colored as a rule, but types occur in which it shows intragranular as well as intergranular color mottling. Darker green coloration also may be conspicuous along fractures. A second generation of jadeite, richer in Na, may vein the older. Albite appears as clear untwinned anhedra or granular masses, usually interstitial, although poikilitic grains have been observed.

Jade occurs as lenses, pods, and veinlike masses in serpentinites or associated with serpentinites in schists. Despite older beliefs, jadeite is not necessarily indicative of high-intensity environments, being stable at low pressures and below 500°C. Some jade, at least, is likely hydrothermal in origin, formed by solutions related to serpentinization. In the United States jade occurs in San Benito County, California. Other occurrences are in Central America, Japan, Celebes, and Burma.

AMPHIBOLE SCHISTS AND GNEISSES AND AMPHIBOLITES

Actinolite Schists

Definition. Actinolite schists are amphibole-rich, schistose rocks containing actinolite as the principal or sole amphibole (Fig. 66a). Many are green in color, and some greenschists are actinolitic.

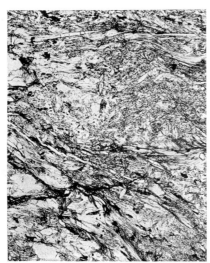

Fig. 66a. Actinolite schist; actinolite, chlorite, biotite, sphene, albite. Shelby, North Carolina. Nicols not crossed, ×10.

Mineralogy. Actinolitic greenschists usually contain the assemblage actinolite, epidote, albite, and chlorite; various modifications result from the presence of quartz, biotite, hornblende, or calcite as essential or accessory constituents. Other accessories include sphene, leucoxene, apatite, stilpnomelane, muscovite, tourmaline, pyrite, and magnetite. Calcareous actinolitic schists contain actinolite, epidote-clinozoisite, and calcite, in some cases in various combinations with albite, quartz, microcline, or biotite. Some actinolite schists consist only of essential actinolite, with just accessory chlorite, talc, epidote, ilmenite, leucoxene, sphene, magnetite, albite, hematite, and pyrite. Actinolite-biotite schists with accessory plagioclase, calcite, quartz, rutile, tourmaline, and sphene are also known, as are actinolite-hornblende schists containing accessory chlorite and talc. Another variation is actinolite-albite schist having accessory chlorite, leucoxene, hematite, pyrite, and pyrrhotite.

Textures and Microstructures. Actinolite, other amphiboles, chlorites, and biotite usually are well oriented, parallel or subparallel, except in those varieties whose texture is in part relict. Bands rich in albite alternating with those containing actinolite-epidote ± chlorite are common. Actinolite forms slender prisms to fibers, with irregular terminations. It may retain ragged cores of green hornblende or diopsidic augite. Inclusions of such minerals as epidote, albite, chlorite, and magnetite may result in a poikiloblastic structure. Some actinolite is in porphyroblasts, usually with inclusions. Actinolite forms pseudomorphs after pyroxene, either in single crystals or in felted aggregates. Chlorite and albite may replace actinolite. Albite, which generally ranges from Ab_{100} to about Ab_{95}, forms a mosaic of anhedra or euhedral to subhedral porphyroblasts, which may be crowded with inclusions of actinolite needles, epidote grains, and chlorite flakes. Some are properly augen, having been broken, rounded, or granulated. Pressure shadows of terminal quartz may outline the porphyroblasts. Relict calcic plagioclase may appear as irregular cores. Epidote forms granular anhedra and some larger subhedra; it may display zoning. Epidote and calcite or epidote and quartz also appear in lenses and veinlets. Chlorite is replaced by biotite or stilpnomelane. Some chlorite appears along shear planes.

Some rocks show relict diabasic, porphyritic, or amygdaloidal textures, with remnants of calcic plagioclase, augite, and hornblende. Some actinolite-rich rocks display a rosette texture, with radially fibrous prisms or needles of the amphibole. Nephrite consists of finely felted fibers of tremolite or actinolite, with some patches of coarser prismatic amphibole and accessory chromite and magnetite.

Occurrence and Origin. Actinolitic schists result from the low-grade regional metamorphism of mafic rocks such as basalts; basaltic tuffs, breccias, and agglomerates; diabases; and gabbros. Calcitic actinolite schists form by similar metamorphism of impure dolomites or dolomitic limestones. The rocks are referred to the biotite-chlorite subfacies of the greenschist facies. Actinolite schists are locally abundant in the Cherry Creek group (pre-Cambrian) of southwestern Montana.

Anthophyllite Schists and Related Rocks

Anthophyllite rocks are varied in mineralogy, the main types being:

Anthophyllite schist: anthophyllite, ± cordierite, ± cummingtonite; accessory biotite (Fig. 66*b*), rutile, magnetite, quartz, ± garnet

Anthophyllite gneiss: anthophyllite, quartz, plagioclase, ± garnet, ±
cordierite; accessory magnetite, rutile, biotite, hornblende
Anthophyllite amphibolite: anthophyllite, plagioclase, ± garnet
Anthophyllite-rich schists: anthophyllite, ± actinolite, ± hypersthene
or enstatite, ± talc, ± cummingtonite; accessory apatite, serpentine, phlogopite, chlorite, rutile, spinel, magnetite, olivine, zoisite

Most of these rocks show a well-developed foliation, owing to near
parallelism of the elongate anthophyllite blades together with other
amphiboles and micaceous minerals. Felted textures are also known.

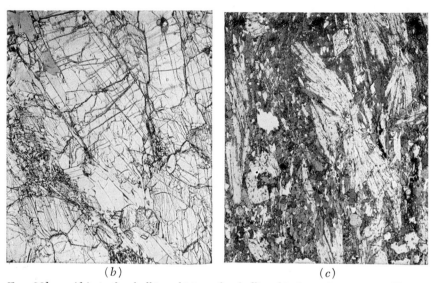

| (*b*) | (*c*) |

FIG. 66*b*, *c*. (*b*) Anthophyllite schist; anthophyllite, biotite, minor quartz. Masons
Mountain, Franklin, North Carolina. Nicols not crossed, ×10. (*c*) Cummingtonite
schist; quartz, hornblende, cummingtonite in semiradial groups. Jardine, Montana.
Nicols not crossed, ×10.

However, some have anthophyllite in radial-fibrous or stellate groups,
and in other coarse anthophyllite amphibolites the arrangement is
decussate. Anthophyllite may be equigranular or appear both in
porphyroblasts, which may be inclusion-rich, and matrix laths. Some
shows zoning and varying degrees of replacement by biotite, cummingtonite, and talc. Plagioclase is commonly oligoclase-andesine, although
labradorite has been identified. Garnets are usually poikiloblastic, as
is cordierite.

Anthophyllite rocks have been formed in the following ways:

1. By magnesian metasomatism of leptites around granitic and granodioritic intrusives
2. By moderate- to high-grade regional metamorphism of peridotites or weathered chloritic greenstones
3. By metasomatism of serpentinites
4. By contact metasomatism of hornblende schists, gneisses, and amphibolites by peridotites or by granitic pegmatites
5. By reaction between amphibolites and dolomitic marbles

Varied anthophyllite rocks occur in the pre-Cambrian Cherry Creek group near Dillon and Ennis, Montana; also in the pre-Cambrian of the Guffey district, Colorado, and near Franklin, North Carolina.

Cummingtonite schists occur mainly in two geological associations: (1) with anthophyllite in rocks formed by metamorphism of or by peridotites and (2) in schists with quartz, resulting from the metamorphism of sediments containing quartz, clay, and Fe-Mg carbonate (ferroan magnesite). The quartz-cummingtonite schists, which resemble some grunerite schists, contain biotite, almandite, and graphite and have cummingtonite in radial tuftlike groups of fibers (Fig. 66c) or in parallel arrangement. Biotite replaces garnet and cummingtonite; chlorite replaces garnet, biotite, and cummingtonite (Homestake formation, Lead, South Dakota). In the cummingtonite schists of the Jardine, Montana district, hornblende is also an essential constituent, replacing cummingtonite. Some examples are banded, and the coarser cummingtonite displays its characteristic twinning.

Glaucophane Schists and Related Rocks

Although glaucophane rocks are relatively rare, they are characterized by a wide variation in mineralogical composition and texture. They generally fall into two groups—glaucophane (and/or crossite) schists and glaucophane (and/or crossite) amphibolites.

GLAUCOPHANE SCHISTS

Definition. Glaucophane schists are schistose rocks that contain glaucophane as one of the principal essential minerals. Other characteristic minerals are lawsonite and pumpelleyite.

Mineralogy. Glaucophane schists display a wide range in mineral composition, but most can be grouped under one of the following main types:

Quartzose ± albite

Glaucophane-muscovite with quartz ± albite, epidote, chlorite (Fig. 67a)

Biotite-glaucophane with quartz

Albite-chlorite-epidote-glaucophane ± calcite, muscovite, quartz; also called prasinite

Chlorite-crossite

Albite-crossite

Lawsonite-glaucophane ± albite

Muscovite-lawsonite-glaucophane ± sodic pyroxene

Lawsonite-albite-crossite

Epidote-glaucophane ± albite

Muscovite-epidote-glaucophane ± albite

Chlorite-epidote-glaucophane ± albite

Muscovite-epidote-crossite

Chlorite-epidote-crossite

Garnet-glaucophane ± epidote

Garnet-lawsonite-glaucophane ± epidote

Garnet-clinozoisite-muscovite-glaucophane

Garnet-muscovite-glaucophane

Garnet-crossite

Sodic pyroxene-muscovite-glaucophane

Glaucophane is the chief amphibole and is conspicuous because of its blue violet pleochroism. It may appear with crossite or riebeckite, or crossite may be the sole sodic amphibole. Within an area the sodic amphiboles may show a considerable range in composition. Actinolite is common in some localities, but hornblende is uncommon except in corroded relicts. Zoned amphiboles are very common; some of the relationships are:

Core	*Margin*
Blue green hornblende	Narrow irregular glaucophane rim
Brownish green hornblende	Glaucophane
Actinolite	Glaucophane
Glaucophane	Deeper blue crossite
Crossite	Glaucophane
Irregular patches of crossite in glaucophane	Glaucophane
Crossite........Intermediate zone of glaucophane	Crossite

Lawsonite, which may show varying degrees of replacement by epidote, sericite, or chlorite, in some rocks contains cores rich in hematite flakes and also includes rutile needles. It is usually polysynthetically twinned. Members of the epidote group include epidote, clinozoisite, pumpelleyite, and uncommon zoisite. Epidote not uncommonly contains allanite cores. Pumpelleyite usually shows simple twins. Garnets show a considerable range in composition: almandite, 45 to 55 per cent; pyrope, 15 to 20 per cent; grossularite, 10 to 30 per cent; andradite, 5 to 25 per cent; and spessartite, maximum 10 per cent. Of the micas, muscovite is the most common; biotite is relatively rare; fuchsite has been reported. In some schists quartz is relatively abundant, in others it is minor. Chlorite, which may be very abundant, is either primary or secondary after lawsonite, garnet, glaucophane, or sodic pyroxene. Among the more common accessories are apatite, rutile, omphacite, sphene, magnetite, allanite, and calcite; less common are pyrite and tourmaline (blue, green, or zoned). Secondary minerals, in addition to chlorite, are antigorite, talc (after amphiboles), sericite (after feldspar), leucoxene, and limonite.

FIG. 67a. Glaucophane schist; glaucophane, muscovite, epidote, chlorite, calcite. Val de Bagna, Valais, Switzerland. Nicols not crossed, × 10.

Textures and Microstructures. Most of the rocks show well-oriented minerals, including glaucophane, crossite, actinolite, muscovite, and chlorite. Glaucophane and crossite occur in slender, subhedral prisms, in broader, stout prisms, or in acicular, felted aggregates. In larger amphibole crystals inclusions of sphene or rutile may be common. Larger crystals also may be broken by cross fractures and healed by a variety of minerals. Lawsonite shows considerable shape variation, forming euhedra to subhedra that are equant, tabular, or prismatic and anhedral angular grains or granular lenticles. Epidote is usually anhedral-granular, rarely euhedral. Pumpelleyite is common locally in crosscutting veinlets. Albite forms anhedra, tabular euhedra, fine-grained veins, and subhedral poikiloblasts. Quartz is anhedral-granular, in small to large irregular grains. It may show undulatory extinction and marginal granulation.

Some rock types are fine- and even-grained. Others contain both fine- and coarse-grained phases. Minerals that appear as porphyroblasts include glaucophane, crossite, epidote (inclusions of glaucophane, crossite, and rutile), lawsonite, muscovite (in some cases markedly poikiloblastic), and garnet (inclusions of glaucophane and sphene). Some porphyroblasts of crossite or glaucophane are fringed by pressure shadows of quartz and other minerals. Albite also forms large porphyroblasts that usually are poikilitic, enclosing grains or granular stringers of lawsonite, glaucophane, epidote, and sphene, some of which trace sigmoid patterns.

Small-scale banding, conspicuous in many varieties, consists of mineralogically contrasting layers. Some bands are monomineralic; others are mineralogically complex: bands of muscovite, of fine-grained glaucophane, of coarse porphyroblastic glaucophane, or bands rich in epidote, or albite, or quartz.

GLAUCOPHANE AMPHIBOLITES AND RELATED ROCKS

Glaucophane amphibolites are commonly coarse-grained, poorly foliated to decussate rocks containing glaucophane (less usually crossite) as the predominating or major constituent, with variable but subordinate amounts of usually garnet or epidote.

The following mineralogical varieties are included:

Epidote-glaucophane amphibolites, including epidote glaucophanites
Garnet-glaucophane amphibolites, including garnet glaucophanites
Lawsonite-glaucophane amphibolites (rare)
Glaucophane metagabbros
Crossite amphibolites ± albite (rare)

In garnet-glaucophane amphibolites (perhaps the most common type) accessories are hornblende, epidote, clinozoisite, chlorite, sphene, rutile, and magnetite. One type, a "glaucophane eclogite," is rich in the rare mineral pseudobrookite. In epidote-glaucophane amphibolites the accessory suite includes hornblende, chlorite, albite, sphene, and magnetite. Chlorite and leucoxene are secondary.

Glaucophane metagabbros are gabbros (and diabases) in which glaucophane (± crossite) forms pseudomorphs after augite, and labradorite has been converted to a mixture of albite and epidote (or lawsonite). Omphacite may also be present, and accessories are chlorite, apatite, rutile, quartz, and magnetite. Chlorite, sericite, and leucoxene are secondary.

Crossite amphibolites are uncommon types containing large unoriented crossite blades. Some varieties contain considerable albite. Accessories are sphene, quartz, and rare zircon and stilpnomelane.

The rocks are nonschistose, with the amphibole blades in decussate to poor orientation. Garnets may form porphyroblasts. Glaucophane forms stout, broad prisms, generally subhedral, and includes sphene grains. Crossite may be in more slender to fibrous crystals, enclosing albite; varied zonal growths with glaucophane are common. In glaucophane metagabbros the fabric is largely inherited.

Occurrence and Origin

Glaucophane schists, glaucophane amphibolites, and related rocks are associated with metamorphosed geosynclinal sediments and lavas and altered ultramafic intrusives. A wide variety of minor rocks occur with the glaucophane rocks, including such types as sodic pyroxene-garnet granulite and schist, hornblende granulite, lawsonite-chlorite schist, sodic hornblende-chlorite-talc schist, and other unusual rocks containing various amphiboles in addition to members of the epidote group, chlorite and talc. Some have considered glaucophane rocks to represent a special metamorphic facies (glaucophane schist facies) of high pressure and low to medium temperature. Other ideas on the origin of these rocks include low- to high-grade regional metamorphism of such alkaline rocks as spilites, sodic rhyolites, various sodic tuffs, and adinoles; hydrothermal metamorphism and local introduction of Na, Fe, Mg into such rocks as graywackes, cherts, and basalts; and retrograde metamorphism of eclogites. Since the rocks are mineralogically, texturally, and chemically highly variable, it is unlikely that they have all originated in the same way. Nor are all glaucophane rocks abnormally rich in Na, but rather a normal Na content has left plagioclase to enter an amphibole in many cases. Glaucophane rocks are conspicuously associated with other metamorphic rocks of the epidote amphibolite facies and also of the greenschist facies. Most glaucophane rocks probably have formed by regional metamorphism of varied sediments and igneous rocks under somewhat specialized conditions of the epidote-amphibolite facies in which, with increasing pressure, plagioclase contributes Na to hornblende or actinolite to form glaucophane and some Ca silicate such as epidote or lawsonite. Some of the parent types would be basalts, gabbros, diabases, peridotites, serpentinites, andesites, graywackes, and eclogites. Undoubtedly some glaucophane rocks that are abnormally rich in Na have either had special sodic parents (spilites, sodic tuffs) or have resulted from local sodic metasomatism of such rocks as sandstones, cherts, and various felsic to mafic igneous types.

Well-known occurrences include those of the California Coast Ranges (Franciscan group—Upper Jurassic), northern Venezuela, Corsica, and Val de Bagne in Valais, Switzerland.

Hornblende Schists

Definition. Markedly foliated rocks, usually dark-colored, consisting of dominant hornblende in association normally with plagioclase and epidote.

Mineralogy. In addition to hornblende, plagioclase, and epidote,

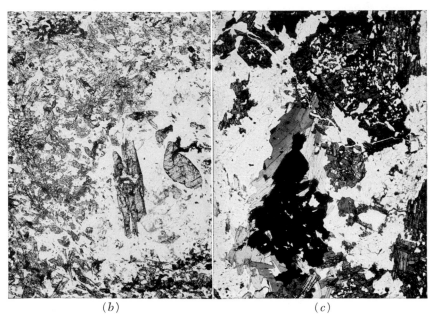

| (b) | (c) |

FIG. 67b, c. (b) Hornblende schist; actinolitic hornblende, albite, quartz, epidote porphyroblasts, sphene. Canon City, Colorado. Nicols not crossed ×10. (c) Hornblende-biotite gneiss; poikiloblastic hornblende, biotite overgrowths on magnetite, oligoclase, minor quartz. Eight Mile Park, Colorado. Nicols not crossed, ×10.

other common essential constituents are quartz, biotite, garnet, and less commonly microcline. Zoisite may proxy for epidote. The hornblende is usually light green to deep bluish green, i.e., "actinolitic" hornblende (Fig. 67b), in contrast to the dark green and brown varieties of higher-grade amphibole rocks, although some quartzose schists have dark green hornblende. The plagioclase is albite or sodic oligoclase, rarely more calcic to andesine, or extraordinarily to labradorite. Garnet is almanditic. In most types plagioclase exceeds quartz or microcline. Accessories include magnetite, hematite, ilmenite, apatite, sphene, and chlorite.

Textures and Microstructures. The amphibole forms slender prisms and needles, with marked parallel orientation and with intergranular epidote. In some cases hornblende also forms porphyroblasts with rims of epidote granules. Biotite flakes also show distinct parallelism. Garnet, which may be concentrated in bands, forms rough porphyroblasts, in some cases poikilitic. Quartz and feldspar are anhedral, in aggregates or interstitial grains. "Feather amphibolites," or Hornblendegarbenschiefer, contain large poikiloblastic hornblende blades, which include quartz, feldspar, and magnetite, and which are flattened in decussate or stellate patterns on foliation planes.

Occurrence and Origin. Hornblende schists are formed by low-grade regional metamorphism of either mafic igneous rocks such as basalts, diabases, basaltic tuffs, gabbros, and some andesites and diorites or of arenaceous sediments containing admixed dolomite, kaolinite, and iron oxide minerals or chlorite and iron oxide minerals. Most of the rocks are referred to the albite-epidote amphibolite facies, chloritoid-almandite subfacies. Some types, with nonactinolitic hornblende and garnet and andesine, were formed under somewhat higher intensity conditions, Examples occur in the Van Horn area, Texas, and in New England.

Hornblende Gneisses and Amphibolites

Definition. Amphibolites are amphibole-rich rocks with essential plagioclase. Some are well foliated, even schistose, but most are poorly foliated or hardly at all. Hornblende gneisses are foliated hornblende-feldspar-quartz rocks.

Mineralogy. The main types are:

Hornblende gneiss: hornblende, plagioclase, quartz. Varieties: ± garnet, ± biotite (Fig. 67c), ± augite or diopside, ± hypersthene, ± epidote or zoisite. Accessories: rutile, magnetite, ilmenite, sphene.

Hornblende amphibolite: hornblende, plagioclase (Fig. 68b). Varieties: ± garnet, ± biotite, ± diopside or augite, ± epidote or zoisite. Accessories: rutile, sphene, apatite, quartz, magnetite, hematite, ilmenite, calcite, chlorite, edenite, actinolite, anthophyllite, pyrrhotite, pyrite, scapolite, tourmaline.

The hornblende is green, dark green, greenish brown, olive brown, or brown. In some examples it is zoned with light green cores and darker green margins. If hornblende occurs both as porphyroblasts and matrix prisms, the two may be different in color. The feldspar commonly is andesine (Fig. 68a), though types as sodic as oligoclase and as calcic as bytownite also occur. Zoning of normal or reversed types may be present. Some amphibolites consist only of essential hornblende, with plagioclase merely accessory.

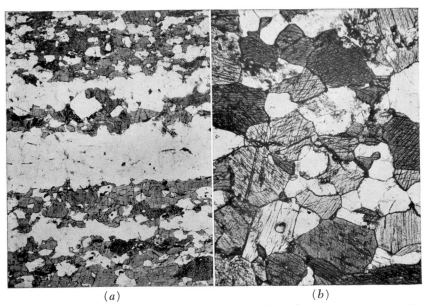

(a)   (b)

FIG. 68. (a) Banded hornblende gneiss; hornblende, andesine, quartz, magnetite. Northeastern Idaho. Nicols not crossed, ×10. (b) Amphibolite; hornblende, andesine. Thirty-one Mile Mountain, Guffey, Colorado. Nicols not crossed, ×32, section cut normal to foliation. (*Courtesy of J. E. Bever.*)

Textures and Microstructures. The hornblende prisms are parallel or subparallel, in decussate arrangement, or less usually in radial groups. They may be uniformly distributed or restricted to or concentrated in layers or in small lenses, pods, or "eyes." In some rocks the amphibole is of uniform size, similar to the other constituents; in other rocks it occurs both as porphyroblasts and matrix units; in still others it is entirely porphyroblastic, commonly with irregular, frayed, or shredded margins. Larger crystals are usually poikiloblastic, including such species as quartz, feldspar, magnetite, ilmenite, and apatite. Matrix hornblende is in slender to stubby prisms or needles or in felted to irregular clusters. Hornblende is replaced by biotite or chlorite or rimmed by edenite; it may retain relict cores of augite. Plagioclase and garnet also form porphyroblasts, the former including quartz or amphibole, and the latter enclosing chiefly quartz, plagioclase, diopside, and magnetite. Inclusions may be zonally or radially arranged or in layers oriented parallel with or at an angle to the foliation. Biotite rarely forms porphyroblasts, but matrix biotite includes hornblende, quartz, and plagioclase. Matrix plagioclase varies in form from anhedral grains to subhedral tabular crystals. Twinning may be inconspicuous, and the feldspar may be saussuritized. Magnetite forms anhedra or skeletal grains; ilmenite is typically in platy subhedra. The two together may form irregular stringers. Sphene occurs in grains and overgrowths on ilmenite.

Many of the rocks show banding (Fig. 68a), usually dark-light with such combinations of alternating layers as hornblende versus plagioclase ± quartz; hornblende versus biotite, plagioclase, quartz; hornblende versus epidote + plagioclase; and hornblende versus diopside. Some minerals also are concentrated in lenses or irregular patches and streaks: quartz; plagioclase; quartz-plagioclase; quartz-garnet; epidote-garnet; and hornblende.

Occurrence and Origin. Hornblende gneisses and amphibolites may originate in the following ways:

1. By medium- to high-grade regional metamorphism (amphibolite facies, staurolite-kyanite subfacies, sillimanite-almandite subfacies) of:

    a. Intermediate and mafic igneous rocks including quartz latites, tonalites, andesites, diorites, basalts, diabases, gabbros, and norites

    b. Marls, calcareous hybrid tuffs, quartzose sediments containing dolomite and kaolinite or calcite-chlorite-quartz sediments

2. By metasomatism of carbonate rocks

From the gross mineralogical composition it is not always possible to decide if the rocks are ortho- or para-amphibolites or gneisses. The following features may be of assistance in some cases:

Orthoamphibolites and orthogneisses

1. Occurrence of common normal zoning in plagioclase
2. Relict diabasic, porphyritic, or granitoid textures
3. Remnants of augite or hypersthene in central parts of hornblende
4. General absence or subordination of bands, particularly biotite-, epidote-, or quartz-rich

5. Crosscutting relations to enclosing metasedimentary rocks in the field
6. Exomorphic and endomorphic mineralogical changes along contacts of layers
7. Relatively high concentration of characteristic trace elements such as Ni, Cr, Sc, Co, and Cu

Para-amphibolites and paragneisses

1. Quartz-rich types
2. Abundance of biotite or microcline
3. Pronounced and variable mineralogical banding, involving quartz, biotite, and epidote
4. Notable amounts of K_2O in the hornblende
5. Large segregations of quartz-garnet, garnet-epidote, or garnet-diopside, which may represent metaconcretions
6. Relatively high concentrations of the trace elements Pb, Ba, Mn, and Au
7. Presence of tourmaline, which is either recrystallized detrital or metasomatic
8. Presence of scapolite
9. Lateral gradation into metasedimentary rocks, such as marbles

Excellent examples are widespread: in the Ammonoosuc Volcanics (Ordovician) of New Hampshire; in the Grenville (pre-Cambrian) of the Adirondacks; in the Roan gneiss (pre-Cambrian) of North Carolina; in the Biwabik (pre-Cambrian) of Minnesota; and in the Swandyke (pre-Cambrian) of Colorado.

EPIDOTE-GROUP ROCKS

General

Foliated rocks in which epidote is an abundant essential constituent have already been described under various other groups: chlorite schists, stilpnomelane schists, calc schists, muscovite schists, biotite schists, hornblende schists and gneisses, and glaucophane schists. Likewise some skarns may be classed as nonfoliated epidote-rich rocks.

Zoisite also is widespread in a variety of metamorphic rocks, including skarns, marbles, biotite-zoisite schists, zoisite amphibolites, and zoisite (± hornblende) granulites. The last is formed by the high-grade regional metamorphism of impure sandstones containing dolomite and kaolinite or chlorite and calcite.

Pumpelleyite may be an abundant constituent of chlorite schists, actinolite schists, and glaucophane schists. It also is formed by the low-grade hydrothermal alteration of a variety of rocks including andesites, basalts, diabases, spilites, skarns, and hornfelses.

The process of saussuritization involves the breakdown of plagioclase with separation of the Na and Ca into different products. Na forms clear albite granules, and Ca appears chiefly in zoisite or epidote, less usually prehnite or grossularite. Other minerals detected in the normally fine-grained greenish to white mixture are quartz, calcite, actinolite, chlorite, rutile, and rare muscovite, orthoclase, and scapolite. The process is usually accompanied by other changes in the rock, including alteration of pyroxene to actinolite or hornblende (uralitization), chlorite and iron oxides, and the alteration of olivine to serpentine, talc, chlorite, or actinolite. Under ideal development it results in fine- to medium-grained rocks consisting chiefly of albite, epidote or zoisite, actinolite, and prehnite. The process is widespread in gabbros but also occurs in diorites and mafic gneisses. In some cases it is hydrothermal, perhaps even autohydrothermal, in origin. In metamorphic rocks it may represent a retrograde metamorphic change.

Piedmontite Schists

Definition. Piedmontite schists are schistose rocks containing piedmontite as an essential to major constituent.

Mineralogy. The main petrologic types are all quartzose:

Muscovite-piedmontite ± hematite
Muscovite-calcite-piedmontite

Minor constituents are albite, epidote, and spessartite. Accessories are magnetite, tourmaline, sphene, rutile, and apatite. Rare accessories are chlorite, barite, and kyanite. The piedmontite, pleochroic in brilliant shades of yellow, violet, and carmine, commonly shows marked zoning. The zoning may differ in different crystals in the same rock. In some rocks both piedmontite and epidote occur together, and the epidote may have a core containing irregular rose (manganiferous) spots. Tourmaline is colorless to pale purple.

Textures and Microstructures. The texture is schistose, with well-oriented piedmontite and muscovite. Quartz grains may also be slightly elongated. Many of the rocks are minutely banded with layers rich in piedmontite alternating with quartzose or micaceous layers. Quartz, anhedral and even-grained, may include piedmontite, epidote, and garnet. Undulatory extinction is common. Albite is finely granular or forms porphyroblasts enclosing piedmontite, epidote, and hematite.

Piedmontite typically forms minute prismatic anhedra, parallelly oriented, in bands or disseminated. Cracks at right angles to the elongation (*b*) are typically present. Some prisms may be bent or broken. Muscovite forms fine to coarse flakes and plates, rarely interleaved with chlorite. Spessarite appears in small euhedra or porphyroblasts that include piedmontite, magnetite, epidote, magnetite, rutile, and hematite. Hematite and magnetite are either anhedral or euhedral, the former in deep red hexagonal plates, the latter in octahedra. Rutile forms rounded grains, euhedral crystals, and knee-shaped twins. Uncommon barite appears in angular anhedral grains. Tourmaline euhedra form single crystals or clusters.

Occurrence and Origin. Piedmontite schists are rare rocks, associated with epidote schists, chlorite schists, stilpnomelane schists, amphibole schists, glaucophane schists, and muscovite schists. Formed by the low-grade, regional metamorphism (muscovite-chlorite subfacies of the greenschist facies) of impure manganiferous sandstones. That Mn has entered epidote instead of forming spessartite may be due to the presence of abundant water. Well-studied examples occur in Japan and in western Otago, New Zealand. Piedmontite-muscovite-quartz schists also occur near Pilar in northern New Mexico.

Unakite, Epidosite, and Related Rocks

Among epidote-rich rocks formed by metasomatism or by metamorphic differentiation are unakites, epidosites, and epidotites.

Unakites are epidote-quartz-feldspar rocks formed from granites, granodiorites, and quartz syenites by hydrothermal replacement of plagioclase, potash feldspar, and mafics by epidote. Where all feldspar and mafics are replaced, unakites grade into epidosites. The potash feldspar is either orthoclase or microcline. Other minerals in unakites are relict biotite, apatite, magnetite, and zircon. Secondary constituents in addition to the epidote are quartz, pyrite, rutile, sericite, kaolinite, chlorite, leucoxene, and limonite. Unakites are medium- to coarse-grained, usually nonfoliated. Epidote occurs in irregular patches of minute granules and in fine-grained veinlets. Quartz is commonly undulatory, may show mortar structure, and is filled with fine rutile needles. Feldspar also may be fractured. Some secondary quartz veinlets may cut other minerals, including epidote. Unakites occur as irregular masses, lenses, and veins in granitic rocks. In the United States the rock was first described from the Unaka Mountains of western North Carolina and eastern Tennessee. Other occurrences are in western Virginia.

Helsinkites are "epidote granites and epidote quartz diorites" probably formed by metasomatic action similar to the development of unakites but on a larger scale.

Epidosites are metasomatic epidote-quartz rocks that occur as veins in greenschists, amphibolites, and granitic rocks. They also contain minor albite, chlorite, actinolite, calcite, and leucoxene. Their texture is usually fine-grained anhedral, but albite may appear as scattered euhedral tablets. Quartz veinlets cut the aggregate. The name epidosite also has been erroneously applied to quartz-epidote-muscovite schists formed by low-grade regional metamorphism of calcareous graywackes.

Epidotite, a variably used term, may be applied to massive or poorly foliated rocks composed mainly of epidote, commonly with minor hornblende, plagioclase, chlorite, quartz, calcite, and garnet. Many are associated with amphibolites intruded by granite sills.

FERRUGINOUS AND MANGANIFEROUS ROCKS

Hydrous Iron Silicate Rocks

Definition. Many hydrous iron silicate rocks have been given various local names, including taconite, which, however, has been used in such a variety of ways both petrographic and economic that its employment may be confusing. Petrographically taconite indicates a rock containing fine-grained quartz (chert), the hydrous iron silicates greenalite, minnesotaite, and stilpnomelane, magnetite ± hematite, and commonly some siderite. The granule texture of the iron silicate minerals is characteristically present. Some of these rocks are banded or very finely laminated ("slaty"); others have a spotted or mottled appearance. The rocks are normally fine-grained.

Mineralogy. The three hydrous iron silicates commonly occur together, but either minnesotaite or stilpnomelane may predominate. Minnesotaite occurs mainly in two ways: as colorless needles or plates arranged in bundles or sheaves or as light green to olive green, rounded granular aggregates of submicroscopic needles in random, felted orientation. Where it occurs as very fine grained granules it resembles greenalite closely but differs in its aggregate polarization and mottled appearance.

Greenalite is apparently isotropic and ranges from olive green to dark olive brown in color, becoming only partly translucent. It characteristically forms oval to elongated granules. Stilpnomelane forms minute needles and plates, commonly radially arranged. In color it varies from olive green to dark brown and is strongly pleochroic. A considerable range in color and indices may be found in a single rock specimen. Much stilpnomelane has apparently been mistaken for grunerite. The extremely fine grained varieties of these minerals require x-ray methods for identification.

Quartz is typically very fine grained to almost submicroscopic. It may be colored reddish by minute hematite inclusions or greenish to brownish by inclusions of iron silicates. Magnetite occurs as fine-grained "dust" and as larger rounded and octahedral grains, commonly in clusters. Siderite forms single rhombohedra, granular patches, or layers. Dolomite and calcite are also found. The magnesium carbonate minerals may show zoning. Other accessory minerals are graphite, pyrite, and apatite.

Mineralogically taconites can be separated into silicate taconite, in which hydrous iron silicates predominate; magnetite taconite, characterized by layers or streaks of granular magnetite, more quartz and less of the iron silicate minerals; carbonate taconite; and hematite or jaspery taconite.

Magnetite alters to hematite (martite). The iron silicates may be leached out, leaving cavities partly filled by goethite. Siderite may also be leached and alters to iron oxide. Minnesotaite and stilpnomelane alter to goethite, hematite, kaolinite, and nontronite.

Textures and Microstructures. The granules vary in shape from smooth elongated ovoids to highly angular, irregular shreds and ribbons that extend out into wispy tails. Any of the rock minerals may occur in granules, but this form is especially characteristic of the hydrous iron silicates. Some granules consist of more than one species: greenalite + minnesotaite + siderite, quartz + minnesotaite + magnetite, stilpnomelane + minnesotaite. In one thin section several different minerals may appear in granules. Minnesotaite may be interstitial to granules of the other iron silicates, as needles radiating from the granules. Stilpnomelane may also be irregular in outline and very finely felted in structure. Some granules contain minute, uniformly sized, ringlike structures of chert or dusty hematite or graphite which are thought to represent relict organic structures. Any type of granule may be cut by veinlets of minnesotaite, quartz, or carbonate, rarely stilpnomelane. Quartz is the most abundant matrix mineral.

In banded varieties magnetite forms layers and continuous stringers, which are wavy, of varying thickness, and branching. Siderite and stilpnomelane also occur in magnetite bands, and carbonate minerals may form bordering layers on both sides of magnetite streaks. Granules in these rocks consist mainly of quartz and are penciled by a very thin dusty rim of hematite, graphite, or needles of iron silicate. Bands of stilpnomelane or of minnesotaite also occur.

In rocks of slaty structure the grains become minute. Very finely divided iron silicates may be interlayered with tiny magnetite or hematite grains. Exact identification of the constituents may require the use of x-rays. Minnesotaite and stilpnomelane range in grain size from microcrystalline to coarsely crystalline.

Occurrence and Origin. Hydrous iron silicate rocks are well represented in the pre-Cambrian iron formations of the Lake Superior region, in association with black slate, ferruginous slate, quartzite, conglomeratic quartzite, and greenstones. Relict algal structures remain in some parts of the iron formation.

The original minerals are believed to have been greenalite, siderite, and very fine grained quartz (chert), perhaps in the form of chalcedony. Some hematite may also have been original. Low-grade regional metamorphism (greenschist facies) has formed stilpnomelane, minnesotaite, and magnetite and recrystallized some of the quartz, but some greenalite and carbonates are preserved. Primary chert tends to be eliminated with metamorphism through formation of iron silicates. One suggestion is that the intimate granule texture favors iron silicate formation and that local metamorphism of the hydrothermal type, around pegmatites, diabases, and quartz veins, has produced much stilpnomelane and minnesotaite. Another investigator believes minnesotaite to be a relict sedimentary mineral.

Jaspilites, Hematite Schists, and Related Rocks

Definition. Jaspilite and related rocks consist mainly of hematite, commonly specularite, and quartz. Jaspilites contain hematite and fine-grained quartz ("chert") so coated by hematite that it appears red in hand specimen. Jaspilites usually are banded but may have a mottled or fragmental texture. If the quartz is not coated and is coarser-grained, the rocks are known as hematite or specularite schists or hematite quartzites.

Mineralogy. In jaspilite or "cherty" rocks the quartz is normally very fine grained, in an interlocking texture, and the individual grains are coated by minute flakes of hematite and may also carry hematite plates as inclusions. Hematite is the second most abundant mineral, occurring as quartz-grain coatings, as individual flakes within quartzose layers, and as the main component of iron-rich bands. Magnetite may be present in varying amounts, and siderite, ankerite, and dolomite may be locally abundant. Accessory minerals are chlorite, muscovite, calcite, and apatite.

Hematite schists, characterized by colorless, coarser quartz, contain hematite as the main iron oxide but may also have some magnetite in variable amounts. Muscovite, oligoclase, and apatite are accessory. Some Swedish types contain only moderate amounts of quartz but more feldspar and biotite, with minor apatite. Itabirite is a variety of banded specularite quartzite from Brazil. Rocks in which magnetite becomes more important can also contain accessory garnet, epidote, or amphibole. There are all gradations between rocks containing mainly hematite and those consisting dominantly of magnetite. Secondary minerals are limonite, goethite, and psilomelane.

Textures and Microstructures. In banded jaspilites quartz-rich layers alternate with layers richer in hematite. Individual quartz grains may be slightly elongated in the plane of the banding. The banding is very fine to coarse, ribbonlike, or even crenulated. In mottled jaspilites ovoid quartz masses with a nucleus clouded red by hematite occur in the silica layers. Other mottled varieties have small rounded to lenticular patches of fine-grained quartz.

Some jaspilites are fragmental, containing pieces of hematitic ore or of jaspery quartz in a matrix of homogeneous jaspilite. The ore fragments are long oval or lenticular masses of very fine grained quartz and tiny hematite flakes cut by veinlets of coarser-grained quartz or hematite. The ore fragment usually is bordered by a rim of dense hematite. The matrix consists mainly of interlocking fine-grained quartz with a few large patches of somewhat coarser grained quartz marginally granulated. Veinlets of finely crystalline matrix quartz transect the patches, which also contain some siderite and hematite. Plates of chlorite may occur in the matrix. The term jaspilite has also been extended to banded martite-jasper rocks in which hematite is pseudomorphous after magnetite. These rocks may show polygonal patterns in the jasper bands, in which dusty hematite areas are bounded by clear silica or even spherulites of fibrous silica with hematite cores.

Hematite schists are banded with quartz layers and hematite ($\pm$ magnetite)-quartz layers. Oriented quartz overgrowths may be seen on detrital quartz grains. Disseminated carbonate rhombohedra may be present, and hematite-free quartz occurs pseudomorphous after carbonate rhombs. In magnetite varieties iron layers can also carry iron silicates, or these minerals may appear in separate streaks.

Occurrence and Origin. Iron-bearing rocks of various types are characteristic of pre-Cambrian areas in many parts of the world, including the Canadian shield, Venezuela, Brazil, India, Fennoscandia, Australia, South Africa, and Manchuria. Jaspilites are common in the iron formations of the Lake Superior region in the United States and in Canada, where they occur in association with greenstones, sideritic slates, magnetite slates, carbonaceous slates, argillites, quartzites, and conglomeratic quartzites. The Brazilian itabirites are found with quartzites, slates, marbles, and locally amphibolites. The banded metamorphic hematite rocks of India are associated with phyllites, some mica schist, chloritic quartzites, carbonaceous quartzites, and metatuffs. The Swedish hematite rocks, many of which contain some magnetite, occur in leptites.

In "cherty" rocks the original silica mineral was nonclastic, probably chalcedony. Some investigators believe the original iron mineral was siderite; others have stated that both iron carbonate and iron oxide were original. Most jaspilites have been subjected only to low-grade metamorphism, as shown by the fine grain of the quartz and the retention of other relict structures. One hypothesis suggests large-scale metasomatic introduction of iron into porous sandy and shaly sediments followed by some metamorphism; another requires silicification of ferruginous slates and schists.

Hematite schists (including itabirite) were formed by low- to medium-grade regional metamorphism of limonitic or hematitic sandstones or, in some cases, perhaps by somewhat more advanced local metamorphism of iron rocks originally containing chalcedonic quartz. The presence of much magnetite is indicative of higher-grade metamorphism.

Magnetite Rocks

Definition. In magnetite rocks abundant magnetite is the predominant iron oxide mineral; hematite may or may not be present. In some varieties quartz is essential, and in other types iron silicate minerals are more common. A banded structure is typical of quartzose types; a schistose structure generally typifies those with abundant iron silicates.

Mineralogy. The quartz–magnetite–iron silicate ratio may show considerable variation. Some types contain only accessory iron silicates. Magnetite is variable in grain size, even in a single section, but usually is relatively coarse grained. It occurs as octahedra or as rounded particles in clusters or elongated groups. It may be altered to hematite (martite), and in some rare varieties it occurs as hexagonal plates, pseudomorphous after hematite. Quartz is uniformly coarse grained, and rocks containing iron silicates in abundance usually have the coarsest quartz of any rocks of the "iron formations." The common iron-bearing silicates include grunerite, actinolite, and garnet. Accessory constituents are biotite, chlorite, epidote, fayalite, hornblende, riebeckite, crossite, hedenbergite, iron-rich hypersthene, siderite, dolomite, pyrrhotite, apatite, barrandite, and zircon. Some South African varieties contain minor muscovite and roscoelite.

Grunerite varies in habit from fibrous to short prismatic with diamond-shaped basal sections. Prism faces can be well developed, but terminations are irregular. Cross striations roughly parallel with (001) are common. The mineral may show very fine lamellar twinning. Less common actinolite is usually fibrous and somewhat finer grained. The garnet is almandite, with almandite-spessartite appearing in rocks richer in MnO, which also may contain a manganiferous amphibole. Rarely, where Ca was abundant, andradite may be formed. Alteration minerals are hematite, goethite, limonite, and chlorite.

Common mineralogical associations are:

Quartz-magnetite (including martite-quartzite)
Quartz-magnetite-grunerite (Fig. 69*b*) ± actinolite
Grunerite-magnetite with subordinate quartz and variable garnet, hypersthene, and hedenbergite
Magnetite-garnet ± hypersthene

At one end the rocks grade into hematite schists and hematite quartzites, at the other into grunerite schists, grunerite eulysites, and eulysites. There are also grunerite-magnetite rocks and actinolite-magnetite rocks in which carbonate minerals, mainly dolomite, greatly exceed quartz. Some magnetite-bearing rocks also contain much chamosite. Contact metamorphosed impure limonites in Brittany consist of magnetite and chamosite, but in general chamosite is not abundant in metamorphic rocks.

Textures and Microstructures. Many of these rocks are markedly banded (Fig. 69*a*), commonly with alternating quartzose layers and magnetite-rich layers. The width of the individual bands varies greatly; some are crenulated. Not uncommonly very tight and intricate small-scale folding is present. The layering may be relatively complex mineralogically, with bands of magnetite-quartz-hornblende, magnetite-quartz-grunerite, magnetite-quartz-apatite, magnetite-pyrrhotite, magnetite-biotite, grunerite-actinolite-quartz, grunerite-apatite, gru-

nerite-actinolite-magnetite, grunerite-riebeckite-magnetite, and gru-
nerite-actinolite, but the bands may also consist essentially of only a
single silicate mineral such as garnet or epidote. Banding may also
result from variations in proportions of the same constituents. In many
cases the needles of actinolite or grunerite are randomly arranged or
may show prominent rosette structure; in other rocks their long axes
are parallel with the banding, in which case the quartz and magnetite

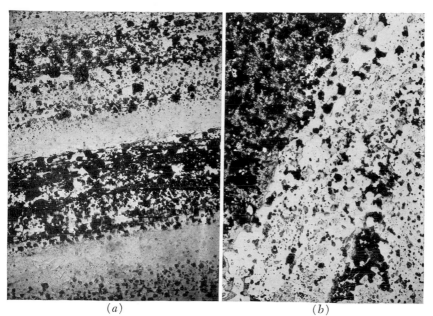

(a)　　　　　　　　　　　　　　(b)

FIG. 69. (a) Magnetite schist; magnetite, hematite, quartz in variously proportioned bands. Cherry Creek, Montana. Nicols not crossed, ×10. (b) Magnetite-
grunerite schist; quartz, magnetite, grunerite in variously proportioned bands.
Cherry Creek, Montana. Nicols not crossed, ×10.

grains are also somewhat elongated. Pyroxenes of these rocks may
show uralitization or intergrowths with amphiboles.

Some rocks are massive, particularly the magnetite-garnet types. In
a variety from Käymäjärvi, northern Sweden, fine-grained magnetite
occurs in rounded blebs that are regarded as metamorphosed greenalite granules.

Occurrence and Origin. Magnetite rocks are common in the pre-
Cambrian of many areas including the Lake Superior region, south-
western Montana, Norway, Sweden, South Africa, India, and Australia.
Associated rocks include grunerite and actinolite marbles, hematite

schists, leptites, pyroxene-garnet gneiss, amphibole gneiss, garnet amphibolite, eulysite, sillimanite-quartz schist, and glassy quartzite. Lower-grade rocks, such as spotted hornfels, calc-silicate rock, and metatuff, occur with some contact types.

Magnetite rocks are usually formed by high-grade regional metamorphism of chert-siderite or chert-greenalite rocks. With increasing metamorphism quartz tends to be eliminated through the formation of silicates. They are also formed by increased metamorphism of lower-grade hematite-quartz metamorphic rocks. Some types are of contact metamorphic origin (Harz Mountains, Germany) and were limonitic sandstones and shales.

Eulysites and Related Rocks

Definition. Eulysites are characterized by the presence of iron-rich olivine, fayalite, as an essential or important constituent. Iron pyroxenes, amphiboles, and garnet are also commonly abundant. The texture is massive to crudely foliated.

Mineralogy. Olivine ranges from about 50 to 75 per cent normally, but some eulysites contain as little as 10 per cent fayalite. The composition of the olivine varies from 55 to 66 per cent FeO; some types are manganiferous with 4 to 9 per cent MnO. A few eulysites are rich in the manganiferous varieties, knebelite and tephroite. Several mineralogical types may be distinguished:

1. Normal eulysite: Fayalite or manganiferous olivine with combinations in varying proportions of diopside-hedenbergite, spessartite-almandite, ferroan anthophyllite, hornblende, magnetite, and accessory zircon, apatite, pyrrhotite, pyrite, grunerite, picotite, biotite, quartz, labradorite, and potash feldspar. Some are relatively rich in quartz; others lack it almost entirely.

2. Hypersthene eulysite: Iron-rich hypersthene and fayalite with combinations of hedenbergite, augite, grunerite, hornblende, and accessory garnet, magnetite, apatite, and pyrrhotite.

3. Grunerite eulysite (collobrièrite): Grunerite and fayalite with magnetite, spessartite-almandite, and accessory zircon, apatite, pyrrhotite, hornblende, biotite, and quartz.

4. Anthophyllite eulysite: Fayalite, ferroan anthophyllite with grunerite, hornblende, and accessory almandite, quartz, hedenbergite, apatite, and magnetite.

5. Cordierite eulysites: Fayalite, cordierite (as much as 33 per cent) with combinations of magnetite, quartz, siderite, garnet, biotite, and accessory hedenbergite, hypersthene, grunerite, anthophyllite, ac-

tinolite, hornblende, crocidolite, potash feldspar, pleonaste, pyrrhotite, and apatite.

6. Other varieties: (*a*) Fayalite, siderite, quartz, pyrrhotite. (*b*) Tephroite, schefferite, manganoan vesuvianite. (*c*) Knebelite, manganoan hornblende, spessartite, rhodonite, rhodochrosite, magnetite, orthoclase.

The proportions of the various minerals in these types may vary considerably. Grunerite eulysites (Fig. 70*a*) grade into grunerite schists

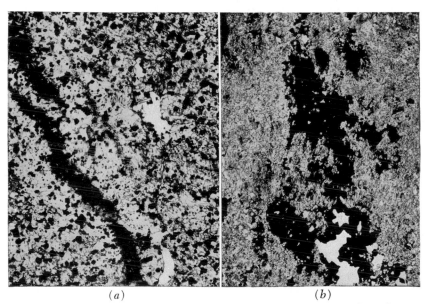

(*a*)   (*b*)

FIG. 70. (*a*) Eulysite; large fayalite crystals enclosing grunerite and much magnetite, some in bands, minor quartz. Beartooth Mountains, Montana. Nicols not crossed, ×10. (*b*) Emery; corundum, spinel, magnetite in streaks. Naxos, Greece. Nicols not crossed, ×10.

or grunerite-almandite schists; anthophyllite eulysites pass into anthophyllite schists and anthophyllite amphibolites; and hypersthene eulysites grade into hypersthene-grunerite-garnet rocks. Alteration minerals are chlorite, serpentine, talc, epidote, magnetite, hematite, and limonite.

Textures and Microstructures. The rocks are commonly rudely foliated, but the texture varies from massive to well banded. Microscopically banding or foliation may also become conspicuous. A granoblastic texture is common, and the grain size varies considerably. Olivine is typically anhedral, tending toward equidimensional, but may form elongated grains. In massive olivine-rich eulysites a mosaic texture may be conspicuous. In some rocks large formless olivine units wrap around other constituents. Olivine may display lamellar twinning and cleavage; minute inclusions of quartz, magnetite, and amphiboles may be abundant. Anthophyllite and grunerite replace olivine. In banded types the layers show much variation in mineralogy: fayalite-magnetite, garnet-pyrrhotite, garnet-apatite, quartz-magnetite, magnetite, hedenbergite, fayalite, and variable hedenbergite-fayalite content. Fayalite and hedenbergite may form porphyroblasts. In some varieties garnet and hypersthene are poikiloblastic, the former with such inclusions as grunerite and magnetite, the latter with included quartz, fayalite, and magnetite. Hypersthene may also contain the typical oriented ilmenite inclusions, and grunerite includes zircon with halos. Pseudohexagonal twinning characterizes cordierite, which may have staurolite inclusions.

Grunerite can be secondary, in veinlets or fibrous groups or sheaves. Prismatic crystals show well-developed lamellar twinning. In some rocks grunerite replaces hypersthene and in others it forms rims between fayalite grains or between pyroxene and quartz and replaces quartz as minute fibers. Hornblende also appears in radial clusters of needles. Finely lamellar intergrowths of pyroxenes are present in some cases, as well as irregular intergrowths of hypersthene in hedenbergite or zoned crystals with cores of hypersthene and margins of hedenbergite. Pyroxene rims may separate fayalite and quartz grains.

Magnetite of two generations can be present, especially in those types in which the olivine is partly replaced by an amphibole.

Occurrence and Origin. Eulysites are commonly found in close association with other types of iron- or manganese-rich metamorphic rocks such as grunerite schists, grunerite-garnet schists, hypersthene-grunerite-garnet schists, hedenbergite-garnet-magnetite rocks, almandite rocks, magnetite-almandite rocks, quartz-magnetite schists, quartz-pyrite rocks, and magnetite-ilvaite rocks.

Eulysites of regional metamorphic origin occur, for example, at Uttervik and Mansjö, Sweden; in northern Sweden; at Collobrières, near Toulon, France (grunerite type); and at Loch Duich, Ross-Shire, Scotland. Contact eulysites have been found at the base of the ultramafic Stillwater complex in the Beartooth Mountains, Montana; along the Duluth lopolith near Gunflint Lake, Minnesota; and in the Harz Mountains of Germany. Contact rocks containing manganiferous olivine have been recorded from Macskomezö, Hungary, and Langban, Sweden.

Eulysites are products of high-grade regional or contact metamorphism. Contact types are associated with ultramafic and mafic intrusives. The original rocks were siliceous iron sediments containing greenalite or ankerite and siderite or perhaps even limonite and hematite, in which reaction of iron oxide with silica produced fayalite. Eulysites may also be formed by contact metamorphism of iron sediments that were first regionally metamorphosed to quartz-magnetite rocks. Some contact types give evidence for limited metasomatism with the introduction of OH, S, Mn, and Fe. Eulysites of replacement origin do not contain quartz in association with fayalite.

Emery

Definition. Essential minerals are corundum, spinel, and magnetite. The corundum-magnetite ratio varies, but normally corundum is more abundant. In some types spinel exceeds corundum. Usually hematite is present. Some types are feldspathic with much plagioclase. The texture is massive or rudely foliated.

Mineralogy. Corundum is normally anhedral and angular, but in some types it occurs in basal plates with elongated lathlike cross sections. It is usually segregated into lenticles. It may also appear as porphyroblasts. Exsolved hematite scales and needles occur along several crystal directions in the corundum, and good parting occurs where exsolution hematite forms mainly needles rather than blebs. The corundum may display twinning. Magnetite is anhedral-granular and of variable grain size, filling interstices between corundum and spinel. The spinel is usually pleonaste but may be hercynite. Other minerals present in varying amounts are margarite, chloritoid, hoegbomite, hematite, and ilmenite (both of which show exsolution intergrowths with the other) and anorthite. Minor accessories are very numerous and reflect in part the type of rock in which the emery occurs: muscovite, biotite, chlorite, tourmaline, vesuvianite, garnet, staurolite, kyanite, sillimanite, cordierite, sapphirine (replacing spinel), amphibole, pyroxene, diaspore, rutile (rounded grains or prismatic crystals or twins), quartz, and pyrite. Corundum alters to sericite, margarite, or diaspore. Magnetite changes to hematite, but most hematite in emery is apparently primary.

Textures and Microstructures. Emery may be massive, lenticularly foliated (Fig. 70b) or layered. Rudely foliated types owe their texture to the segregation of corundum, spinel, or magnetite into small lenses. In banded varieties the individual layers range in thickness from a millimeter to several centimeters and are caused by variations in the proportions of the three main minerals or by alternation of corundum and metallic minerals. In well-foliated rocks most of the corundum crystals are oriented parallel with the banded structure. The metallic constituents may form as a network of interconnected, interstitial patches.

Occurrence and Origin. Various geological associations characterize emery. The deposits at Peekskill, New York, are irregular lenses and pods in exomorphosed schist xenoliths enclosed in the Cortlandt mafic complex (pyroxenite and norite). The Virginia deposits consist of lenses in granite and in quartzite and schist. Sericite schists and amphibolite are associated with emery at Chester, Massachusetts. Lenticular bodies of emery occur at Naxos, Greece, and at Aidin, Turkey, in marble. Elsewhere such rocks as phyllite, cordierite-corundum hornfels, mica schist, chlorite schist, talc schist, and hornblende schist occur with emery.

Emery is formed by regional or high-temperature contact metamorphism of ferruginous bauxite and lateritic clay or their metamorphosed equivalents. In contact deposits metasomatic processes may be important. This is attested to not only by the presence of such minerals as tourmaline and pyrite but also by the presence of relict schist foliation which has been inherited by the emery.

Manganese Silicate Rocks

Definition. The manganiferous metamorphic rocks are a rather special group characterized by an abundance of various manganese silicates as essential constituents. These include such rocks as the gondites of India in which spessartite, rhodonite, and manganophyllite are the chief nonmetallic manganese minerals. Some varieties also contain considerable rhodochrosite, and another associated type is a piedmontite marble. Some eulysites are also strongly manganiferous. The textures are massive to banded.

Mineralogy. The chief types are:

1. Gondite: Spessartite, quartz. Quartz may become subordinate and the typical gondite grades into a spessartite rock. Magnetite may also become abundant.

2. Rhodonite gondite: Rhodonite, spessartite, quartz. Some types contain pyroxene; others, with declining garnet, pass into rhodonite-quartz rocks, and with quartz subordinate too, into rhodonite rocks.

3. Pyroxmangite quartzite: Pyroxmangite, quartz, rhodonite.

4. Amphibole gondite: Manganiferous amphibole, spessartite, quartz. Some varieties contain considerable orthoclase.

5. Manganophyllite rocks with magnetite, barite, and manganese phosphates.

The accessory suite shows wide variations: combinations of plagioclase, microcline, wollastonite, piedmontite, grunerite, graphite, apatite, rhodochrosite, calcite, and specularite. Manganese ore minerals are found in considerable amounts locally, particularly braunite, pyrolusite, psilomelane, hollandite, sitaparite, and vrendenbergite. The rocks alter rather readily to mixtures of manganese oxide minerals and quartz.

Textures and Microstructures. Manganese silicate rocks are commonly well banded with quartz layers alternating with silicate layers. The quartz may be strained. Garnets are rounded to idioblastic and contain dusty inclusions. Quartz veinlets transect them. Rhodonite is anhedral, and pyroxmangite has been observed in porphyroblasts as much as 12 cm across, containing inclusions of quartz, calcite, graphite, and magnetite. Some gondites are characterized by fine-grained idioblastic garnet in a quartz mosaic.

Occurrence and Origin. In India manganiferous rocks occur as layers in quartzites, phyllites, mica schists, conglomeratic gneiss, and piedmontite marbles. Some of the schists contain manganese tourmaline and ottrelite. Similar rocks from the Gold Coast occur with quartz schist, quartz-kyanite schist, quartzite, phyllite, and chlorite schist. Pyroxmangite quartzites have been found at Simsiö, Finland.

Formed through medium-grade to low-grade regional metamorphism of manganiferous sedimentary rocks, perhaps from such types as rhodochrosite-chert rocks, shales with manganiferous carbonate, or manganese oxide nodules and concretions.

Migmatites

Migmatites, because of the scale on which the intermingling of igneous and metamorphic material takes place, are not normally usefully studied in their entirety by thin-section methods. They are hybrid rocks, composed in part of metamorphic remnants and in part of material of igneous composition and texture. The igneous fraction (usually of granitic composition) is in many cases injected but according to the beliefs of some petrologists may also be metasomatically introduced or even developed *in situ* by metamorphic differentiation. Other names that correspond generally to migmatite are mixed gneiss, composite gneiss, and injection gneiss. The alternation of conformable layers of igneous intrusions and metamorphic hosts is called lit-par-lit injection structure. Sederholm called veined gneisses phlebites, which he believed to include two genetic types: veinites, in which the vein material was derived from the rock itself, and arterites, in which it was injected. French petrologists have attempted to distinguish three classes of migmatites on the basis of increasing intermingling of the two phases:

1. Diadysites: the igneous material forms a network of generally connecting small sills and dikes (eruptive breccia) or forms swarms of parallel lenses, more or less isolated

2. Embrechites: the foliation of the metamorphic is still distinct but partly destroyed or encroached upon by abundant parallel sills or pods of igneous material (phlebites)

3. Anatexites: the metamorphic foliation remains only as relicts, and the rock in general approaches a granite in composition and texture

BIBLIOGRAPHY

GENERAL

The Principles of Petrology, by G. W. Tyrrell, 2d ed., E. P. Dutton & Co., Inc., New York, 1929.

Petrographic Methods and Calculations, by Arthur Holmes, rev. ed., Thomas Murby and Co., London, 1930.

Petrography and Petrology, by Frank F. Grout, McGraw-Hill Book Company, Inc., New York, 1932.

Igneous Rocks and the Depths of the Earth, by Reginald A. Daly, McGraw-Hill Book Company, Inc., New York, 1933.

Die Entstehung der Gesteine, by Tom. F. W. Barth, Carl W. Corens, and Pentti Eskola, Springer Verlag OHG, Berlin, 1939.

Theoretical Petrology, by Tom. F. W. Barth, John Wiley & Sons, Inc., New York, 1952.

Petrology for Students, by Alfred Harker, 8th ed., rev. by C. E. Tilley, S. R. Nockolds, and M. Black, Cambridge University Press, New York, 1954.

A Historical Survey of Petrology, by F. Y. Loewinson-Lessing, trans. from Russian by S. I. Tomkeieff, Oliver and Boyd, Ltd., Edinburgh and London, 1954.

Rocks and Mineral Deposits, by Paul Niggli, trans. by Robert L. Parker, W. H. Freeman and Co., San Francisco, 1954.

Petrography, by Howell Williams, Francis J. Turner, and Charles M. Gilbert, W. H. Freeman and Co., San Francisco, 1954.

IGNEOUS ROCKS AND PROCESSES

The Evolution of the Igneous Rocks, by N. L. Bowen, Princeton University Press, Princeton, N.J., 1928.

Interpretative Petrology of the Igneous Rocks, by Harold L. Alling, McGraw-Hill Book Company, Inc., New York, 1936.

A Descriptive Petrography of the Igneous Rocks, vols. I–IV, 2d ed., by Albert Johannsen, University of Chicago Press, Chicago, 1939.

Eruptive Rocks, by S. James Shand, 3d ed., John Wiley & Sons, Inc., New York, 1947.

Igneous Minerals and Rocks, by Ernest E. Wahlstrom, John Wiley & Sons, Inc., New York, 1947.

Origin of Granite, James Gilluly (chairman), *Geol. Soc. Amer. Mem.* 28, 1948.

Introduction to Theoretical Igneous Petrology, by Ernest E. Wahlstrom, John Wiley & Sons, Inc., New York, 1950.

Igneous and Metamorphic Petrology, by Francis J. Turner and Jean Verhoogen, McGraw-Hill Book Company, Inc., New York, 1951.

SEDIMENTARY ROCKS AND PROCESSES

On the Mineralogy of Sedimentary Rocks, by P. G. H. Boswell, Thomas Murby and Co., London, 1933.

Manual of Sedimentary Petrography, by W. C. Krumbein and Francis J. Pettijohn, Appleton-Century-Crofts, Inc., New York, 1938.

Methods of Study of Sediments, by W. H. Twenhofel and S. A. Tyler, McGraw-Hill Book Company, Inc., New York, 1941.

Sequence in Layered Rocks, by Robert R. Shrock, McGraw-Hill Book Company, Inc., New York, 1948.

Sedimentary Rocks, by Francis J. Pettijohn, Harper & Brothers, New York, 1949.

Stratigraphy and Sedimentation, by W. C. Krumbein and W. H. Sloss, W. H. Freeman and Co., San Francisco, 1951.

Sedimentary Petrography, by Henry B. Milner, 3d ed., Thomas Murby and Co., London, 1952.

Problems of Clay and Laterite Genesis, Symposium at Annual Meeting, St. Louis, February 19–22, 1951, American Institute of Mining and Metallurgical Engineers, New York, 1952.

Petrographie des roches sedimentaires, by Albert Carozzi, F. Rouge and Co., Lausanne, 1953.

METAMORPHIC ROCKS AND PROCESSES

Metamorphism, by Alfred Harker, Newthen and Co., Ltd., London, 1932.

Mineralogical and Structural Evolution of the Metamorphic Rocks, by Francis J. Turner, *Geol. Soc. Amer. Mem.* 30, 1948.

Igneous and Metamorphic Petrology, by Francis J. Turner and Jean Verhoogen, McGraw-Hill Book Company, Inc., New York, 1951.

The Origin of Metamorphic and Metasomatic Rock, by Hans Ramburg, University of Chicago Press, Chicago, 1952.

INDEX

275